MECHANISMS OF
COLOUR DISCRIMINATION

MECHANISMS OF
COLOUR DISCRIMINATION

PROCEEDINGS OF AN
INTERNATIONAL SYMPOSIUM ON THE
FUNDAMENTAL MECHANISMS
OF THE CHROMATIC DISCRIMINATION
IN ANIMALS AND MAN
HELD IN PARIS AT THE COLLÈGE DE FRANCE
25-29 JULY 1958

SPONSORED BY THE
INTERNATIONAL COUNCIL
OF SCIENTIFIC UNIONS

SYMPOSIUM PUBLICATIONS DIVISION
PERGAMON PRESS
NEW YORK · LONDON · OXFORD · PARIS
1960

PERGAMON PRESS INC.
122 East 55th Street, New York 22, N.Y.
1404 New York Avenue, N.W., Washington 5, D.C.
P.O. Box 47715, Los Angeles, California

PERGAMON PRESS LTD
4 & 5 Fitzroy Square, London, W.1
Headington Hill Hall, Oxford

PERGAMON PRESS S.A.R.L.
24 Rue des Écoles, Paris V^e

PERGAMON PRESS, G.m.b.H.
Kaiserstrasse 75, Frankfurt am Main

Library of Congress Card No. 59-13719

PRINTED IN GREAT BRITAIN IN THE CITY OF OXFORD AT THE ALDEN PRESS

CONTENTS

CONTENTS

PARTICIPANTS

CHAIRMAN : PRÉSIDENT

Piéron, H., Collège de France, Paris

REPORTERS : RAPPORTEURS

Dartnall, H. J. A., Ophthalmological Research Unit, Institute of Ophthalmology, London.
Von Frisch, K., Zoologisches Institut der Universität, München, D.B.R.
Galifret, Y., Laboratoire de Neurophysiologie Générale, Collège de France, Paris.
Le Grand, Y., Laboratoire de Physique, Muséum National d'Histoire Naturelle, Paris.
Hurvich, L. M., Department of Psychology, New York University, New York.
Rushton, W. A. H., Trinity College, Cambridge, England.
Stiles, W. L., National Physical Laboratory, Teddington, England.
Viaud, G., suppléé par Médioni, J., Laboratoire de Psychologie Animale, Faculté de Sciences, Strasbourg, France.

DISCUSSANTS : DISCUTANTS

Arnulf, A., Institut d'Optique, Paris.
Auerbach, E., Vision Research Laboratory, Hadassah Medical School, Hebrew University, Jerusalem.
Autrum, H., Zoologisches Institut der Universität, München, D.B.R.
Baumgardt, E., Laboratoire de Physiologie Générale de la Sorbonne, Paris.
Benoit, P., Laboratoire de Physiologie Générale, Faculté de Sciences, Marseille, France.
Bishop, P. O., Department of Physiology, University of Sidney, Sidney, Australia.
Bouman, M. A., Institut v. Zintuigfysiologie, Soesterberg, Holland.
Dekking, H. M., Clinique Ophtalmologique de l'Université, Groningue, Holland.
Dubois-Poulsen, A., Clinique Ophtalmologique des Quinze-Vingts, Paris.
Farnsworth, D., U.S. Department of the Navy, Office of Naval Research, Branch Office, London.
Fessard, A., Laboratoire de Neurophysiologie Générale, Collège de France, Paris.
Hansel, C. E. M., Department of Psychology, Manchester University, Manchester, England.
Hurvich, Dorothea, Department of Psychology, New York University, New York.
Ingvar, D. H., Department of Physiology, University of Lund, Lund, Sweden.
Krinsky, N., Biological Laboratories, Harvard University, Cambridge, Mass., U.S.A.
Kruger, L., Department of Physiology, Johns Hopkins University School of Medicine, Baltimore, U.S.A.
Lennox, Margaret, Universitetets Neurofysiologiske Institut, Copenhagen.
Marriott, F. H. C., University Laboratory of Physiology, Oxford, England.
Monnier, M., Physiologisches Institut der Universität Vesalianum, Basle, Switzerland.
Pirenne, M. N., University Laboratory of Physiology, Oxford, England.
Riggs, L. A., Walter S. Hunter Laboratory of Psychology, Brown University, Providence, U.S.A.
Scheglman, L., Psychologischen Institut de Universität, Tubingen, D.B.R.
Stevens, S. S., Psychological Laboratories, Harvard University, Cambridge, Mass., U.S.A.

Tansley, Katherine, Ophthalmological Research Unit, Institute of Ophthalmology, London.

De Valois, R. L., Departments of Psychology and Ophthalmology, University of Michigan, Ann Arbor, U.S.A.

Verriest, G., Clinique Ophtalmologique de l'Université, Gand, Belgium.

Walraven, P. L., Clinique Ophtalmologique de l'Université, Groningue, Holland.

Weale, R. A., Ophthalmological Research Unit, Institute of Ophthalmology, London.

Wirth, A., Clinica Occulistica dell'Universita, Rome, Italy.

Wolken, J. J., Biophysical Research Laboratory, University of Pittsburg, School of Medicine, Pittsburg, U.S.A.

Wright, W. D., Technical Optic Section, Imperial College of Science and Technology, University of London, London.

Zanen, J., Department d'Ophtalmologie, Hôpital Universitaire Brugman, Brussels, Belgium.

ALLOCUTION INTRODUCTIVE
DU PRÉSIDENT

ALLOCUTION INTRODUCTIVE
DU PRÉSIDENT

LE PROFESSEUR HENRI PIÉRON

Le Professeur Henri Piéron, président, souhaite la bienvenue aux participants. Puis,

Il est remarquable que, en dépit de l'ampleur des recherches, de la multiplicité des rencontres entre spécialistes, de l'importance des perfectionnements techniques, des moyens qui sont fournis aux laboratoires, le problème des mécanismes fondamentaux sur lesquels repose la vision des couleurs n'est pas actuellement résolu de façon satisfaisante.

Nous voyons toujours essayer de nouveaux schémas, et les deux schémas classiques, celui de Young-Helmholtz et celui de Hering, s'opposent encore aujourd'hui.

A certains moments, l'un des deux l'a emporté, à d'autres moments, c'est l'autre schéma, et, à l'heure actuelle, vraiment, on se trouve dans une situation où l'on peut hésiter entre ces deux modalités, la trichromatique ou celle des couples antagonistes.

Ce retard, évidemment, il tient un peu à ce que le domaine de la couleur n'est pas celui des armes de guerre, mais il tient aussi à ce qu'il implique des compétences extrêmement diverses.

Il est bien certain que nous avons toujours la grande tradition des physiciens, mais qui ont la tentation d'envisager le problème sous l'angle pratique de la colorimétrie, avec un observateur standard qui est commode, mais auquel ne correspond souvent aucune individualité précise.

Nous avons des psychologues qui, eux, au contraire, se préoccupent surtout de perceptions interprétatives. Les biochimistes sont bien soucieux d'atteindre des substances pures, et ce n'est pas commode. Les neurophysiologistes ne sont pas toujours suffisamment soucieux de conditions de stimulation physique rigoureuses, et ils ont longtemps négligé les aboutissements psychologiques, les processus corticaux qui interviennent toujours. Les zoologistes sont surtout des éthologistes, c'est-à-dire des observateurs. Ils n'ont pas été toujours au courant des difficultés que pose l'expérimentation correcte. Aussi, le rapprochement des spécialistes est fructueux. Nous en avons eu des exemples ces dernières années. Ils se sont, en effet, multipliés.

Nous avons ici le Dr. Stiles et le Dr. Wolken, à qui on peut être reconnaissant de leur effort pour les symposia qu'ils ont organisés récemment. Eh bien, c'est dans cette perspective de l'utilité de ces rapprochements, c'est avec une certaine confiance en leur fécondité qu'a été conçu notre symposium inter-unions, qui a été patronné par le Conseil international des Unions scientifiques: La physique, la biochimie, les sciences biologiques, les sciences physiologiques, la psychologie scientifique. Nous espérons que l'on pourra arriver à faire le point, dans une certaine mesure, des données qui sont le plus solidement acquises, et, en même temps, d'indiquer des voies nouvelles de recherche qui s'annoncent particulièrement fructueuses, en se mettant en garde contre des illusions et des erreurs. Il faut bien reconnaître qu'il est utile que nous nous familiarisions, les uns et les autres, avec des langages et des modes de pensée qui sont assez différents. Eh bien, c'est par le contact direct que cette familiarisation peut être le mieux obtenue.

Les sciences biologiques sont évidemment au centre, car c'est une vérité première, mais elle est quelquefois oubliée: la lumière est un phénomène biologique, et, à plus forte raison, la couleur. La couleur, nous le savons bien, n'a pas d'existence physique réelle, et cependant elle joue dans la vie courante un rôle extrêmement considérable. C'est donc sur des êtres vivants que les recherches doivent nécessairement porter — des êtres vivants, aussi bien les animaux que les hommes. Mais les conditions expérimentales et les méthodes ne peuvent pas être entièrement identiques dans les deux cas.

Pour les hommes, on a cet avantage de la communication verbale qui nous fournit des informations précieuses, et une bonne volonté de collaboration, sur laquelle nous ne pouvons pas compter chez les animaux.

Mais il y a des inconvénients. Le langage est quelquefois dangereux, car il y a bien des incertitudes dans la signification des mots, et vous savez que quand on comptait sur le langage pour déceler des dyschromatopsies, eh bien, la plupart du temps, on n'arrivait pas à les connaître parce que les daltoniens emploient les mots de 'rouge' et de 'vert' comme si, réellement, les impressions de rouge et de vert étaient parfaitement connues. D'autre part, toute l'expérimentation neurophysiologique chez l'homme est extrêmement difficile. Et enfin — j'y reviendrai — il y a des influences suggestives qui peuvent aussi s'exercer de façon réellement dangereuse.

Chez les animaux, alors, nous avons l'avantage, évidemment, de ne pas craindre la subjectivité — de ne pas craindre les influences suggestives. On est obligé d'utiliser des méthodes purement objectives — ceci est évidemment précieux; mais il est quelquefois délicat de trouver une méthode objective qui soit tout à fait satisfaisante et sûre. On a, dans bien des cas, commis des erreurs qui ont été à la base d'innombrables discussions. Le professeur von Frisch se souvient de celles qu'il a longtemps poursuivies avec Hess.

Dans bien des travaux on voit qu'on identifie pratiquement les différences d'action qui peuvent s'observer sous l'influence de longueurs d'ondes différentes comme dues à des différences de couleurs.

On compare des radiations de basse fréquence qu'on appelle 'rouges', d'autres de fréquence double qu'on appelle 'bleues', et on est conduit à admettre des spécificités chromatiques correspondantes, alors que, fort souvent, il s'agit seulement de l'intervention de deux systèmes de réception qui existent chez un grand nombre, chez la plupart des Vertébrés — et cela est une confusion qui est extrêmement commune.

Elle a été à la base des erreurs de Le Gros Clark, quand il a étudié le corps genouillé. On y reviendra. Il est certain que les travaux de De Valois ont montré, comme les critiques de Walls, que les interprétations de Le Gros Clark n'avaient aucune valeur.

Ou bien, une simple différence dans l'efficacité lumineuse est aussi attribuée à une différence de couleur, en particulier dans de nombreuses études sur les animaux inférieurs — toutes les recherches sur les phototropismes. Cela tient à ce que l'on ne vérifiait pas l'égalité lumineuse sur laquelle on prétendait s'appuyer. Il y a une nécessité de connaître l'isophanie, l'égalité lumineuse. C'est le point sur lequel on doit s'appuyer quand on veut déterminer une capacité de discrimination chromatique. Pour toutes les méthodes que l'on emploie: de conditionnement, de dressage à la couleur des stimuli lumineux, c'est évidemment nécessaire.

Mais, dans la plupart des cas, on ne s'adresse pas à des stimulations lumineuses directes, en éclairant l'appareil récepteur avec une source lumineuse.

Ce qu'on examine, c'est la capacité de discrimination pour des objets vus, pour des surfaces vues, dans la mesure où ils sont éclairés. Par exemple, la méthode de Schlieper est fondée sur une réaction opto-cinétique à la rotation d'une surface présentant une hétérogénéité, hétérogénéité fondée sur la couleur, avec des stries colorées juxtaposées. Eh bien, cette méthode, elle est valable, dans la mesure où on s'assure d'une égalité dans la perception de la réflectance, de l'albedo des surfaces. C'est l'isoleucie, c'est l'égalité de 'lightness', qu'il est nécessaire de connaître. Or, les déterminations d'égalité — égalité phanique et, plus encore, égalité leucique — sont extrêmement variables, non seulement d'une espèce animale à une autre, mais même d'un individu à un autre. Et cela est vrai pour les individus humains.

On peut faire, comme de Vries, la comparaison de la luminosité, de la lucivité spectrale, à une radiation de 550 millimicrons, et comparer les valeurs obtenues: il l'a fait sur vingt-deux sujets — en prenant comme égale à 100 la valeur qu'il observait sur lui-même — et il a trouvé des variations, chez ces vingt-deux individus, allant de 100 à 236 — par conséquent une variabilité énorme qui fait que, si l'on croit pouvoir, sur un opérateur standard, déterminer la véritable lucivité d'une radiation spectrale, on commet des erreurs qui peuvent se traduire et entraîner quelquefois des conclusions tout à fait fausses. Nous n'avons malheureusement pas, à la base, actuellement, de la détermination de l'observateur standard, des données statistiques qui soient réellement satisfaisantes. On n'a pas étudié d'une façon statistique correcte, comme on le fait pour la taille des individus, cette constante qu'est la lucivité spectrale.

Dans un article de 1957 de l'Optical Society, Nimeroff signale qu'il faudrait au moins connaître, à côté des valeurs significatives que l'on adopte, les indices de dispersion, les variances, pour qu'on se rende mieux compte de la possibilité d'erreur, de la marge d'erreur probable que l'on commettra.

Evidemment, on arrive, dans les études animales, à vaincre cette difficulté — et c'est en particulier ce qu'a fait le professeur von Frisch, chez les abeilles, comme il nous l'exposera lui-même, si l'on confronte à une surface colorée une série, mais assez complète, de surfaces achromatiques comportant, d'après le taux de la réflectance, des graduations de leucies à peu près continues entre le noir et le blanc.

Mais l'interprétation de ce qu'on appelle l'homochromie, que l'on observe chez certaines espèces animales, comme faisant partie de la notion de mimétisme, et sur laquelle on fonde souvent la réalité d'une vision chromatique, est très souvent erronée.

L'adaptation se limite généralement à une certaine homoleucie avec le substrat. C'est ce que j'ai observé pour des Isopodes, en particulier, en 1914, et il n'y a pas de doute que l'apparence d'homochromie dans ce cas était une homoleucie, c'est-à-dire que cela ne signifiait rien du tout au point de vue d'une capacité de discrimination chromatique.

Nous aurons l'occasion, peut-être, de reparler de ce point en étudiant l'inventaire de la vision des couleurs, mais je vous signale tout de suite cette cause d'erreur considérable.

Dans la recherche des critères objectifs satisfaisants, l'on a évidemment la tentation d'utiliser cette manifestation assez facilement enregistrable, même chez l'homme, que fournit l'électrorétinogramme.

Mais là on s'est aperçu de la difficulté du problème, du fait que l'onde b, cette onde positive, qui paraît marquer l'efficacité de l'excitation lumineuse, est surtout dominée par le système récepteur des bâtonnets qui ne fournissent pas du tout de capacité de discrimination chromatique.

Evidemment, on tend à distinguer — et c'est là un progrès fort intéressant — une onde que l'on appelle l'onde x, et qui n'est plus l'onde b des batonnets, mais la différenciation est souvent extrêmement difficile.

Aussi est-il extrêmement important — et c'est un des points auxquels, je crois, on ne fera jamais assez attention — de se rappeler qu'il y a des animaux dont les rétines sont dépourvues de bâtonnets. Par conséquent, il y a là une possibilité d'éliminer une de ces causes d'erreurs essentielles qui est l'intervention de différentes actions en fonction de la longueur d'onde, par la différence de sensibilité de la rhodopsine ou de la porphyroxine vis-à-vis des récepteurs photosensibles des cônes.

Aussi des données intéressantes ont déjà été acquises par Forbes dans des rétines de tortue avec une égalité d'amplitude de l'onde b pour des stimulations hétérochromatiques; il a pu constater l'existence, dans certains changements de longueurs d'ondes, d'une réaction spécifique, qui pouvait être attribuée, cette fois, à un changement de système récepteur. Il n'y avait pas d'influence ni d'intervention variable du récepteur photopique, d'un coté, et scotopique, de l'autre.

Je pense que nous aurons des renseignements très intéressants, qui seront donnés par le professeur Autrum, dans ses recherches sur *Calliphora*, où il a utilisé aussi des manifestations d'électrorétinogrammes, avec des stimulations alternées.

Nous avons distingué l'homophanie, c'est-à-dire l'égalité dans l'impression subjective de luminance (*subjective brightness*) qui est une sensation élémentaire, lorsqu'on ne cherche pas à la traduire en une impression quantitative. Mais cette homophanie doit être distinguée complètement de l'homoleucie, ce que l'on ne fait pas toujours, car celle-ci est une appréciation perceptive qui, sous des éclairements qui peuvent être très inégaux, avec des sensations lumineuses, des sensations de phanie, très variables, permettent de se rendre compte d'une certaine constante des surfaces et des objets que nous reconnaissons ainsi: appréciation d'une réflectance, d'un albedo. Evidemment, dans cette appréciation, la sensation lumineuse que nous fournit la surface examinée joue un très grand rôle, mais avec des éléments correcteurs qui tiennent à tout un *pattern* d'ensemble de nos impressions. Il faut insister sur l'importance capitale de cette distinction qui ne s'est imposée que très tardivement et qui, vous le savez, a été complètement méconnue par Hering, qui a envisagé le blanc et le noir comme des sensations élémentaires.

Les perceptions constituent toujours des interprétations d'ensembles plus ou moins complexes, qui comprennent des sensations d'origines parfois diverses, des souvenirs, assurant une connaissance du monde extérieur propre à diriger des comportements adaptés. Mais elles comportent une marge considérable de variabilité, variabilité inter-individuelle et variabilité, même, intra-individuelle, chez le même individu.

La leucie nous fournit une caractéristique perceptible des objets maintenus dans des conditions variées d'éclairement, et la caractéristique se complète de l'électivité de la réflectance, de la couleur de l'objet qui est une chromoleucie. Là encore, nous n'avons pas de sensation élémentaire, par exemple, de marron, de brun, de rose.

Nous savons isoler les stimulations réflexives sans qu'on puisse avoir de renseignements par ailleurs sur les éclairements; ces impressions qui nous paraissent des sensations de couleurs tout comme les autres, ne sont plus alors perceptibles, elles n'existent plus! On ne peut pas, avec de la lumière, faire — à volonté, du rose ou du brun. Ce n'est que dans des conditions artificielles que ces réflexions, par des surfaces d'objets, peuvent nous donner des sensations élémentaires. Mais alors, ce sont toujours des impressions lumineuses et qui nous donnent les mêmes sensations de couleurs que l'on peut déterminer avec des ondes spectrales.

Il en est de même pour les grandeurs et les formes visuelles des objets. Vous savez qu'elles ne sont pas en correspondance univoque avec les images rétiniennes. Lorsque l'on a placé des prismes déformants devant les yeux d'un sujet, et qu'on les a laissés devant lui durant un temps assez long — l'expérience a été nettement faite par Ivo Kohler — les déformations s'l'atténuent peu à peu et les perceptions correctes se rétablissent. Et c'est lorsqu'on enlève les prismes que la déformation en sens inverse, momentanément au moins, se manifeste. De même, pour les grandeurs d'objets: nous savons très bien que la grandeur de l'image rétinienne ne donne pas directement la grandeur de l'objet, mais qu'elle est fonction d'une certaine appréciation des distances.

Eh bien, il en est tout à fait de même en ce qui concerne les leucies. Des recherches récentes de Sanders et Wyszecki se sont adressées aux possibilités de connaître d'après des examens de surfaces colorées et non pas d'objets — en évitant, évidemment, des causes d'erreurs supplémentaires — avec des échelles, des papiers de Munsell — s'il y avait une équivalence possible entre la réflectance de la surface colorée et la réflectance achromatique des échelons du gris.

Or, on a constaté qu'il y avait des variations considérables, des variations individuelles. Chez trois sujets, par exemple, observant des équivalents de leucies avec des échantillons Munsell, alors qu'on leur présentait des échantillons qui avaient même réflectance au point de vue lumineux, d'après les calculs, on avait des valeurs qui, au lieu de la valeur 1, représentant cette égalité réelle, allait, chez un sujet, de 0,84 à 1,20 — chez un autre, de 0,85 à 1,22 — chez un troisième, de 0,90 à 1,54.

Passons à une autre cause d'erreur qui tient à une très forte tendance, dans la vision animale, à attribuer à la vision photopique comme telle la capacité de discrimination chromatique, et, dès lors, à admettre que, si l'on obtient, chez un individu animal, une courbe de visibilité, de lucivité spectrale, de type photopique, dans des conditions déterminées, on peut, de ce chef, conclure à la réalité de la vision chromatique.

Or, vous savez qu'il y a là, au contraire, des contestations. On a même nié la vision des couleurs chez tous les mammifères autres que les primates, comme l'a fait Miles, en particulier; c'est certainement excessif, mais cela repose sur des faits qui ont une valeur réelle, au moins pour certaines espèces. D'autre part, l'existence d'une achromatopsie totale — évidemment exceptionnelle — chez des hommes ayant une vision fovéale bien conservée, avec la courbe normale de lucivité spectrale, a bien montré l'indépendance possible des deux termes habituellement associés. Walls et Heath purent établir que c'étaient les cônes qui étaient bien en jeu dans cette réception achromatique. On a pensé qu'il y avait, quelquefois, dans ce cas-là, un monochromatisme; mais quand on peut comparer — en l'absence, naturellement, d'anomalies monoculaires — le repère de la vision scotopique avec la vision photopique, on constate qu'il n'y a pas, dans ce cas-là, de vision colorée du tout. Corélativement, je pense que l'on peut fortement douter que la courbe de lucivité photopique soit nécessairement, comme dans le schéma primitif, le simple résultat additif de courbes composantes d'absorption relevant de systèmes récepteurs qui assurent les électivités chromatiques.

Lorsque l'on fait des adaptations monochromatiques, comme je l'ai constaté en 1930, comme Wright l'a vu en 1934, comme Mandelbaum et Mintz en 1941 l'ont constaté chez Hecht — et Hurvich et Rushton également — s'il y a une certaine électivité dans la dépression lumineuse qui est entraînée par l'adaptation tout au long du spectre, le spectre entier se trouve générale-ment atteint. D'autre part, les données récentes de Graham et Hsia sur les courbes de lucivité des daltoniens, y compris ce cas typique, qu'ils ont particulièrement étudié, d'une deutéranope monoculaire, ont bien mis en évidence une moindre excitabilité spectrale dans une moitié ou dans l'autre du spectre. Mais les différences dans les courbes de lucivité sont-elles impor-tantes? En réalité, elles restent minimes. Elles sont évidemment très faibles chez le deutéranope; parfois, même, les chiffres sont jugés normaux. Les seuils s'élèveraient au triple au maximum, dans les régions les plus atteintes par la dépression.

Et même chez les protanopes, dont le spectre paraît raccourci — ce qui tient à une moindre sensibilité générale — les seuils sont multipliés au maxi-mum par treize — un peu plus d'une unité logarithmique, à 700 millimicrons.

Chez les tritanopes de Wright, les différences obtenues sont évidemment beaucoup plus faibles, et nous savons que ce qu'on attribue à la composante *bleue* — au point de vue de la luminosité — est très faible. Il a trouvé que les différences moyennes par rapport à lui de sept de ces tritanopes, allaient simplement de 1 à 1,8. Mais quand il distingue les courbes individuelles de ces sept tritanopes, la variation entre les extrêmes va de 1 à dix. Par conséquent la variation de 1 à 1,8 est peu significative, dans un cas déterminé, ou un individu déterminé.

Il paraît n'y avoir, en réalité, qu'une participation très limitée des com-posantes chromatiques dans l'excitation lumineuse qui fournit l'intensité de la phanie.

En ce qui concerne les modalités d'excitation, vous savez quelles différences essentielles se manifestent suivant que l'on envisage la sensation de phanie ou celle de couleur.

D'un côté, en effet, les stimulations des diverses régions spectrales ont des

B

effets excitateurs additifs, non tout à fait intégralement toutefois à l'encontre de la loi d'Abney: à cet égard, il s'est trouvé que, réellement, dans les couples complémentaires, sans aucun doute, l'addition intégrale n'existe pas. Mais, de l'autre, il y a, en revanche, des effets antagonistes, jusqu'à annulation de toute sensation chromatique, et si la sensation lumineuse est diminuée en général par l'adaptation monochromatique, la sensation de couleur correspondante arrive parfois à disparaître totalement, et, en même temps, la couleur dite 'complémentaire' et 'antagoniste' se trouve exaltée jusqu'à une saturation qui ne se trouve jamais atteinte dans une rétine au repos.

La valence lumineuse d'une radiation est largement indépendante d'un individu à un autre par rapport à la valence chromatique.

Vous savez qu'on a actuellement tendance à admettre la possibilité de récepteurs photopiques achromatiques, qui fourniraient les éléments les plus importants pour la sensation lumineuse proprement dite, pour la sensation phanique qui semble intervenir indépendamment de la sensation de couleur.

Pour la vision des couleurs, il faut certainement envisager, au premier plan, l'intervention de mécanismes nerveux secondaires d'interaction, après la stimulation primaire des récepteurs. Leur importance est capitale, mais leur complexité est telle que l'on a énormément de mal, à l'heure actuelle, à voir clair au point de vue de ces mécanismes neurophysiologiques sur lesquels j'espère que les données que vous apporterez fourniront de la lumière.

On peut, évidemment, s'appuyer sur quelque chose qui est vraiment solidement acquis, car c'est une donnée pleinement démontrée aujourd'hui: l'intervention initiale d'un processus photochimique dans l'excitation normale de l'appareil visuel ne peut plus faire aucun doute.

Pour ce qui concerne l'excitation lumineuse scotopique, la détermination du mécanisme est déjà fort avancée. L'œuvre persistante de nombreux chercheurs y a contribué, dans laquelle on ne peut pas oublier le rôle important de Wald, qui s'est attelé aussi, maintenant, au problème de l'excitation photopique.

Mais, après les déceptions qu'ont causées les recherches de von Studnitz, qui paraissaient pleines de promesses, l'identification provisoire que tente Wald de trois substances photosensibles à la base des réceptions chromatiques se heurte à de bien graves difficultés. Il envisage la rhodopsine, d'un côté, ou un pigment du même type, en tout cas; l'iodopsine, de l'autre; et la cyanopsine, enfin. Mais, que la rhodopsine intervienne dans la vision des couleurs, comme le soutient Willmer — c'est là quelque chose qui, à l'heure actuelle, ne peut pas être accepté.

Il est assez curieux que les conceptions de Willmer aient conduit un éminent biologiste, Sir Gavin de Beer, à s'appuyer sur cette interprétation pour défendre la conception darwinienne du rôle de la sélection dans l'évolution.

En effet, l'une des objections que l'on fait à la théorie darwinienne de la sélection, c'est que bien des variations sont parfaitement inutiles avant d'avoir atteint un certain degré de développement; et on ne comprend pas, alors, pourquoi ce développement s'est effectué si la sélection ne jouait pas.

Or, il pense qu'il peut y avoir tout de même un rôle de ces variations qui sont inefficaces, semble-t-il, dans certains cas, dont il donne comme exemple la vision des couleurs.

'La vision des couleurs', dit-il, s'est développée indépendamment dans beaucoup de groupes animaux. Parmi les éléments de l'œil sensibles à la lumière, certains sont spécialement sensibles à la lumière faible; d'autres confèrent l'acuité de la vision en lumière forte grâce à leur innervation individuelle, les stimuli étant alors perçus séparément, par des petites surfaces de la rétine. 'Dans chacune des deux fonctions, vision en obscurité relative, et vision précise à la lumière, une efficacité accrue confère une chance plus grande de survie, à partir du début même du perfectionnement. Mais quand ces deux fonctions sont réalisées dans le même œil, il se produit un mécanisme — comme l'a montré Willmer — où les éléments visuels sont sensibles d'une manière différentielle à différentes longueurs d'ondes: et ceci constitue la base de la vision des couleurs. L'acquisition de cette vision est donc un avantage inattendu qui résulte du perfectionnement des deux autres fonctions.'

Eh bien, il est difficile d'admettre, comme le fait Sir Gavin de Beer, que la vision des couleurs soit née obligatoirement de la dualité comme condition suffisante et nécessaire, car toutes les données — sur lesquelles je n'insisterai pas maintenant — montrant qu'il ne peut pas s'agir de la rhodopsine dans la perception du bleu, éliminent cette conception.

Il y a un cas qui paraît particulièrement crucial: c'est de savoir quelle est exactement la vision du bleu dans les cas d'avitaminose où la rhodopsine a disparu.

Il faut reconnaître qu'il n'y a pas, malheureusement, d'étude systématique satisfaisante de cette vision du bleu chez des héméralopes par avitaminose.

On l'a constatée chez des héméralopes congénitaux; par exemple, Abney, en 1917, a montré qu'il y avait une perception du bleu exigeant une énergie stimulatrice plus grande, mais, alors, sans intervalle photochromatique. Aussitôt que le bleu était perçu, il était perçu avec sa couleur, et l'année suivante un autre cas a été signalé à l'Académie des Sciences à Paris par un ophtalmologiste, Pollack, donnant les mêmes résultats.

On peut naturellement dire qu'il n'en est pas ainsi dans l'avitaminose, mais là, nous n'avons pas la réponse. Nous savons, évidemment, que, dans la vision périphérique de ces héméralopes, le bleu est beaucoup moins efficace; la lumière bleue est beaucoup moins efficace; mais nous n'avons pas de données sur la perception réelle du bleu dans la région centrale de la rétine.

Ainsi, un des éléments de Wald ne paraît pas solide, mais je crois que cela vaut la peine de le discuter plus complètement.

En ce qui concerne les deux autres pigments qu'il a invoqués, il est regrettable que, jusqu'à présent, on n'ait pas pu extraire de rétines entièrement dépourvues de bâtonnets l'iodopsine qu'il a isolée; il l'a isolée dans des rétines de poulets. Et enfin, quand il fait appel à la cyanopsine, c'est une possibilité, puisqu'il l'a obtenue en la synthétisant artificiellement, mais on ne l'a jamais trouvée encore dans les substances photosensibles naturelles.

On commence à entreprendre des recherches chez des Invertébrés possédant la vision des couleurs, et en particulier chez les Abeilles — si bien étudiées par von Frisch — mais les difficultés paraissent bien grandes. Jusqu'à présent, vous savez que le seul élément positif, c'est la récente découverte par le collaborateur de Wald, Goldsmith, qui n'a malheureusement pas pu venir, et qui a trouvé qu'à la base des pigments des abeilles il y avait bien un rétinène à vitamine A, avec un maximum d'absorption à 440 millimicrons, ce qui laisse penser que, peut-être, c'est bien ce pigment qui intervient dans la vision de l'ultraviolet, que von Frisch a mis en évidence.

Il est certain que, si l'on envisage les courbes d'absorption de tous les pigments que l'on a signalés, on a décelé ceux-ci, mais généralement on ne les a pas extraits — comme l'a noté Morton.

Il y a des maxima qui pourraient rendre compte des électivités dans la photosensivité des récepteurs. En tout cas, nous pouvons beaucoup compter sur les données que l'on peut obtenir par l'originale méthode de Rushton, données obtenues justement sur l'œil humain, difficile à étudier au point de vue de la photochimie directe.

Peut-on espérer des résultats d'une histomicrochimie? Les travaux histologiques qui portent sur l'identification d'un pigment aussi évident que le pigment scotopique, que la rhodopsine, dans les travaux histologiques de Mme Berger et de Ségal, de Karli, de Vilter, ne sont pas très encourageants à cet égard, pour des essais d'identification de pigments purement photopiques.

En tout cas, une collaboration particulièrement étroite des biochimistes et des histologistes serait vraiment nécessaire. Mais le travail devrait surtout porter sur des rétines purement photopiques.

C'est l'intervention de récepteurs scotopiques qui a empêché Granit, dans les belles recherches dont il avait pris l'initiative, de dégager de ses résultats sur les réponses des cellules ganglionnaires de la rétine à des radiations de différentes longueurs d'ondes des interprétations certaines; vous connaissez l'état actuel de la question.

Quand Le Gros Clark a cru pouvoir attribuer à des couches du corps genouillé chez les singes une spécificité chromatique, il se fondait sur des différences qui tenaient à ce que les deux lames ventrales laminaires de ce centre contiennent les grandes cellules qui assurent la transmission synaptiques des récepteurs scotopiques, tandis que les quatre lames dorsales à petites cellules assurent les synapses de vision photopique.

Dans tout le système nerveux, la projection est d'origine topographique, et les différences qualitatives ne se marquent pas par des différences de sièges. On peut essayer d'èliminer les bâtonnets — on l'a fait — en utilisant de très forts éclairements. Mais, à cet égard, on s'est aperçu que les bâtonnets possédaient une excitabilité qui s'étendait bien au delà des limites qu'on leur attribue généralement, tant du côté des luminances très élevées que des très grandes longueurs d'ondes. On n'exclut pas facilement leur participation dans l'excitation des rétines mixtes.

A l'heure actuelle, on tire de grands espoirs de l'expérimentation par les microélectrodes qui ne porte plus maintenant sur des cellules ganglionnaires seulement, mais sur des récepteurs des couches profondes de la rétine, des récepteurs — on le croit — mais un doute persiste, et il est bien possible que les recherches de Tomita et Funaishi, Svaetichin et Motokawa, portent sur des bipolaires.

En tout cas, nous savons très bien, à l'heure actuelle, que, dans les niveaux infra-ganglionnaires de la rétine, ce ne sont pas des potentiels d'action obéissant au tout ou rien qui interviennent — mais des potentiels gradués, qui commandent ensuite le message par tout ou rien. Ceci, nous l'avions, avec Galifret, dégagé, dans le cas de modifications de surface, comme une conclusion nécessaire: l'existence de modes d'excitation graduée. A l'heure actuelle, il ne fait plus de doute qu'il en est bien ainsi. En tout cas, les recherches sur les cellules centrales et les cellules synaptiques dans les corps genouillés — sur les cellules du cortex — toutes ces recherches qui se multiplient actuellement, en particulier les recherches de Grüsser, les recherches de De Valois, etc. — toutes ces recherches paraissent être susceptibles de montrer des spécificités chromatiques — mais avec des interactions, des influences, qui ne permettent pas encore de conclure d'une façon satisfaisante.

En tout cas, il a fallu renoncer à certains faits qui étaient assez tentateurs, comme la notion de trois catégories de fibres optiques, ayant des vitesses de transmission différentes et engendrant, dans le cortex, avec un retard variable, trois ondes corticales qui auraient représenté les trois spécificités chromatiques.

Nous savons, à l'heure actuelle, qu'il n'en est rien, et vous pourrez vous en assurer d'après le rapport sur les processus neurophysiologiques dans les centres.

Il est très regrettable que, chez les Invertébrés, le Limule, si magnifiquement étudié par Hartline, ne possède pas une vision discriminative des couleurs; cela aurait, évidemment, beaucoup facilité une étude neurophysiologique précise.

Mais dans la neurophysiologique des Insectes, les nouvelles méthodes d'Autrum peuvent apporter des faits du plus haut intérêt.

C'est, en tout cas, dans l'ensemble des données fondamentales que la psychophysiologie de la fonction visuelle ne cesse d'accumuler, que s'est dessiné un cadre général pour les hypothèses théoriques avec une utilisation scientifique, qui aurait besoin d'être beaucoup plus poussée, des cas d'anomalies ou d'atteintes pathologiques que les ophtamolgistes sont appelés à connaître.

Vous savez que c'est bien le daltonisme qui a joué le principal rôle pour l'édification de la théorie trichromatique de Young. C'est encore lui qui fournit actuellement à Graham et Hsia les éléments d'une conception qui paraît être cohérente.

Quant au dichromatisme qui paraît exister chez certaines espèces animales, et qui serait un type primitif de vision des couleurs, comme dans la théorie de Ladd Franklin, ce type, s'il existe, devrait être analysé de plus près. On devrait rechercher, dans ce cas, les possibilités de vérification d'équations chromatiques qui nous permettraient de comparer d'une façon plus satisfaisante ces modes de vision animale avec les modes de vision humains.

Chez les chimpanzés, nous savons que nous avons vraiment les mêmes modes, et que, quand on utilise l'équation de Rayleigh, on obtient chez le chimpanzé à peu près les mêmes résultats que l'on trouve chez les hommes normaux.

Nous avons aussi des données nouvelles qui paraissent particulièrement intéressantes: ce sont les analyses à base quantique de Bouman qui prouvent un intervalle photochromatique fovéal, comme si un récepteur plus sensible suffisait pour la réception lumineuse, pour la phanie, tandis qu'il y aurait une inégalité d'exigences pour les récepteurs du rouge et du vert.

Enfin, il y a les essais d'analyse factorielle, et je vous en reparlerai; il me semble qu'il y a là un avenir extrêmement intéressant. Jusqu'ici, les données ne sont pas satisfaisantes, c'est bien certain, mais il pourrait y avoir un programme de recherches d'ensemble qui permettrait, avec les machines dont on dispose actuellement, d'obtenir des corrélations très nombreuses chez un grand nombre d'individus, desquelles pourraient peut-être se dégager des résultats de l'analyse factorielle.

Je vous disais tout à l'heure que l'inconvénient, chez l'homme, était la suggestibilité. Je crois que les théoriciens ne se méfient pas toujours assez du danger que peut présenter une conviction préalable, non seulement dans leurs propres observations, mais dans celles des gens sur lesquels, à leur insu, ils peuvent exercer une influence.

Certainement, les données de Kravkov, autrefois, m'ont paru, quand je suis allé le voir, découler de facteurs qui étaient, justement, des facteurs de suggestibilité.

A l'heure actuelle, la méthode de Motokawa, qui fait appel à des seuils de phosphènes, me paraît également soumise à cette grave cause d'erreurs.

Les physiciens ne se sont pas toujours assez méfiés de ce rôle de la suggestibilité dans les observations visuelles — ayant affaire généralement à des objets de la nature qui ne sont pas susceptibles d'être directement influencés.

Je me permets de rappeler que j'ai décelé assez vite le rôle — dans la pseudo-découverte des rayons N, par les physiciens de Nancy, en 1904 — d'une suggestion qui s'est exercée sur les savants dans une ville entière, fondée sur l'apparence d'un changement de luminosité juxtaliminaire qui jouait alors; et l'on pouvait montrer combien il était facile de provoquer une apparence d'un changement de cet ordre, sous des influences extérieures.

Je n'oublie pas, en revanche, que c'est bien aux physiciens qu'il appartient de préciser les modalités de stimulation qui risquent de rester trop grossières, en particulier pour le monochromatisme — ce qui entraîne d'importantes erreurs d'interprétation — et la notion de lumière blanche, ce repère achromatique qui n'est pas encore suffisamment défini, joue évidemment dans certaines interprétations un rôle dangereux.

Un dernier danger, c'est de rester trop soumis au cadre — c'est bien encore une influence suggestive — des interprétations qui ont pris une force extraordinaire.

Evidemment, l'interprétation trichromatique, le rôle qu'elle joue, et qu'elle joue très utilement, d'ailleurs, en colorimétrie, tend à lui donner une valeur telle que l'on hésite beaucoup à renoncer à ce schéma.

J'ajoute que je ferai, à cet égard, un peu mon *mea culpa*, car j'ai évidemment critiqué beaucoup les schémas de Hering — en grande partie, justement, à cause de sa confusion du blanc et du noir avec des sensations; et je ne voyais aucun moyen de rendre compte de ses actions opposées dans les couples antagonistes des récepteurs rétiniens.

A l'heure actuelle, avec les données de Svaetichin et de divers autres, qui montrent des influences inhibitrices pouvant résulter d'une stimulation, on arrive à redonner, à la possibilité de couples antagonistes, une très grande importance.

Nous aurons l'occasion d'y revenir, naturellement, dans les discussions générales, mais je dois avouer que j'ai reconnu maintenant que j'ai été aussi trop influencé par la notion traditionnelle du trichromatisme.

En tout cas, j'ai grand espoir que les faits qui nous seront apportés, que les discussions qui vont s'ouvrir, nous fourniront des éléments pour diriger les nouvelles recherches et pour nous permettre de gagner encore au point de vue de notre connaissance des mécanismes fondamentaux qui sont en jeu dans la vision chromatique.

RÉFÉRENCES

ABNEY, W. DE W. (1917) *Proc. Roy. Soc. London*, **90**, 69.
BEER, G. DE (1958) *Endeavour*, **17**, 61.
FORBES, A. (1958) *J. Neurophysiol.*, **21**, 247.

GALIFRET, Y. & PIÉRON, H. (1950) *Année Psychol.*, **49**, 1.
GOLDSMITH, T. H. (1958) *Proc. Nat. Acad. Sci. (U.S.)*, **44**, 123.
GRAHAM, C. H. & HSIA, Y. (1957) *Proc. Nat. Acad. Sci. (U.S.)*, **43**, 1011 et (1958) **44**, 46.
KOHLER, IVO (1951) *Österr. Akad. Wiss. Math-naturw. Kl. Sitzber*, **227**, 1.
MANDELBAUM, J. & MINTZ, E. V. (1941) *Am. J. Ophthalmol.*, **24**, 1241.
MILES, R. C. (1956) *J. Comp. and Physiol. Psychol.*, **51**, 152.
NIMEROFF, I. (1957) *J. Opt. Soc. Amer.*, **47**, 697.
PIÉRON, H. (1914) *Bull. Sci. Fr. et Belg.*, **48**, 32.
PIÉRON, H. (1942) *Année Psychol.*, **40**, 52.
POLACK, A. (1918) *Compt. rend.*, **166**, 501.
SANDERS, C. L. & WYSZECKI, G. (1957) *J. Opt. Soc. Amer.*, **47**, 398, 840.
SCHLIEPER, C. (1927) *Z. vergleich. Physiol.*, **6**, 493.
SVAETICHIN, G. (1956) *Acta Physiol. Scand.*, **39**, sup. 134, 17 et 67.
VILTER, V. (1949) *Compt. rend. soc. biol.*, **143**, 781, 830 et 1509.
VRIES, HL. DE (1946), *Nature*, **157**, 736.
WALLS, G. L. & HEATH, G. G. (1954) *Acta Ophthalmol.*, **32**, 253.
WILLMER, E. N. (1955) *Doc. Ophthalmol.*, **9**, 235.
WRIGHT, W. D. (1934) *Proc. Roy. Soc. London*, **B119**, 49.
WRIGHT, W. D. (1952) *J. Opt. Soc. Amer.*, **42**, 509.

INVENTAIRE ZOOLOGIQUE

I

ÜBER DEN FARBENSINN DER INSEKTEN

K. von Frisch

Bei Bienen sind wir über den Farbensinn besser unterrichtet als bei allen übrigen Insekten. Ich möchte daher zuerst über den *Farbensinn der Bienen* sprechen, dann unsere Kenntnisse bei *anderen Insekten* vergleichend behandeln und schliesslich etwas über die *blütenbiologische Bedeutung* der Befunde sagen.

I

Schon Lubbock (1885) und Forel (1910) haben gezeigt, dass man Bienen durch Fütterung auf farbigem Papier an diese Farbe gewöhnen kann und dass sie z.B. Blau von Rot mit Sicherheit unterscheiden.

v. Hess wies darauf hin, dass solches 'Farbenunterscheidungsvermögen' noch kein Beweis für 'Farbensinn' ist. Denn auch ein total farbenblinder Mensch kann Blau und Rot unterscheiden, und zwar nach der Helligkeit. Rot erscheint ihm viel dunkler als Blau. Nach v. Hess (1913) sollen die Fische und alle wirbellosen Tiere total farbenblind sein. Er begründete diese Ansicht mit seinem Befund, dass die Fische und die wirbellosen Tiere in ihrem *Helligkeitssinn* mit dem total farbenblinden Menschen übereinstimmen (Spektrum am langwelligen Ende verkürzt, hellste Stelle im Gelbgrün bis Grün). Das ist aber kein Beweis für totale Farbenblindheit. Überdies gilt diese Übereinstimmung nicht für alle Insekten (Schlieper, 1928).

Im Gegensatz zu v. Hess konnte ich zeigen (1914, 1915), dass Bienen, die durch Fütterung auf Blau 'dressiert' sind, diese Farbe von Graustufen jeder Helligkeit sicher unterscheiden. Sie sehen die Farbe qualitativ verschieden von Grau, sie haben also Farbensinn. Der Versuch gelang auch mit anderen Farben, jedoch mit zwei Ausnahmen: Scharlachrot verwechselten die Bienen mit Dunkelgrau und Schwarz, und nach Dressur auf ein blaugrünes Papier beflogen sie Graupapiere von mittlerer Helligkeit ebenso stark wie das Blaugrün. Vor die Aufgabe gestellt, die Dressurfarbe unter anderen Farben herauszufinden, verwechselten die Bienen Gelb mit Orange und Grün, sowie anderseits Blau mit Violett und Purpurrot. Ihr Verhalten erinnerte an die Rot-Grün-Blindheit des Menschen, speziell an die Protanopie. Ich habe darum nach jenen Versuchen die Bienen für rotgrünblind gehalten.

Seither sind unsere Kenntnisse vom Farbensehen der Bienen zweimal wesentlich vertieft worden. Beidemale hat sich gezeigt, dass wir ihre Fähigkeiten unterschätzt hatten.

Der erste Fortschritt kam durch Kühn & Pohl (1921). Sie wiederholten die Dressurversuche, die ich mit Heringschen Farbpapieren gemacht hatte, mit Spektralfarben. Hierbei fanden sie, dass die Bienen Ultraviolett sehen und als besondere Farbe qualitativ von den anderen Spektralbereichen unterscheiden. Ferner, dass sie auch spektrales Blaugrün als spezifische Farbe sehen. Das Misslingen meiner Dressur auf Blaugrün war auf die Verwendung von Farbpapieren zurückzuführen, die neben Blaugrün auch Ultraviolett reflektieren (dieses ist für unser Auge nicht erkennbar, für die Bienen aber sichtbar und zu Blaugrün komplementär, s.S. 22). Das Ergebnis umfangreicher Versuche von Kühn (1927) lässt sich dahin zusammenfassen, dass für Bienen die Sichtbarkeitsgrenzen des Spektrums nach der kurzwelligen Seite verschoben sind und dass sie nur 4 Farbqualitäten sehen: 'Gelb' (650-500 mμ), 'Blaugrün' (500-480 mμ), 'Blau' (480-400 mμ) und 'Ultraviolett' (400-300 mμ). Zwischen 'Gelb' und 'Blaugrün' sowie zwischen 'Blaugrün' und 'Blau' fand er schmale Übergangsgebiete, die für die Bienen mit beiden Nachbargebieten Ähnlichkeit hatten.

Kühn gelang auch der Nachweis des simultanen Farbenkontrastes für das Bienenauge. Auf Blau dressierte Bienen beflogen einen grauen Streifen, wenn er in gelber Umgebung geboten wurde. Wenn eine so typische Erscheinung des menschlichen Farbensehens auch bei Bienen besteht, so darf man daraus schliessen, dass trotz der anatomischen Verschiedenheiten zwischen dem Linsenauge des Menschen und dem Facettenauge der Biene die physiologischen Grundlagen des Farbensehens in beiden Fällen ähnlich sind.

Die zweite Vertiefung unserer Kenntnisse verdanken wir meinem Schüler Daumer (1956). Wir wussten bisher nicht, ob die Gesetze der Farbenmischung, wie sie vom Menschen bekannt sind, auch bei Insekten bestehen oder ob diese etwa in einem Gemisch die einzelnen Wellenlängen erkennen, wie wir im Bereich der Schallwahrnehmung. Daumer konstruierte einen für Bienendressuren geeigneten Apparat, bei dem eine Mischung der Farben mit Einschluss des Ultraviolett möglich war.

Als Lichtquelle diente eine Xenon-Hochdrucklampe, zur Zeit die beste Lampe, um 'Tageslicht' künstlich zu erzeugen. Sie war im Inneren einer Trommel untergebracht, in der durch Interferenzfilter die gewünschten Farben gewonnen, in ihrer Intensität messbar abgestuft und in Reflexionsmischkammern, die mit geknitterter Aluminiumfolie ausgekleidet waren, nach Belieben miteinander gemischt werden konnten. Mit den verschiedenen reinen oder Misch-Lichtern wurden im Deckel der Trommel 4 Ausschnitte von unten beleuchtet. Der Apparat stand in einem halbdunklen Raum, in den die Bienen durch eine Fensteröffnung einfliegen konnten. Über dem Dressurlicht stand ein Quarzfuttergefäss mit Zuckerwasser, über dem Vergleichslicht ein ebensolches Quarzgefäss mit reinem Wasser. Im Versuch, nach vollzogener Dressur, gab es natürlich nur saubere Gefässe mit reinem Wasser. Es zeigte sich dann, ob die Bienen ein bestimmtes Dressurlicht von einem anderen Licht oder Lichtgemisch unterscheiden können oder nicht.

Es stellte sich rasch heraus, dass dem *Ultraviolett* im Farbensehen der Bienen eine besondere Bedeutung zukommt. Es ist sowohl die hellste, wie auch die gesättigteste Farbe im Bienenspektrum. Das geht aus Versuchen hervor, in welchen nach Dressur auf eine Spektralfarbe die minimale Intensität dieser Farbe bestimmt wurde, die eben hinreicht, damit die Bienen das beleuchtete Feld von einem nicht farbig beleuchteten unterscheiden können. Je geringer die Intensität, die zum Erkennen der Farbe ausreicht, desto grösser ist deren *Reizwirksamkeit*. Bezogen auf Energiegleichheit, ergab sich als relative Reizwirksamkeit der Farben (wenn man jene von Grün = 1 setzt): Orange 0,3 — Blaugrün 0,5 — Gelb 0,8 — Grün 1,0 — Blauviolett 1,5 — Ultraviolett 5,6.

An dieser Reizwirksamkeit ist sowohl die Helligkeit der Farbe (für das Bienenauge) wie ihre Sättigung beteiligt. Die *Sättigung* lässt sich gesondert feststellen indem man prüft, wieviel von einer bestimmten Farbe nötig ist, um einem Weisslicht von bekannter Intensität einen für Bienen eben erkennbaren Farbton zu geben. Ultraviolett zeigt die grösste, Blaugrün die geringste Sättigung.

Das *Unterscheidungsvermögen für Farbtöne* ist besser, als wir früher angenommen hatten. Orange, Gelb und Grün sind für Bienen im Farbton einander ähnlich, aber nicht identisch. Mit dem Apparat von Daumer gelang eine Differenzdressur zwischen den 3 genannten Farben — aber nicht mit jener Sicherheit, mit der eine jede dieser Farben von Blaugrün oder von Blau oder Ultraviolett unterschieden wird. Auch Blau und Violett sind einander ähnlich, aber unterscheidbar.* Die alten Begriffe des 'Gelbbereiches' und 'Blaubereiches' für das Farbensehen der Bienen bleiben also giltig in dem Sinne, dass die Farben innerhalb dieser verhältnismässig breiten Spektralbezirke für Bienen viel ähnlicher sind als für uns.

Ein unerwarteter Reichtum an Farbtönen enthüllte sich aber bei Berücksichtigung des *Ultraviolett*: Innerhalb des Ultraviolett konnten (weil nicht mehr geeignete Filter vorhanden waren) nur die Wellenlängen 375 mμ und 360 mμ gegeneinander geprüft werden. Die Differenzdressur ist trotz des geringen Unterschiedes von 15 mμ gut gelungen. Die Biene sieht also auch im Ultraviolett selbst noch verschiedene Farbtöne.

Wie für uns durch Mischung von Rot und Violett die Purpurfarben entstehen und das farbige Band des Spektrums zum Kreis schliessen, so lassen sich

* Schon Kühn & Fränkel (1927) hatten mit einer abgeänderten Methodik eine gewisse Unterscheidbarkeit der Farben innerhalb des 'Gelbbereiches' und 'Blaubereiches' gefunden. Lotmar (1933) konnte das bestätigen, machte aber hauptsächlich die verschiedene Helligkeit der Farben für diese Unterscheidung der Nuancen verantwortlich. Daumer konnte bei seinen Versuchen den Einfluss der Helligkeit und Sättigung ausschliessen.

für Bienen durch Mischung der Endbezirke des *für sie* wahrnehmbaren Spektrums, also durch Mischung von Gelb und Ultraviolett, Farben erzeugen, die im Spektrum für sie nicht vorhanden sind (*'Bienenpurpur'*). Innerhalb dieses Bereiches können sie 2 Farben sehr sicher (5 Farbtöne mässig gut) unterscheiden. — Durch Mischung von Blauviolett und Ultraviolett entstehen weitere, bisher unbekannt gewesene Farbqualitäten (3 sicher, 7 mässig gut unterscheidbar), die als *'Bienenviolett'* bezeichnet werden können.

Wie man für das menschliche Auge farbloses Weiss nicht nur aus der Mischung aller Spektralfarben erhält, sondern auch dann, wenn man nur die 3 Grundfarben Rot, Grün und Blau im richtigen Verhältnis miteinander mischt, so lässt sich für Bienen ein neutrales Licht, das für sie mit keiner Spektralfarbe Ähnlichkeit hat, durch Mischung von 55 Prozent Gelb + 30 Prozent Blauviolett + 15 Prozent Ultraviolett herstellen (*'Bienenweiss'*).

Da am 'Bienenweiss' das für uns unsichtbare Ultraviolett beteiligt ist, können Gegenstände, die uns einheitlich weiss erscheinen, für Bienen verschieden aussehen:* 'weiss' dann, wenn sie alles für Bienen sichtbare Licht, also auch Ultraviolett, zurückwerfen. Wenn sie nur wenig oder kein Ultraviolett reflektieren, werden sie farbig gesehen. Ein ultraviolettarmes Weiss wird von Bienen mit Blaugrün verwechselt. Ein blaugrünes Papier, das auch (für uns nicht erkennbar) Ultraviolett reflektiert, verliert dadurch für Bienen seine Farbigkeit. Hertz (1938, 1939) betrachtete daher Blaugrün und Ultraviolett als Komplementärfarben für das Bienenauge. Das konnte Daumer bestätigen. Dagegen hat sich ihre Annahme, dass auch Gelb und Blau für die Bienen Komplementärfarben sind, als irrig erwiesen.†

Komplementärfarben für Bienen, die durch Mischung im richtigen Verhältnis 'Bienenweiss' ergeben, sind nach Daumers Versuchen:

> 'Gelb' und 'Bienenviolett'
> 'Blaugrün' und 'Ultraviolett'
> 'Blau' und 'Bienenpurpur'.

Die bisher bekannten 4 Hauptqualitäten der Bienenfarben haben sich durch 'Bienenviolett' und 'Bienenpurpur' auf 6 vermehrt. Das Farbensystem der Bienen kann als trichromatisch angesehen werden, wie das des Menschen, von dem es sich hauptsächlich durch die Verschiebung des ganzen Empfindlichkeitsbereiches nach der kurzwelligen Seite des Spektrums unterscheidet (Abb. 1).

---

* Das hat schon Lutz (1933) erkannt, vgl. auch Hertz (1937) und Engländer (1941).

† Wie es zu erklären ist, dass Kühn trotzdem mit blauem und gelbem Farbpapier den simultanen Farbenkontrast bei Bienen nachweisen konnte, kann ohne neue, darauf gerichtete Versuche nicht gesagt werden. Das Gelb hatte vielleicht mit Bienenpurpur (Komplementärfarbe zu Blau) genügend Ähnlichkeit. Vielleicht erschien es aber infolge von Reflexion ultravioletten Lichtes den Bienen tatsächlich als 'Bienenpurpur'.

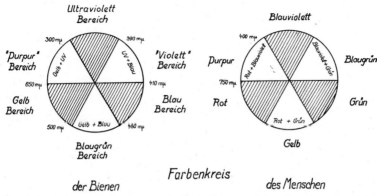

ABB. 1. Farbenkreis der Bienen und des Menschen. Schraffiert die drei Grundfarbbereiche. Dazwischen die durch additive Mischung der ersteren darstellbaren
Zwischenfarbbereiche. Gegenüberliegende Sektoren bezeichnen Kompementär-
farbenpaare (Nach Daumer).

II

Das Farbensehen ist keine Spezialität der Honigbiene. Knoll (1926)
studierte eingehend die Fliege *Bombylius fuliginosus* und den Schwärmer
Macroglossum stellatarum. Zum Nachweis des Farbensinnes übernahm er die
Graustufen-Methode mit Pigmentpapieren, er benützte aber meist, statt
künstlicher Dressur, die natürliche Bindung der Insekten an eine Farbe, wie
sie beim Blumenbesuch zustande kommt. Die von ihm untersuchten Fliegen
und Schmetterlinge erwiesen sich als rotblind und konnten einen 'Gelb-
bereich' und einen 'Blaubereich', voneinander, sowie von allen Graustufen
sicher unterscheiden. Das Ultraviolett blieb ausser Betracht.

Da nicht alle Insekten natürliche Bindungen an bestimmte Farben eingehen
oder zu Dressurversuchen geeignet sind, hat man zum Nachweis eines
Farbensehens noch andere Methoden herangezogen.

Hamilton (1922) benützte die positive Phototaxis von *Drosophila* um zu
zeigen, dass Lichter verschiedener Wellenlänge für diese Fliegen qualitativ
verschieden sind. Wenn man zwei Farben in ihrer Intensität so abstuft, dass
sie die phototaktischen Tiere gleich stark anlocken, und die Fliegen dann
längere Zeit mit *einer* der beiden Farben bestrahlt, so erweisen sie sich als
spezifisch für diese Farbe ermüdet und die vorher eingestellte Gleichung ist
zugunsten der anderen Farbe verschoben.

Eine weitere Methode bedient sich der optomotorischen Reaktionen.
Schlieper (1927) fand, dass bei Drehung eines Streifenzylinders, der aus
abwechselnd grauen und farbigen Streifen zusammengesetzt ist, der *Hellig-
keitswert* der Farben für die Auslösung der Reaktion massgebend ist. Zu jeder
Farbe lässt sich eine Graustufe finden, bei der die optomotorische Reaktion

unterbleibt oder auf ein Minimum sinkt. Es wird angenommen, dass diese Graustufe dem Tier gleich hell erscheint wie die Farbe. Sucht man nun *zwei Farben*, die für das Tier gleich hell sind — z.b. ein Blau und ein Gelb, die beide bei *derselben* Graustufe ihr Minimum der optomotorischen Reaktion haben — so erhält man mit Streifenzylindern, die aus *diesen beiden Farben* zusammengesetzt sind, trotz gleicher Helligkeit klare optomotorische Reaktionen. Die beiden Farben müssen also qualitativ verschieden gesehen werden. So konnte Schlegtendal (1934) bei verschiedenen Fliegen, Käfern und Schmetterlingen ein Farbensehen nachweisen.

Auf grundsätzlich gleiche Art zeigten Autrum & Stumpf (1953) mit elektrophysiologischer Methodik an Hand der Erregungspotentiale, dass das Auge der Fliege *Calliphora* bei Darbietung von Flimmerlicht auf Farben spezifisch anspricht. Es liegen auch andere elektrophysiologische Versuche an Insektenaugen vor. Im Gegensatz zum Verhaltensversuch geben sie über intime Vorgänge an bestimmter Stelle des Nervensystems Aufschluss. Ihre Deutung ist aber noch so unsicher, dass sie entscheidende Beiträge zu unseren Vorstellungen über das Farbensehen der Insekten bisher nicht geliefert haben.

Ein Farbensinn ist schon bei so vielen Insektenordnungen nachgewiesen, dass die Frage berechtigt ist, ob es total farbenblinde Insekten überhaupt gibt. Schlegtendal (1934) vermutet, dass Stabheuschrecken (*Dixippus*) und die Baumwanze *Troilus* (Pentatomide) farbenblind seien. Rokohl (1942) nimmt Farbenblindheit für den ventralen Augenteil des Rückenschwimmers (*Notonecta*) an. Diese Befunde stützen sich auf die optomotorische Methode, die mir aber nur bei positiven, nicht bei negativen Ergebnissen beweiskräftig scheint. Versuche von Hundertmark (1937) an *Dixippus* sind gleichfalls mit der Annahme totaler Farbenblindheit vereinbar, ohne sie zu beweisen. Walther (1958) erhielt bei elektrophysiologischen Untersuchungen an der Küchenschabe (*Periplaneta*) Ergebnisse, die für Farbenblindheit der unteren Augenteile sprechen, doch hält er selbst eine solche Folgerung nicht für zwingend. Ich kenne keinen einwandfreien Nachweis für totale Farbenblindheit bei einer Insektenart.

Auch das Auftreten von totaler Farbenblindheit im Zustande der Dunkeladaptation — wie bei Wirbeltieren — konnte für Insekten bisher nicht erwiesen werden. *Drosophila* soll nach Fingerman & Brown (1953) im Dämmerlicht farbenblind werden, doch sind die Versuche nicht überzeugend. Denn die beobachteten Veränderungen der Reaktionsweise könnten auch auf andere Ursachen zurückzuführen sein (Pigmentwanderung im Auge, geringere Ermüdung bei schwacher Belichtung). Knoll (1925) fand bei dem Schwärmer *Deilephila livornica*, dass bei sehr schwachem Dämmerlicht, bei welchem das menschliche Auge farbenblind war, die Farben sicher erkannt wurden. Bei noch schwächerer Beleuchtung stellten die Tiere den Flug ein.

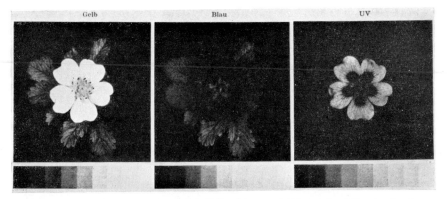

ABB. 2. *Potentilla reptans*, durch das Gelb-, Blau- und Ultraviolett-Filter in den 3 Grundbereichen des Bienenfarbsystems aufgenommen. In der Ultraviolett-Aufnahme erscheint ein für uns unsichtbares Saftmal. Die mitphotographierten Blätter reflektieren in allen 3 Bereichen ziemlich gleichmässig und erscheinen den Bienen fast farblos, schwach gelblich (nach Daumer).

Bei manchen Insekten sind die vorliegenden Kenntnisse mit der Annahme eines dichromatischen Farbensinnes vereinbar, doch ist ein solcher in keinem Falle erwiesen. Es blieb ja auch das Ultraviolett bei den Untersuchungen meist unberücksichtigt. Verschiedenheiten bestehen in der Wahrnehmungsgrenze am langwelligen Ende des Spektrums. So fanden Kühn & Ilse (1925) und Ilse (1929), dass gewisse Tagfalter nicht rotblind sind. Der Leuchtkäfer *Photinus pyralis* reagiert nach Buck (1937) noch auf tiefrote Blinklichter (690 mμ). Eine Empfindlichkeit für ultraviolettes licht ist auch für *Drosophila* erwiesen (Bertholf, 1932) und scheint bei Insekten sehr allgemein verbreitet zu sein. Denn *Masochin-Porschnjakow* (1955, 1956) machte die Erfahrung, dass beim Köderfang mit Licht von ultraviolettreichen Lampen Insekten fast aller Ordnungen sehr viel stärker angelockt werden als bei Anwendung gewöhnlicher Lampen.

III

Die Blumenfarben erleichtern den Insekten das Entdecken der Blüten und, bei gegebener 'Blütenstetigkeit', das Herausfinden der beflogenen Art aus einem Meer verschiedenartiger Blumen. Um uns die Bedeutung der farbigen Abhebung von einem gleichmässigen Hintergrund zu vergegenwärtigen, brauchen wir nur an eigene Erfahrungen zu denken: Wie leicht sind blühende Vergissmeinnicht, Lichtnelken oder andere Blumen in Menge zu einem Strauss zu sammeln — und wie schwer ist es, diese Pflanzen im einheitlichen Grün der Wiese aufzufinden, sobald die Blüte vorüber ist!

Offensichtlich besteht ein tiefer Zusammenhang zwischen den Farben der Blumen und dem Farbensinn der regelmässigen Blütengäste. Das 'Kolibrirot', das für ornithophile Blüten so bezeichnend ist, kommt dem für Rot besonders empfindlichen Vogelauge entgegen. Für rotblinde Insekten wären solche scharlachrote Blüten nicht sinnvoll. Tatsächlich sind sie bei entomophilen Blüten eine Seltenheit. Purpurfarbige Blüten mit relativ viel Rot sind von Blüten bekannt, die durch Tagfalter bestäubt werden — und diese sind nicht rotblind (Ilse, 1929). Rote Mohnblüten und rote Bohnenblüten reflektieren neben Rot viel Ultraviolett und erscheinen den Bienen als 'ultraviolette' Blumen (Lotmar, 1933; Daumer, 1958).

Daumer (1958) suchte einen Überblick über das Aussehen der Blumen für das Bienenauge dadurch zu gewinnen, dass er von mehr als 200 verschiedenen Blüten photographische Aufnahmen durch 3 Farbfilter machte, deren Durchlässigkeitsbereiche der spektralen Ausdehnung der 3 Grundfarbbereiche der Bienen entsprachen. Mit der Blüte wurde eine 10 stufige Grauleiter mit aufgenommen, die es gestattete, die Reflexion der Blütenteile für jeden der 3 Spektralbezirke in Prozent von Weiss (MgO-Reflexion) auszumessen. Ohne auf die quantitativen Daten einzugehen, soll hier nur das Hauptergebnis

c

besprochen werden: Dass Bienen *mehr* verschiedene Blumenfarben sehen, als wir bisher geahnt haben und dass sich viele für uns gleich aussehende Blüten infolge verschiedener Ultraviolett-Reflexion für das Insektenauge deutlich voneinander unterscheiden. So sind z.B. die Cruciferen *Erysimum helveticum*, *Brassica napus* und *Sinapis arvensis* für uns gleichmässig gelb, sie sind einander auch in der Blütenform sehr ähnlich — aber sie reflektieren in verschiedenem Masse Ultraviolett. Nur die erstgenannte Art hat auch für Bienen rein gelbe Blüten, da sie kein Ultraviolett zurückwerfen, die beiden anderen Arten haben 'bienenpurpurne' Blüten in zwei verschiedenen Tönungen. Dressur-versuche bestätigten, dass diese drei Blütenarten von den Bienen an ihrer Farbe sicher unterschieden werden. Für uns blaue Blüten können auch für Bienen 'blau' sein, oder durch gleichzeitige Ultraviolett-Reflexion 'bienen-violett'.

Uns *weiss* erscheinende Blumen absorbieren fast ausnahmslos das Ultra-violett. Dadurch werden sie für Bienen — und wahrscheinlich für alle Insekten — farbig, und zwar 'Blaugrün' (Hertz, 1937; Daumer, 1958). Ihre Farbigkeit ist wichtig, weil Farben für Bienen eindrucksvoller sind als 'Weiss'. Eine Dressur auf unbunte Lichter gelingt verhältnismässig schwer. Auch heben sich farbige Blumen vom Laub wirksamer ab als farblose, denn das Grün der Blätter ist — nach Daumers Messungen an 60 verschiedenen Pflanzenarten — für Bienen ein fast farbloses, blass gelbliches Grau. Die grünen Blätter reflektieren das Licht in den drei Grundfarbbereichen der Bienen nahezu in dem Verhältnis, das für sie bei additiver Mischung neutrales 'Grau' gibt. Abb. 2 zeigt eine Blüte von *Potentilla reptans* mit einigen Blättern durch die 3 Farbfilter aufgenommen. Die Blätter reflektieren ziemlich gleichmässig, nur im Gelb ein wenig mehr.

Das Bild bringt noch eine andere überraschende Erscheinung. Die Blüte ist für uns gleichmässig gelb. Sie reflektiert stark im Gelb, fast nicht im Blau. Im Ultraviolett erscheint ein prächtiges, *für uns unsichtbares* 'Saftmal'. Da nur die äusseren Teile der Blumenblätter neben Gelb auch Ultraviolett reflektieren, ist die Farbe dieser Blüte ein 'Bienenpurpur' mit zentralem, rein gelbem Saftmal. Dass es so etwas gibt, hat schon Lutz (1924, 1933) erkannt (vgl. auch Richtmyer, 1923; Vogel, 1950). Aber dass für das ultraviolett-sichtige Bienenauge für uns unsichtbare Saftmale sogar häufiger vorkommen als entsprechende, auch für uns sichtbare Blütenmuster, haben erst Daumers Aufnahmen ans Licht gebracht.

Die Bedeutung der Saftmale als Wegweiser zur Nahrung ist wiederholt bezweifelt worden, aber mit Unrecht. Sie ist heute erwiesen (Knoll, 1923, 1926; Kugler, 1943, 1950, 1951; Manning, 1956) und von Daumer (1958) erneut bestätigt, auch für jene Blütenzeichnungen, die unseren ultraviolettblinden Augen verborgen bleiben. Das Saftmal ist, ganz im Sinne Sprengels (1793) eine Markierung der Stelle, wo in der Blüte das Futter zu finden ist, und wirkt darüber hinaus wie eine Einladung zu Tisch. Denn die Biene beantwortet nach dem Anflug an die Blüte die Erscheinung des Saftmales mit einer, nachweislich angeborenen Reaktion, indem sie den Kopf senkt und den Rüssel ausstreckt, auch wenn daselbst — im Experiment — gar nichts zu holen ist.

Zweifellos werden den Insekten auch ihre eigenen Körperfarben wesentlich anders erscheinen als uns (vgl. Crane, 1954; Masochin-Porschnjakow, 1954). Die bunten Kleider der Schmetterlinge und Käfer sind geradezu herausfordernd für eine kritische Betrachtung in diesem Sinne. Aber wir sollten erst wissen, wie weit die gewonnenen Kenntnisse über das Farbensehen der Bienen auch bei anderen Insekten gelten. Den Beziehungen zwischen dem Farbensinn der Insektenarten, ihrer eigenen Körperfärbung und den Blumenfarben weiter nachzugehen, ist eine reizvolle Aufgabe für die Zukunft.

Literatur-Verzeichnis

Autrum, H. & Stumpf, H. (1953) *Z. vergleich. Physiol.*, **35**, 71.
Bertholf, L. M. (1931a) *J. Ag. Research*, **43**, 703.
Bertholf, L. M. (1931b) *J. Ag. Research*, **42**, 379.
Bertholf, L. M. (1932) *Z. vergleich. Physiol.*, **18**, 32.
Buck, J. B. (1937) *Physiol. Zoöl.*, **10**, 412.
Buddenbrock, W. v. & Moller-Racke, I. (1952) *Experientia*, **8**, 62.
Crane, J. (1954) *Zoologica, Contr. N.Y. Zool. Soc.*, **39**, 85.
Daumer, K. (1956) *Z. vergleich. Physiol.*, **38**, 413.
Daumer, K. (1958) *Z. vergleich. Physiol.*, **41**, 49.
Engländer, H. (1941) *Archiv f. Bienenkunde*, **22**, Heft 5/6.
Fingerman, M. & Brown, F. A. (1953) *Physiol. Zoöl.*, **26**, 59.
Forel, A. (1910) *Das Sinnesleben der Insekten*, München.
Frisch, K. v. (1914a) *Verh. Deutsch. Zoolog. Ges.*, Freiburg, 50.
Frisch, K. v. (1914b) *Der Farbensinn und Formensinn der Bienen*, Jena; auch in (1915) *Zool. Jahrb. Phys.*, **35**, 1.
Frisch, K. v. (1919) *Biol. Zentr.*, **39**, 122.
Frisch, K. v. (1923) *Naturwiss.*, 470.
Hamilton, W. F. (1922) *Proc. Nat. Acad. Sci. (U.S.)*, **8**, 350.
Hertz, M. (1937) *Z. vergleich. Physiol.*, **24**, 413.
Hertz, M. (1938) *Z. vergleich. Physiol.*, **25**, 239.
Hertz, M. (1939) *J. Exper. Biol.*, **16**, 1.
Hess, C. v. (1913a) *Zool. Jahrb. Phys.*, **34**, 81.
Hess, C. v. (1913b) Die Entwicklung von Lichtsinn und Farbensinn in der Tierreihe, *Vortrag Vers. d. Naturf. u. Aerzte*, Wien, Wiesbaden 1914.
Hundertmark, A. (1937a) *Biol. Zentr.*, **57**, 228.
Hundertmark, A. (1937b) *Z. vergleich. Physiol.*, **24**, 42.
Ilse, D. (1929) *Z. vergleich. Physiol.*, **8**, 658.
Ilse, D. (1949) *Nature*, **163**, 255.
Ilse, D. & Vaidya, K. G. (1956) *Proc. Indian Acad. Sci.*, **43**, 23.
Knoll, F. (1923) *Ber. deut. botan. Ges.*, **40**, 30.
Knoll, F. (1925) *Z. vergleich. Physiol.*, **2**, 329.
Knoll, F. (1926) *Abhandl. d. Zool. Bot. Ges.*, in Wien, **12**.
Koehler, O. (1924) *Verh. deut. Zool. Ges.*, **29**, 83.
Kühn, A. (1927) *Z. vergleich. Physiol.*, **5**, 762.
Kühn, A. & Fraenkel, G. (1927) *Nachr. Ges. d. Wissensch. math. physik.*, Kl. Göttingen.

28 *Inventaire Zoologique*

KÜHN, A. & ILSE, D. (1925) *Biol. Zentr.*, **45**, 144.
KÜHN, A. & POHL, R. (1921) *Naturwiss.*
KUGLER, H. (1943) *Ergeb. Biol.*, **19**, 143.
KUGLER, H. (1950a) *Naturw. Rundschau*, 269.
KUGLER, H. (1950b) *Z. vergleich. Physiol.*, **32**, 328.
KUGLER, H. (1951) *Ber. Physik. mediz. Ges.*, Würzburg, N.F. **66**, 28.
KUGLER, H. (1952) *Ber. deut. botan. Ges.*, **44**, 327.
LOTMAR, R. (1933) *Z. vergleich. Physiol.*, **19**, 673.
LUBBOCK, J. (1885) *Ants, Bees and Wasps*, London.
LUTZ, F. E. (1924) *Ann. N.Y. Acad. Sci.*, **29**, 181.
LUTZ, F. E. (1933a) *Am. Museum Novitates*, nr. **641**, 1.
LUTZ, F. E. (1933b) *Natural History*, **33**, 565.
MANNING, A. (1956) *J. Animal Behaviour*, **9**, 114.
MASOCHIN-PORSCHRJAKOW (1954) *Akad. Wiss. UDSSR, Zhur. allg. Biol.*, **15** (russisch).
MASOCHIN-PORSCHRJAKOW (1955) *Ber. Akad. Wiss. d. UDSSR*, **102**, 729 (russisch).
MASOCHIN-PORSCHRJAKOW (1956) *Zhur. Zool.*, **35**, (russisch).
MASOCHIN-PORSCHRJAKOW (1957) *Acad. Wiss. UDSSR, Biophysik*, Nr. **3**, 358 (russisch m. engl. Zus. Fassung).
MOERICKE, V. (1950) *Z. Tierpsychol.*, **7**, 265.
MOLLER-RACKE, I. (1949) *Verh. deutsch. Zool. Ges.*, Mainz.
RICHTMYER, F. K. (1923) *J. Opt. Soc. Amer.*, **7**, 151.
ROKOHL, R. (1942) *Z. vergleich. Physiol.*, **29**, 638.
SCHLEGTENDAL, A. (1934) *Z. vergleich. Physiol.*, **20**, 545.
SCHLIEPER, C. (1927) *Z. vergleich. Physiol.*, **6**, 453.
SCHLIEPER, C. (1928) *Z. vergleich. Physiol.*, **8**, 281.
SCHREMMER, F. (1941) *Z. vergleich. Physiol.*, **28**, 457.
SPRENGEL, C. C. (1793) *Das entdeckte Geheimnis der Natur im Bau und in der Befruchtung der Blumen*, Berlin.
SÜFFERT, F. & GÖTZ, B. (1936) *Naturwiss.*, **24**, 815.
VOGEL, S. (1950) *Österr. Botan. Z.*, **97**, 44.
WALTHER, J. B. (1958) *Biol. Zentr.*, **77**, 63.
WALTHER, J. B. & DODT, E. (1957) *Experientia*, **13**, 333.

DISCUSSION

PIÉRON

Je remercie le Pr. von Frisch de son exposé. Il a montré un domaine de la vision colorée qui ne correspond pas tout à fait à celui de l'homme, mais qui lui correspond tout de même avec un certain décalage — ce qui est, évidemment, particulièrement intéressant et rend désirable que l'on puisse en faire une étude aussi systématique que possible avec des équations de couleurs, comme on le fait chez l'homme, de manière que nous puissions mieux pénétrer la nature exacte de ce système, qui serait aussi trichromatique.

Mais maintenant je vais demander à ceux, entre vous, qui veulent poser des questions au Pr. von Frisch, de bien vouloir venir ici pour les poser directement.

HURVICH

I have one or two short questions. I should like to know what the transmission of the facets of the bee's eye is; have they been analysed in this respect? The second question relates to experiments in which humans who are aphakic have viewed spectral light and reported on its appearance at the spectral extremes. There are several experimental reports on this, and I can't at the moment recall what hues these observers reported that they saw in the low wavelength region. Do you know what the human observer does see in the near ultra-violet?

VON FRISCH

Mir sind keine genauen Untersuchungen bekannt über die Ultraviolett-Wahrnehmung von Menschen ohne Augenlinse. Dass das Auge der Insekten für Ultraviolett durchlässig ist, ergibt sich schon daraus, dass sie auf ultraviolettes Licht so deutlich reagieren. Genaue Messungen über die Durchlässigkeit der Cornea, der Kristallkegel und der anderen Augenteile sind mir nicht bekannt.

PIÉRON

La vision humaine de l'ultraviolet, n'est-ce pas? C'est ce que l'on signale dans le cas où il n'y a plus de cristallin, et on a pu montrer surtout qu'avec des énergies suffisantes il y avait possibilité de rendre décelables des rayonnements ultraviolets jusque vers 300 millimicrons, c'est-à-dire, au fond, tout l'ultraviolet qui atteint la terre dans le rayonnement du soleil.

Seulement, chez l'Abeille le fait est très important et très différent: l'ultraviolet qui s'ajoute chez l'homme n'ajoute pas une couleur particulière et différente, et ce qui fait la grosse différence avec le système des abeilles, c'est que les abeilles ont comme un décalage, qui fait que l'ultraviolet représente la couleur extrême du spectre, tandis que celui-ci ne va pas jusqu'au rouge de l'autre côté, et que la lumière se situe dans une partie spectrale qui va depuis la région jaune jusqu'à la limite de l'ultraviolet du rayonnement solaire.

Il y a donc là, n'est-ce pas, une différence extrêment intéressante au point de vue des systèmes récepteurs de l'abeille d'un côté, et de l'homme, de l'autre.

LE GRAND

Je crois que la grande différence entre la vision des insectes, telle que les très belles recherches du Professeur von Frisch et de son école l'ont révélée, et la vision des vertébrés doit biologiquement provenir de la différence dans la structure de formation d'images; l'image, en général, dans l'œil des vertébrés, est obtenue par des moyens dioptriques, c'est-à-dire par un système qui projette sur une surface réceptrice une image au moyen d'une lentille — enfin, d'un dispositif assurant une projection point par point.

Au contraire, dans l'œil des insectes, nous avons un ensemble d'ommatidies, dans l'œil composé, dont chacune est un récepteur individuel, si bien que l'acuité visuelle est obtenue, évidemment, par des moyens extrêmement différents.

Si l'œil du type des vertébrés possédait la vision jusqu'à 300 millimicrons, l'aberration chromatique qui est extrêmement importante dans cette longueur d'onde, même pour l'eau, donnerait une image pratiquement inutilisable.

Évidemment, pour l'abeille, l'aberration chromatique ne joue pas, puisque chaque ommatidie assure une individualité d'acuité, quelle que soit la longueur d'onde.

Il est vraisemblable que c'est la raison biologique pour laquelle ces deux types d'yeux très différents ont des répartitions de sensibilité et de couleur si différentes.

D'ailleurs, il suffit de prendre une photographie dans l'ultraviolet pour voir qu'en plus, la vision des lointains devient extrêmement mauvaise, pour une raison supplémentaire: parce que le voile dû au bleu de l'air prend une telle importance qu'à partir de quelques centaines de mètres on ne voit pratiquement plus, dans l'ultraviolet, par suite de la diffusion sélective, alors qu'il semble que, pour les insectes, ce soit une vision rapprochée qui joue, surtout pour leur permettre d'aller vers les fleurs, alors que pour les vertébrés — du moins, pour les oiseaux et pour les mammifères — la vision lointaine est utile pour la reconnaissance de la proie.

Ce sont donc probablement les deux raisons principales qui tendraient à expliquer — si tant est que nous devions expliquer cette différence — que l'ultraviolet joue un rôle important dans les yeux composés, et n'en joue pas dans les yeux non-composés.

D'autre part, tous les chimistes savent la variété de bandes d'absorption que l'on trouve dans tous les colorants naturels dans l'ultraviolet, et il était donc très tentant, pour des yeux que l'ultraviolet ne gêne pas dans leur vision, d'utiliser cette région spectrale où les différences de réflectance sont beaucoup plus marquées certainement que dans la partie visible du spectre telle qu'elle existe pour nous.

MEDIONI

Je voudrais demander au Professeur von Frisch quelle validité, selon lui, on peut attribuer aux anciennes expériences de Hamilton (1922), tendant à démontrer l'existence du sens chromatique chez la *Drosophile*, expériences qui utilisent le phototropisme positif de cet Insecte (les animaux en expérience étant placés dans un tube de verre éclairé aux deux extrémités par deux faisceaux lumineux opposés).

J'ai eu récemment l'occasion d'étudier le phototropisme de la *Drosophile*, et je puis affirmer que cette espèce n'est pas photopositive de façon absolue et constante.

Le phototropisme, chez la *Drosophile*, présente des phases alternantes d'attraction et de répulsion par la lumière, lesquelles dépendent de la capacité photopathique individuelle, très variable.

Compte tenu de ce fait, je doute qu'on puisse attribuer une validité quelconque aux expériences de Hamilton, ainsi qu'à celles, beaucoup plus récentes, de Fingerman et Brown, que vous avez vous-même critiquées dans la suite de votre rapport.

Je souhaiterais vivement avoir l'opinion du Professeur von Frisch sur cette question.

VON FRISCH

Ich habe die Versuche Hamiltons nicht wiederholt. Es ist nicht leicht ein Urteil abzugeben über Versuche, die man nicht gesehen hat. Aber nach seiner Beschreibung scheinen sie mir überzeugend.

Er belichtete Fliegen von entgegengesetzten Seiten mit zwei verschiedenen Farben, die in ihrer Intensität so eingestellt waren, dass die positiv phototaktischen Fliegen weder der einen, noch der gegenüber stehenden Farbe zustrebten. Die beiden Lichter waren im phototaktischen Gleichgewicht. Dann wurden die Tiere längere Zeit nur mit einer der beiden Farben belichtet. Wurde sodann die zweite Farbe dazu wieder eingeschaltet, so sammelten sich die Fliegen bei dieser, sie war jetzt stärker wirksam. Gegenüber der anderen Farbe, mit der sie länger belichtet worden waren, waren sie spezifisch ermüdet. Wenn sie farbenblind wären, wären die beiden, phototaktisch gleich wirksamen Lichter für sie identisch, sie müssten also gleich wirksam bleiben und es könnte keine spezifische Ermüdung für eine der beiden Farben geben. — Habe ich etwas missverstanden?

MEDIONI

L'existence d'un phototropisme positif n'est pas évidente.

VON FRISCH

Darauf kann ich nichts entgegnen, weil ich die Versuche nicht selbst gesehen habe. Hamilton gibt an, dass die Fliegen positiv phototaktisch waren.

MEDIONI

L'expérience montre que le phototropisme positif n'est pas constant; les Drosophiles sont tantôt attirées, tantôt repoussées par la lumière.

VON FRISCH

Wenn das phototaktische Verhalten der Fliegen schwankend ist, dann sind sie für solche Versuche nicht geeignet.

MEDIONI

Nach meiner Meinung ist es so.

PIÉRON

Je remercie le Professeur von Frisch.

Je demanderai maintenant si quelqu'un a apporté un document sur la vision des insectes qu'il désire faire connaître. Est-ce que le Professeur Autrum pourrait nous parler de la *Calliphora* et de sa méthode d'examen, qui lui a permis de déceler des différences par alternance?

AUTRUM

The capacity for colour discrimination presupposes certain properties of the receptor systems and the neurophysiological responses: at least two receptor systems of differing spectral sensitivity must be present; these two systems must either have specific connections within the CNS, or must vary their signal with the colour. In this connection, the concept of receptors or receptor systems should not be too narrowly defined, especially in morphological respects. The nature and function of receptor systems is being analysed through investigation of the primary processes and following neurophysiological events. Whether animals *attend* to colours can only be decided by behavioural studies.

(I). A necessary condition for the discrimination of two colours is that the neuro-physiological responses conducted to the CNS are always different, regardless of the intensity of the two colours. There must be no intensity pairs of the two colours which give identical neurophysiological responses. Autrum & Stumpf* have flickered alternately two different monochromatic lights of variable intensity, in *Calliphora* (method of heterochromatic flicker), and recorded the electroretinogram. In this method, to a monochromatic stimulus of λ_1 and given intensity I_1 was matched a stimulus of λ_2 with an intensity I_2 such that both stimuli gave potentials of equal amplitude and were therefore equally effective. These two lights were then alternately flickered, without pause, in such a way that during the flicker the effective brightness of the collective stimulus remained constant and only its wavelength was rhythmically altered (Fig. 1).

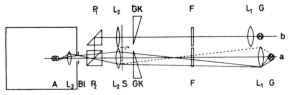

FIG. 1. Schematic representation of the light paths for heterochromatic flicker: a, b, two light paths, each with one light source (G), lenses (L_1, L_2), monochromatic interference filters (F), one wedge-shaped neutral filter (GK); P_1, total reflecting prism; P_2, semi-reflecting prism; Bl, diaphragm; S, sector shutter for alternate flickering of the two rays (after Autrum & Stumpf, 1953).

With this method the following results were obtained for the eye of the fly, *Calliphora erythrocephala*:

Heterochromatic light, which appears white (colourless) to the human eye, gives flicker potentials with all colours of the spectrum between 400 and 690 mμ; therefore no equalization of brightness between white light and spectral colours can be

* Autrum, H. & Stumpf, H. (1953) *Z. vergleich. Physiol.*, **35**, 71-104.

established. An exception is yellow light of 580 mμ, which is exchangeable with white light; white light can be flickered against yellow (580 mμ) so that no flicker potential arises. If lights in the 690-630 mμ range are flickered against each other, only slight responses are obtained; no response is obtained if the wavelengths of the two colours are too narrowly separated. The region between 630 and 580 mμ always gives flicker potentials against lights with wavelengths under 580 or over 630 mμ; in the region of 630 to 580 mμ small differences in wavelength are consistently sufficient to release responses. Similarly, the region between 580 and 480 mμ can be set apart, giving flicker responses with all longer wavelengths. However, there are two wavelengths, one on each side of 480 mμ, which when flickered against each other give no response, and are therefore interchangeable.

The height of the heterochromatic-flicker potential obtained between two colours separated by 10 mμ wavelength, can be used as a measure of the relative sensitivity for colour discrimination. One then obtains the curve of Fig. 2 which expresses the

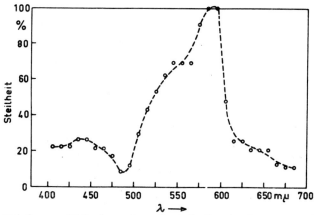

FIG. 2. Relative sensitivity for colour discrimination in the compound eye of *Calliphora*. The height of the curve gives a measure of the relative ability for colour discrimination; large values of the ordinate signify better ability for colour differentiation. Ordinate: slope $\Delta h/\Delta h$ in per cent of maximum value (h = amplitude of the potential, λ = wavelength; $\Delta\lambda$ = 10 mμ). Abscissa: wavelength (after Autrum & Stumpf).

ability of the eye to discriminate colours. A higher ordinate expresses a greater colour-discrimination sensitivity, a smaller wavelength difference being required to produce an effect of a given amplitude.

(II). The difference in characteristics of the electrical responses of the eye of *Calliphora* to equally potent (subjectively equally bright) stimuli of various wavelengths has not yet been investigated. The procedure of heterochromatic flicker gives no information about the spectral sensitivities of the receptor systems, or about the properties of the receptor systems themselves. The response potential in heterochromatic flicker is the result of very complex processes, which are summated in ways as yet poorly understood. In order to be able to say something about the establishment of this complex response, it is necessary to isolate the basic component processes involved.

One route to this goal is to investigate first the form of the electrical response of the eye to single stimuli of various wavelengths. Two methods offer themselves: (1) The intensities I_1 and I_2 of two colours λ_1 and λ_2 can be so chosen that the *response potentials* are first alike in *one* property, for example in the amplitude of the on-effect; then one can test whether or not the potentials are different in other characteristics. (2) The effectiveness (efficacy) curves for different colours of equal quantal level can be determined, in the largest possible range from very small to very large quantal levels.

In *Calliphora* (with complex, diphasic potentials)*† the electrical responses of a given on-effect amplitude to red light have a different form from responses to yellow-green, green, blue or violet light *of equal on-effect amplitude* (Fig. 3). In stimulation by red light there is never a negative initial wave, the latency is greater,

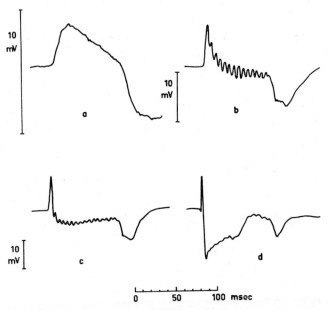

FIG. 3. Compound eye of *Calliphora*: differences in form of the on-effect of the diphasic ERG: (a), 401 mμ; (b), 630 mμ. The intensities are so selected that the on-effects are of the same amplitude. (c, d), the on-effects can have the same amplitudes at lower intensities (c, rel. intensity 0.074; d, rel. intensity 1); however, the form is different. For (c, d) wavelength $\lambda = 511$ mμ (Autrum & Hoffmann, unpublished).

decay of the on-effect is less steep than with stimulation by light of shorter wavelengths (Fig. 3). The potentials obtained cannot be made congruent by alteration of the light intensity of the two stimulus wavelengths (for example 630 and 400 mμ).

The same phenomenon is found in certain eye areas of the cockroach, *Periplaneta*:‡ the responses to various wavelengths which are recorded from the *lower* part of the

* Autrum, H. (1950) *Z. vergleich. Physiol.*, **32**, 176-227.

† Autrum, H. (1953) *Zool. et biol. animale*, **14**, Sér. 11, 439-447.

‡ Walther, J. B. (1958) *Z. Ins. Physiol.*, **2**, 142-151.

compound eye can be made exactly congruent in form by modification of the intensity of the light stimulus used (Fig. 4). However, this is not the case for the

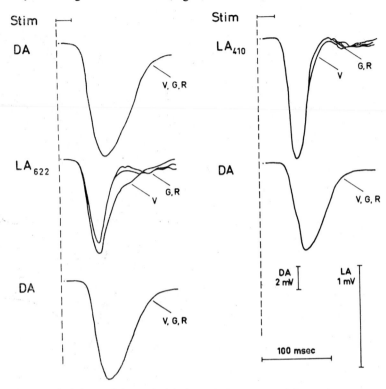

FIG. 4. Typical shape of the potentials from the lower part of the compound eye of *Periplaneta americana* (cockroach); stimulation by different colours following dark adaptation (DA), and their change through light adaptation (LA_λ) to monochromatic light of wavelength λ. DA and LA_λ are alternating with each other in each case (various calibration signals). The intensities of the three colour stimuli are defined in terms of equal effectiveness during the first DA, and remain constant during all further recordings. For each state of adaptation the potentials from stimuli of 407, 507, 605 mμ are superimposed. The difference in form during rise of the potentials to a maximum and in the more gradually declining phase are not significant. The potentials show no selective adaptation (after Walther, 1958).

potentials obtained from the *upper* part of the eye (Fig. 5). One is forced to conclude, therefore, that in at least the upper part of the eye two different receptor systems are present. It is, naturally, not permissible to conclude that only one receptor system is present in the lower part of the eye. The diphasic potentials of the eye of *Calliphora* contain components from the visual cells and components from the ganglia.*†‡ (By operative removal of the optic ganglia one can investigate the

* AUTRUM, H. (1950) *Z. vergleich. Physiol.*, **32**, 176-227.

† AUTRUM, H. & GALLWITZ, U. (1951) *Z. vergleich. Physiol.*, **33**, 407-435.

‡ AUTRUM, H. & HOFFMANN, E. (1957) *Z. Naturforsch.*, **12b**, 752-7.

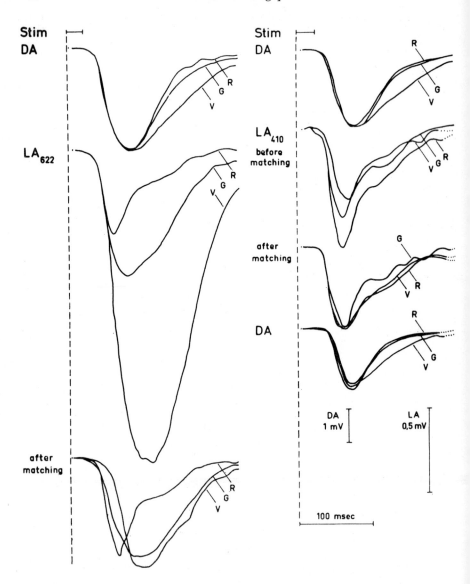

Fig. 5. Typical form of the potentials from the upper part of the compound eye of *Periplaneta americana*. In dark adaptation, the stimuli of 407, 507, 605 mμ are equalized. After light adaptation with violet (410 mμ, LA_{410}) or red (622 mμ, LA_{622}) light; the middle series of the figure is produced by the same stimuli as those used in dark adaptation. For the second series the stimulus intensities were so selected that they produced potentials of equal amplitude. Then differences in shape remain; selective adaptation exists here (after Walther, 1958).

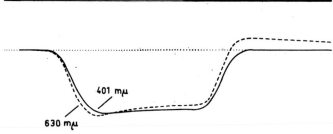

FIG. 6. Compound eye of *Calliphora* (mutant white-apricot): differences in form (at wavelengths λ = 620 and 401 mμ) of the monophasic ERG after removal of the optic ganglia (isolated retinula); relative quantal levels at 401 mμ 1, at 630 mμ 98. (Autrum & Hoffmann, unpublished).

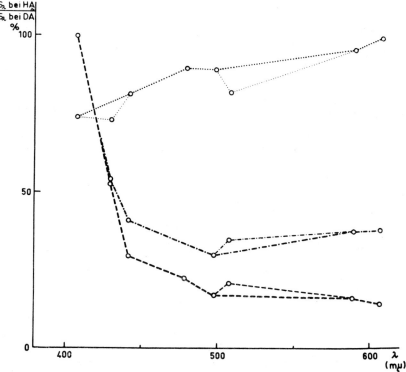

FIG. 7. Compound eye of *Periplaneta americana*. Mean relative changes of the relative spectral sensitivity (Sλ) through monochromatic light adaptation (LAλ), as compared with dark adaptation (DA). Abscissa: wavelength in mμ. Ordinate: Sλ at LA over Sλ at DA in per cent of respective maximum. Parameter: colour of the respective adaptation light (410 mμ ...... ; 488 mμ—·—·—·; 605 mμ————). The points not incorporated in the curve show influences of secondary UV maxima of the respective filters (after Walther, 1958).

responses of the visual cells themselves. They are in general negative, especially at rather low stimulus intensities. The form of these primary responses is also dependent on the wavelength of the stimuli (Fig. 6; Autrum & Hoffmann, unpublished).)

If the spectral sensitivities of these two receptor systems are different, one can

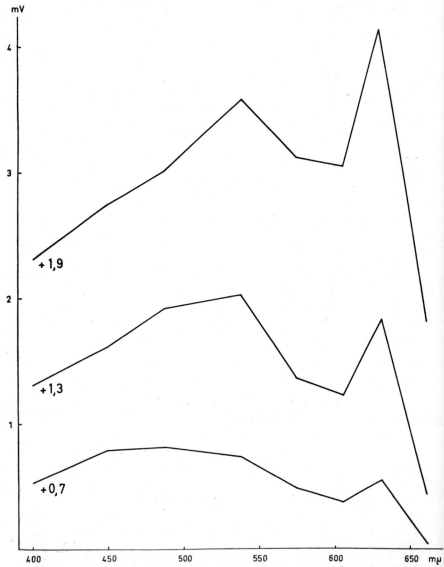

FIG. 8. Red-eyed (normal) *Calliphora erythrocephala.* Spectral effectiveness of equal-quantum stimuli for various quantum numbers. Abscissa: light wavelength. Ordinate: millivolts. Parameter: log of the relative quantum number (after Autrum, 1955).

expect that their responses will be differently influenced by *selective adaptation*. Indeed, Walther found, in *Periplaneta*, that after adaptation with red light (622 mμ), the sensitivity of the upper part of the eye was more strongly decreased for the long wavelengths than for short wavelengths. In animals which have been sufficiently dark adapted the maximum spectral sensitivity of the eye is at 507 mμ; after adaptation to light of 622 mμ the maximum sensitivity may be shifted as far as 407 mμ. Adaptation to violet light (410 mμ), in comparison, has very little influence on the *relative* spectral sensitivity (Fig. 7).

The relative spectral sensitivity of the lower part of the eye is not influenced by adaptation.

These results are a further argument for the assumption that at least in the upper part of the eye of *Periplaneta* two receptor systems of different spectral sensitivity are present.

(III). In the eye of vertebrates one finds, as a rule, two receptor systems simultaneously, rods and cones, which are recognizable by various physiological properties. One of the basic phenomena is different spectral sensitivity maxima, and different absolute light sensitivities. In low light intensities, the relative sensitivity maximum is at a shorter wavelength than in high intensities (Purkinje phenomenon).

Analogous — although by no means comparable — phenomena occur in the insect eye (*Calliphora erythrocephala*) when one determines electrophysiologically the effectiveness (efficacy) curves for various quantal levels.

For determination of the effectiveness of a given light the on-effect of the diphasic electroretinogram is convenient (Fig. 8). At high quantal levels (relative intensity = 1) the maximum effectiveness lies at 620 mμ. At I = 0.01 this maximum is still present, but a second, relatively even higher maximum appears at 520 mμ; and at I = 0.0001 only one maximum is present, at 490 mμ. From this one can conclude that there are present two receptor systems with different intensity dependencies: a more sensitive system with a maximum in the region between 480 and 500 mμ, and a less sensitive receptor system in the red region of the spectrum. Therefore, the physiological basis for colour discrimination is present; whether these animals are able to discriminate colours remains uncertain.

PIÉRON

Il y a espoir, par conséquent, d'arriver à des progrès dans le mècanisme de cette vision des insectes, évidemment encore assez complexe et difficile à interpréter.

Je rappelle que nous n'avons, comme données biochimiques, que les expériences de Goldschmidt, qui a trouvé du rétinène, tout de même, chez l'abeille, avec un maximum à 440 mμ.

Mais il y a un gros problème, alors, que je voudrais poser en ce qui concerne la vision par les yeux composés, c'est-à-dire par ommatidies.

En effet, il semble — je dis: il semble — que chaque ommatidie a une seule fibre qui transmette les messages.

Il y a, évidemment, dans chaque ommatidie une série de cellules. Par conséquent, on pourrait envisager un mécanisme faisant appel à plusieurs éléments récepteurs.

Mais, s'il y a un message unique qui sort de l'ommatidie, alors nous ne voyons plus de composition possible, et il faudrait savoir s'il y a des spécialisations réceptrices d'ommatidies différentes, ou si chaque ommatidie est réellement capable de faire de la discrimination chromatique. C'est là le problème essentiel.

Il s'est posé — le Professeur Autrum s'en souvient — à propos de la lumière polarisée et de sa réception dans cet œil, et au point de vue de l'orientation grâce à la lumière polarisée qu'a démontrée le Professeur von Frisch.

Est-ce que chaque ommatidie peut fournir une donnée d'orientation? ou bien faut-il un ensemble d'ommatidies pour que l'orientation vis-à-vis de la lumière polarisée soit possible?

C'est là-dessus que l'on a discuté beaucoup — sur la possibilité d'envoyer plusieurs messages ou un seul message par ommatidie.

Sur le Limule, là où les choses sont plus faciles, puisque l'on a le récepteur et que l'on peut suivre les données de Hartline; elles semblent indiquer qu'il n'y a qu'un seul message, une seule fibre envoyant le message par potentiel se déplaçant, par influx.

Il y a là, donc, un problème qui est extrêmement délicat. Est-ce que nous pouvons prévoir une réception de la couleur par un jeu d'ommatidies différentes, ou à l'intérieur d'une seule des ommatidies?

PIRENNE

That is the difficulty, of course, that Dr. Hartline finds. I think that with regard to *Limulus*, it is believed that all recordings so far have been made from the eccentric cell. What happens in the other cells is not known. In each *Limulus* ommatidium there are a number of cells; there is a peculiar cell at the side, the eccentric cell, and it has been shown in delicate experiments* that all the recordings are probably made from this eccentric cell.

In connection with the problem of colour differentiation and the functioning of ommatidia, I remember discussing with the late Selig Hecht the idea that one should measure the visual acuity of insects using different monochromatic lights and compare the results with those for white light. But I have never tried this myself.

PIÉRON

En tout cas, il est extrêmement souhaitable qu'avec microélectrodes on puisse arriver à déterminer si réellement vous avez des potentiels d'action qui circulent dans des fibres isolées à la sortie de l'œil composé.

Évidemment, c'est très délicat, mais il serait extrêmement souhaitable, n'est-ce pas, qu'avec des microélectrodes très fines — puisque nous arrivons maintenant à des diamètres très petits — on puisse faire une exploration systématique.

Eh bien, je pense que nous voyons un état de la question, et qu'il y a beaucoup à faire dans cette voie, que l'on n'exploite pas encore, au point de vue de la physiologie sensorielle, du domaine des Insectes, aussi complètement qu'il est possible.

Il y a un travail initial magnifique du Professeur von Frisch. Maintenant on a besoin de la neurophysiologie fine, pour tâcher d'analyser les mécanismes qui sont à la base de phénomènes parfaitement démontrés à l'heure actuelle.

Nous allons laisser, si vous le voulez bien, pour un instant, le problème limité aux Insectes, et demander à M. Medioni, qui vient de la part de M. Viaud, de nous parler du problème de la vision chez d'autres animaux, et en particulier chez les Vertébrés.

* HARTLINE, H. K., WAGNER, H. G. & MacNICHOL, E. F. (1952) *Cold Spring Symposia Quant. Biol.*, **17**.

II

LA VISION CHROMATIQUE CHEZ LES ANIMAUX (SAUF LES INSECTES)

G. Viaud*

Nous disons qu'il y a vision chromatique ou perception des couleurs lorsqu'un animal réagit de manière spécifique à des radiations de diverses longueurs d'onde, quel que soit le degré d'intensité (ou de luminosité) des stimuli employés dans l'expérience.

Les expériences sur la vision chromatique chez l'Homme sont relativement faciles, car les réponses, verbales ou motrices du sujet, dépendant de consignes, peuvent aisément donner la preuve d'une distinction et d'une reconnaissance des couleurs dans diverses circonstances expérimentales.

Mais la question de la vision chromatique des animaux est très difficile, puisque les seules preuves de l'existence de cette fonction ne peuvent être données que par des expériences de physiologie ou de psychophysiologie utilisant des comportements moteurs. Aussi, bien que cette question ait fait, depuis 50 ans environ, l'objet d'innombrables travaux, est-elle encore relativement peu avancée. Beaucoup de résultats sont contradictoires. Ces contradictions tiennent souvent à des défauts de méthode.

Les buts de cet exposé sont précisément:

(1) de montrer quel degré de confiance on peut accorder aux diverses méthodes employées pour l'étude de la vision chromatique chez les animaux;

(2) d'étudier la répartition de la vision chromatique dans les divers groupes zoologiques, d'après nos connaissances actuelles.

I. LES MÉTHODES D'INVESTIGATION DE LA VISION CHROMATIQUE CHEZ LES ANIMAUX

D'un point de vue logique, on peut diviser ces méthodes en deux grands groupes:

(1) les méthodes qui utilisent le raisonnement par analogie;

(2) celles qui visent à donner des preuves expérimentales directes de la vision chromatique.

Les premières sont essentiellement des méthodes histophysiologiques ou

* Rapport présenté par J. Médioni.

neurophysiologiques. Rappelons qu'un raisonnement par analogie est fondé
sur des rapports de ressemblance; il ne donne pas la certitude, mais seulement
une probabilité. Les méthodes de ce groupe sont fondées sur des *analogies*
entre des propriétés physiologiques de telle ou telle partie de l'appareil
visuel chez des animaux et les propriétés physiologiques de l'appareil visuel
humain. Si ces analogies paraissent suffisamment étroites, on conclut à
l'existence d'un sens chromatique chez les animaux étudiés.

Le défaut de ces méthodes éclate déjà dans les anciennes recherches de von
Hess (1909-1919 environ). Von Hess, se fondant sur la ressemblance de la
courbe de la luminosité des radiations spectrales chez nombre d'animaux dits
inférieurs (Vers, Mollusques, Crustacés, Poissons, etc.) — courbe en cloche
avec un maximum vers 530 mμ — avec la courbe de sensibilité spectrale pour
l'Homme achromatopsique, en concluait que tous ces animaux sont aveugles
aux couleurs. La fausseté de ce raisonnement a été démontrée d'une part
a priori — car rien n'indique qu'il y ait une liaison nécessaire et générale
entre la sensibilité visuelle aux radiations spectrales du type de celle de
l'achromatopsique humain et la cécité aux couleurs; d'autre part, *a posteriori*,
par des expériences démontrant l'existence d'un sens chromatique chez
certains animaux inférieurs (par exemple, les expériences de von Frisch, à
partir de 1914 environ).

Tout le monde est d'accord aujourd'hui sur cette critique des conclusions
de von Hess. Cependant, on fait souvent grand cas d'autres méthodes
physiologiques employant également le raisonnement par analogie. Citons:
les méthodes histologiques, cherchant à mettre en évidence un dualisme
morphologique rétinien (avec un phénomène de Purkinje); les méthodes
spectrochimiques, tendant à montrer la présence de plusieurs pigments dans
les cônes rétiniens de certains animaux; les méthodes électrophysiologiques,
prouvant l'existence de 'modulateurs', au sens de Granit, par l'étude des
potentiels d'action recueillis par micro-électrodes, ou montrant l'analogie
des ERG obtenus chez des animaux possédant des rétines à cônes avec les
ERG de l'Homme à vision normale, etc. ...

Or toutes ces méthodes ne peuvent montrer que la possibilité, au mieux la
probabilité, de l'existence d'un sens chromatique. La combinaison ou la
convergence de plusieurs de ces méthodes peut augmenter cette probabilité;
elle ne peut donner de preuve décisive. Car toutes les conditions de la vision
des couleurs ne sont pas réunies dans la rétine, ni même dans les diverses
parties de l'appareil visuel, mais *dans l'ensemble fonctionnel nerveux* de la
perception visuelle.

La tentative de Le Gros Clark (1949) de trouver un rapport entre les
couches de neurones décelables dans les corps genouillés externes et la vision
colorée des Mammifères est bien un essai d'investigation histophysiologique
totale de l'appareil visuel; mais Walls (1953) a montré que cette structure

laminaire du corps genouillé externe, visible chez certains Primates, n'a pas de signification générale.

En l'état actuel de nos connaissances, seules peuvent amener la certitude les méthodes du second groupe, qui sont *psychologiques* ou *psychophysiologiques*. Parmi celles-ci nous distinguerons:

(*a*) Les méthodes utilisant les *réactions perceptives*, innées ou acquises. On appelle réaction perceptive toute réaction qui dépend de la perception d'un *signe*, instinctivement connu ou reconnu à la suite d'un learning. Il est évident que si un animal est capable de reconnaître des stimuli lumineux colorés, quelle que soit leur intensité ou leur luminosité relatives, c'est qu'il voit les couleurs, du moins certaines couleurs. D'où:

(i) *La méthode de discrimination spontanée*: on observe que certains animaux préfèrent instinctivement telle couleur à telle autre dans leurs réactions alimentaires ou reproductrices; exemple: la Piéride du chou affamée, selon Ilse (1937), réagit positivement au rouge-jaune et au bleu-violet, mais non au vert; le mâle, à l'époque de la pariade, réagit au jaune par des réactions d'accouplement; la femelle, au moment de la ponte, réagit à toutes les surfaces vertes. Le mâle de l'Epinoche à trois épines perçoit la couleur rouge du ventre d'un congénère, qui est un signe distinctif du sexe mâle à l'état de maturité sexuelle (Tinbergen, 1940).

(ii) *La méthode de conditionnement, d'apprentissage ou de dressage*. Par exemple, l'animal est dressé à venir chercher sa nourriture dans une boîte à choix, dans le compartiment signalé par un stimulus coloré. S'il distingue ce stimulus de tous les autres qui lui sont opposés, indépendamment du facteur de luminosité ou leucie, c'est qu'il en perçoit la qualité chromatique. Bien entendu, il faut éviter que la récompense soit signalée par un autre stimulus que le stimulus lumineux conditionné. Von Frisch (1923) et Kühn (1927) ont employé cette méthode avec le succès que l'on sait chez l'Abeille. Nous en verrons plus loin de nombreux autres exemples.

On peut ajouter à ces méthodes des réactions perceptives une méthode fondée sur les phénomènes d'*homochromie*. Il est évident que si un animal cherche un fond d'une couleur voisine de celle de son corps, ou s'il modifie la coloration de son corps de manière à l'harmoniser à celle du fond, c'est qu'il perçoit cette couleur. Mais il faut que cette réaction soit à point de départ *oculaire*, ce que l'expérience seule peut décider, et, de plus, qu'il ne s'agisse pas d'une simple réaction d'*homoleucie* (Piéron, 1941).

Autre restriction: le phénomène que Cuénot (1927) a appelé l'*homochromie anti-spectrale* n'apporte pas la preuve de la vision des couleurs. Ainsi la Crevette *Hippolyte varians* cherche un abri sous des algues de la couleur de son corps — les individus bruns sous les algues brunes, les individus verts sous les algues vertes — parce que ces algues forment un filtre de radiations. Cette réaction est une simple réaction de défense contre l'action de la lumière et ne prouve absolument pas la perception de qualités chromatiques.

(*b*) *La méthode des réflexes oculo-moteurs*, préconisée par von Buddenbrock (1927); elle consiste à produire chez l'animal étudié un nystagmus optocinétique, en le plaçant au centre d'un tambour tournant portant des bandes verticales colorées. Pour que le nystagmus se manifeste, il faut, bien entendu, opérer en-dessous de la fréquence critique de fusionnement: dans ces conditions l'animal réagit s'il distingue les bandes par leur luminosité ou leucie, et éventuellement par leur chroma. Si le nystagmus s'observe encore quand on utilise des bandes d'égale luminosité, on peut en conclure que l'animal possède un sens chromatique. Mais le nystagmus est plus aisément déclenché par des variations de luminosité que par des différences chromatiques, et il peut se faire qu'il ne se produise pas quand on confronte des bandes jaunes, par exemple, avec des bandes grises de même leucie. Doit-on en conclure que l'espèce étudiée est forcément achromate? Pas encore: on cherchera un bleu qui, combiné avec le même gris, ne donne pas non plus de nystagmus, puis on combinera ce bleu avec le jaune de même luminosité. Si le nystagmus est déclenché par cette confrontation de deux couleurs complémentaires, qui donne lieu à un contraste plus accusé que la combinaison d'une d'entre elles avec le gris, on pourra conclure à l'existence d'un sens chromatique. On le voit, cette méthode n'est pas d'un emploi très facile; elle exige beaucoup de doigté de la part de l'expérimentateur. Mais elle est fort précieuse, en particulier pour prouver la vision des couleurs chez des espèces difficiles à conditionner. Elle a été largement employée par von Buddenbrock et ses élèves chez les Arthropodes et, ensuite, par bien d'autres auteurs. Récemment, elle vient d'être appliquée à un Mammifère, le Cobaye, par Trincker & Berndt (1957).

(*c*) Une autre méthode psychophysiologique serait celle du *phototropisme ou de la phototaxie*. Certains auteurs ont pensé que les différences d'efficacité des radiations spectrales dans la causation de réactions phototropiques pouvaient constituer une preuve de l'existence d'un sens chromatique. Von Hess (1922) avait combattu cette manière de voir, disant qu'en jouant sur l'intensité des radiations on pouvait toujours égaliser l'efficacité de l'une à celle d'une autre pour la production de phototropisme positif ou négatif. Nous avons maintes fois vérifié la justesse de cette opinion. C'est probablement Lemke (1935) qui, la première, a nettement insisté sur l'impossibilité de mettre en évidence une vision chromatique chez les Planaires par le moyen de leur phototropisme. Elle dit en substance que, tant qu'on n'aura pas réussi à dresser les Planaires à reconnaître les couleurs, on n'aura pas prouvé qu'elles sont capables de les distinguer.

Mais divers auteurs, à la suite de von Frisch & Kupelwieser (1913), ont affirmé que des Crustacés inférieurs, les Daphnies, étaient dotés d'un sens chromatique, et ce, en se fondant sur le comportement phototropique de ces animaux. Or, nous avons montré, dès 1938, que l'attraction phototropique ne dépend nullement de l'excitation du sens visuel, mais de celle du sens dermatoptique. Ce qui rendait évidemment caduques les preuves de l'existence de la vision chromatique obtenues par l'étude du phototropisme. Par ailleurs, nous avons refait récemment l'expérience de von Frisch et Kupelwieser, et les résultats que nous avons trouvés ne s'accordent nullement avec ceux de ces auteurs; ils ne prouvent rien ni pour, ni contre l'hypothèse d'une vision discriminative des couleurs chez les Daphnies, mais montrent seulement que ces animaux sont attirés au maximum par les lumières les moins excitantes, ce qui dépend de leur capacité photopathique.*

En conclusion de la première partie de ce travail, nous dirons donc que les seules méthodes donnant la preuve certaine d'une vision chromatique chez les animaux sont des méthodes *psychologiques* utilisant des réactions *perceptives*; principalement des réactions acquises par conditionnement ou apprentissage et, à défaut de celles-ci, la méthode fondée sur le nystagmus optocinétique, *à l'exclusion des expériences mettant en jeu le phototropisme.*

II. RÉPARTITION DE LA VISION CHROMATIQUE DANS LES DIVERS GROUPES ZOOLOGIQUES

De premières constatations, très générales, s'imposent:

(1) La vision chromatique est absente chez tous les animaux inférieurs.

(2) On n'a pu la mettre en évidence que chez les *Arthropodes supérieurs* (Crustacés Décapodes, Arachnides, Insectes) d'une part; et, d'autre part, chez un assez grand nombre de *Vertébrés*. Le cas des Mollusques Céphalopodes doit encore être réservé.

(3) Si on marque sur un arbre généalogique du Règne animal (par exemple celui de Cuénot, 1940) les groupes zoologiques dont un nombre plus ou moins grand de représentants sont sensibles aux couleurs, on constate que, dans l'ensemble, la vision chromatique ne se rencontre guère que *dans les phylums les plus évolués et vers l'extrémité de ces phylums* (Fig. 1). Ce fait apparaît nettement chez les Décapodes, les Insectes, les Poissons Téléostéens, les Reptiles, les Oiseaux, les Primates, etc. ... Il montre évidemment que *la vision chromatique est un produit ultime de l'évolution de l'appareil visuel.*

(4) Mais l'évolution de la vision chromatique a été assez capricieuse. Beaucoup des complications qu'elle présente semblent tenir au mode de vie des animaux, diurne ou nocturne. Ainsi, presque tous les Rongeurs sont nocturnes et achromates, mais les Ecureuils, Rongeurs adaptés à la vie diurne, ont une vision des couleurs, récemment démontrée par Meyer-Oehme (1957).

* Pour plus de détails sur ce point, nous renvoyons le lecteur à la discussion qui suit ce rapport.

Voyons maintenant les détails les plus intéressants de la répartition de la vision chromatique dans les divers groupes.

D'abord, en ce qui concerne les *Invertébrés*. Un certain nombre d'auteurs ont affirmé l'existence, chez des Vers et des Crustacés inférieurs, d'un sens dichromatique, comportant des récepteurs électivement sensibles aux ondes courtes et aux grandes ondes du spectre visible pour l'Homme, la limite entre ces deux groupes de radiations se situant dans le vert. Par exemple: Beuther (1928) chez des Planaires; Denzer-Malbrandt (1935) chez des Hirudinées; von Frisch & Kupelwieser (1913), Ewald (1914), Koehler (1924), Heberdey (1936), Smith & Baylor (1953), chez divers Cladocères et, en particulier, *Daphnia magna* et *D. pulex*; Heberdey (1936) sur le Copépode *Diaptomus zachariae*. Toutes ces expériences ont porté sur le phototropisme des animaux en question. Comme nous l'avons dit plus haut, Lemke (1935) a montré que de telles expériences ne prouvent nullement l'existence d'une vision chromatique. Le fait que tous ces animaux préfèrent les radiations à grande longueur d'onde aux courtes longueurs d'onde tient tout simplement à ce que les premières ne les excitent pas excessivement, au contraire des secondes. Nous avons montré nous-même (à partir de 1938) sur *Daphnia pulex* et sur diverses Planaires (*Planaria lugubris, Fonticola vitta, Castrada sp., Mesostoma lingua*), ainsi que sur des Rotifères (*Brachionus pala, Hydatina senta, Polyarthra trigla …*) que tous les animaux *oculés* de ces espèces présentent *deux* modes de photoréception: la *sensibilité visuelle* et la *sensibilité dermatoptique*, les animaux non-oculés n'ayant que le sens dermatoptique. Le sens visuel se manifeste dans l'orientation axiale des animaux et le sens dermatoptique règle leurs déplacements par rapport à une source de lumière monochromatique. Ce dernier phénomène n'est donc nullement en relation avec une problématique vision chromatique oculaire. Un récent travail de Scheffer, Robert & Médioni (1958) a établi que, non seulement le phototropisme, mais aussi les réactions oculo-motrices de *Daphnia pulex* dépendent à la fois du sens visuel et du sens dermatoptique.

Concernant les Mollusques, il ne semble pas que les Gastéropodes et les Lamellibranches soient dotés d'un sens chromatique. En tout cas, les résultats des expériences de von Buddenbrock & Moller-Racke (1953) sur le *Pecten* sont entièrement négatifs. Et les données de Liche (1934) signalant l'existence d'un sens chromatique chez *Limnaea stagnalis* ne sont pas dignes de foi, étant donnés les graves défauts de la technique expérimentale mise en œuvre. Chez les Céphalopodes, l'existence d'un sens chromatique reste douteuse, malgré les recherches de Kühn (1930 et 1950) sur *Octopus* et sur *Sepia* et celles de Boulet (1956) sur *Sepia officinalis*. Néanmoins elle est assez probable à cause des phénomènes d'homochromie très nets qui s'observent chez ces animaux.

Pour les Crustacés Décapodes, la vision colorée ne fait pas de doute, à al suite des recherches de von Buddenbrock & Friedrich (1933) sur *Carcinus moenas*, et celles d'Annelise Schlegtendal (1934) sur *Crangon vulgaris* et *Leander* (=*Palaemon*) *adspersus*, recherches menées par l'ingénieuse méthode des réactions optomotrices, décrite plus haut. Il faut citer aussi la méthode de Koller (1929), fondée sur des réactions perceptives de choix spontané des Pagures: les Pagures *Eupagurus anachoretus* et *Clibanarius misanthropus*, privés de la coquille où ils s'abritent, sont amenés à choisir entre plusieurs coquilles de *Cerithium*, les unes vides et colorées, les autres grises et bouchées à la paraffine; les Pagures ont manifesté une répulsion nette pour les coquilles bleues et jaunes; ils ont toujours recherché les coquilles vertes, rouges ou grises. Ces animaux sont donc capables de distinguer au moins trois couleurs, peut-être quatre.

En ce qui concerne les *Vertébrés*, on ne sait encore rien de certain sur les Cyclostomes et les Poissons inférieurs. Par contre, l'existence d'un sens chromatique chez les Téléostéens a été établie par les travaux de nombreux auteurs. Citons en particulier ceux de Burkamp (1923), Schiemenz (1924), von Frisch (1925), Wolff (1926), Hamburger (1926) sur le Vairon (*Phoxinus phoxinus*), de Burkamp (1923) sur la Bouvière (*Rhodeus amarus*), de von Frisch (1925) sur le Goujon (*Gobio fluviatilis*), etc. ... Les expériences bien connues de von Frisch sont particulièrement intéressantes: il a dressé des Vairons à venir chercher leur nourriture dans de petits godets signalés par des papiers colorés de la série de Hering. Résultats: (1) les Vairons sont capables de distinguer une douzaine de nuances, mais ils confondent le rouge et le violet, ce qui est l'indice d'un cycle fermé des couleurs comparable à celui qui s'observe dans la vision chromatique humaine; (2) le maximum de la finesse de la discrimination chromatique est dans la région moyenne du spectre, comme chez l'Homme; (3) en vision scotopique, les Vairons deviennent achromates: l'étude histologique d'yeux fixés immédiatement après des expériences de discrimination chromatique montrent que le passage de la vision des couleurs à l'achromatopsie s'accompagne d'une *extension* des cônes rétiniens, dont l'article externe s'enfouit dans l'epithelium pigmentaire, et d'une *rétraction* des bâtonnets qui viennent se placer dans le plan de formation de l'image rétinienne. Ces faits s'accordent bien avec la théorie du dualisme rétinien et ils la complètent. Toutefois, ils ne s'observent pas chez le Goujon, qui a une vision des couleurs assez voisine de celle du Vairon. Ajoutons que la Tanche (*Tinca tinca*), poisson de nœurs nocturnes qui possède de gros bâtonnets et peu de cônes, n'en perçoit pas moins les couleurs (Burkamp, 1923).

Parmi les Batraciens, le genres *Rana* et *Hyla* ont un sens chromatique bien développé, mis en évidence par Birukow (1949, 1950) grâce à la méthode du nystagmus optocinétique, et confirmé par les expériences de Thomas (1955).

Cet auteur a pu montrer aussi, par des expériences de dressage à l'aide d'attrapes colorées que les Bufonidés, les Pélobatidés, et, en général, tous les Anoures nocturnes ne voient pas les couleurs. Par contre, le sens chromatique des espèces diurnes est bien développé; elles distinguent le rouge, l'orangé, le jaune, le vert-jaune, le bleu-vert et le bleu. L'accord est remarquable entre les résultats de la méthode du conditionnement et de celle du nystagmus optocinétique. C'est cette dernière qui a permis à Burgers (1952) de montrer que *Xenopus laevis* ne voit pas les couleurs, mais qu'il possède seulement une bonne sensibilité différentielle à la brillance. Rappelons enfin que les recherches de Granit (1942) ont montré l'existence, chez la Grenouille, de trois 'modulateurs', sensibles au maximum, respectivement à 580, 530 et 460 mμ. On ne possède encore que peu de données sur l'existence d'une vision des couleurs chez les Batraciens Urodèles: un travail de Birukow (1950) indique toutefois que la méthode optocinétique révèle chez les Salamandres l'existence d'un sens chromatique bien dévoloppé; celui des Tritons serait beaucoup plus fruste.

Dans la classe des Reptiles, les Tortues *Emys europea* et *Clemmys caspica* ont été bien étudiées par Wojtusiak (1933); cet auteur a montré qu'elles distinguent au moins cinq qualités chromatiques: rouge, jaune, vert, bleu, violet, avec un maximum de discrimination chromatique dans le rouge et le jaune. De nombreux autres reptiles, Ophidiens et Lacertiliens, ont fait l'objet de recherches plus ou moins approfondies. Citons: celles de Grodzinska (1948) sur les Lézards *Lacerta agilis* et *L. viridis* (dressage); de Musolff (1955) sur l'Iguanidé *Anolis carolinensis* (réactions optomotrices). Il ressort de ces résultats que la discrimination des couleurs est bonne chez les espèces étudiées: le Lézard perçoit au moins huit qualités chromatiques différentes, et l'Iguane en perçoit au moins quatre. Quant au Caméléon et au Geckonidé *Ptychozoon homalocephalon*, ils voient certainement les couleurs aussi, puisqu'ils présentent des réactions d'homochromie à point de départ oculaire (Boschma, 1925).

Dans l'ensemble, les données morpho-physiologiques s'accordent bien avec les résultats de l'étude du comportement, chez les Reptiles: on sait, par exemple, que la rétine des Lézards ne contient pas de bâtonnets, mais uniquement des cônes. De plus, Granit a trouvé, chez *Testudo graeca*, trois modulateurs, vers 600, 530 et 470 mμ. Hosoya, Okita & Akune (1938) ont isolé, chez la Tortue *Ocadia sinensis*, trois pigments rétiniens photosensibles hydrosolubles, présentant un maximum d'absorption, respectivement à 460, 570 et 670 mμ.

Dans la classe des Oiseaux, les Carinates diurnes ont été passablement étudiés; ils paraissent dotés d'une bonne sensibilité différentielle chromatique; c'est le cas de la Poule (Lashley, 1916; Révész, 1921), du Faisan et de la Perdrix (v. Törne, 1941), du Pigeon (Hamilton & Coleman, 1933; v. Törne,

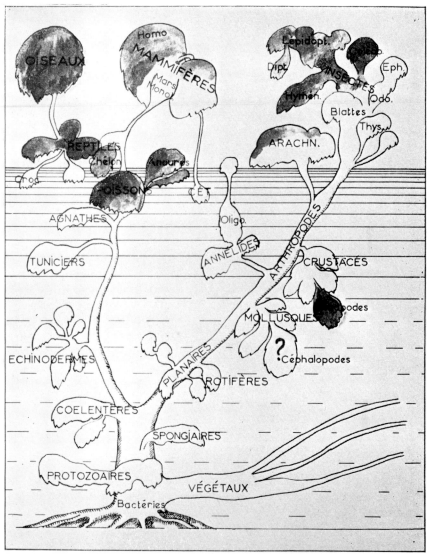

Fig. 1. Arbre généalogique du règne animal (d'après Cuénot, 1940). Sont figurés en rouge les groupes comportant des espèces qui perçoivent les couleurs.

1941), du Tétras (Hoglund, 1956), de la Grive (van Eck, 1939) et des Perruches: *Stilorhynchus violaceus* (Morrison-Scott, 1937), *Melopsittacus undulatus* (Bailey & Riley, 1931; Plath, 1935). Selon Plath, la Perruche ondulée discrimine huit nuances spectrales: le rouge, l'orangé, le jaune, deux verts, deux bleus et le violet. Les Rapaces nocturnes ont été très peu étudiés; selon Walls, il est probable qu'ils ne voient pas les couleurs.

Au point de vue morpho-physiologique, tous les Oiseaux possèdent une rétine mixte à cônes et à bâtonnets bien différenciés; les cônes prédominent chez les espèces diurnes, les bâtonnets chez les espèces nocturnes. Les cônes sont pourvus d'une boule huileuse, dont la couleur peut varier du rouge au jaune, et qui joue le rôle d'un écran coloré. Ce fait contribuerait au décalage vers les grandes longueurs d'onde du maximum de la courbe de la vision photopique (580 mµ, au lieu de 560 chez les Mammifères). Cette hypothèse est confirmée par le fait que ce décalage ne s'observe pas chez les Rapaces nocturnes, qui ont des cônes à boule huileuse quasi-incolore. Enfin, Donner (1953) a montré que la rétine du Pigeon est dotée de trois modulateurs: 600, 540 et 480 mµ.

Nous en arrivons maintenant aux Mammifères. François & Verriest (1957), dans leur revue de la question de la vision colorée chez les Animaux, disent qu'en dehors des Primates, dont le sens chromatique ne fait aucun doute, les autres Mammifères, sauf exception, sont essentiellement nocturnes, pauvres en cônes et dotés d'une vision chromatique très déficiente, quoique rarement tout-à-fait absente. Cette appréciation nous paraît quelque peu exagérée. C'est ainsi que, dans le groupe des Rongeurs, le Cobaye a une vision des couleurs assez bien développée, distinguant au moins le rouge, le jaune, le vert et le bleu de toute une gamme de gris, comme le prouvent les résultats convergents de Sgonina (1936), obtenus par des expériences de dressage dans une boîte à choix, et les données de Trincker & Berndt (1957), qui ont employé la méthode du nystagmus optocinétique.* Ce fait ne s'accorde guère, d'ailleurs, dans le cadre de la théorie du dualisme rétinien, avec l'absence quasi-totale de cônes dans la rétine du Cobaye, signalée par O'Day (1947).

Parmi les Muridés, il semble que le Rat albinos soit doté d'une certaine vision des couleurs: Muenzinger & Reynolds (1936) ont démontré que cet animal est capable de discriminer le rouge de toute une gamme de gris. Puis des travaux de Walton & Bornemeier (1938 et 1939) ont établi que le Rat albinos discrimine le bleu, le vert et le jaune du rouge, et le bleu du jaune (à leucie égale). Par contre, les discriminations vert-jaune et bleu-vert ne sont pas apprises. D'autre part, le Rat de race sauvage et la Souris seraient à peu près achromates (Hopkins, 1927; Walls, 1942). En dépit de la rareté des

---

* Toutefois, selon un travail récent de Miles, Ratoosh & Meyer (1956), le Cobaye serait achromate.

cônes dans la rétine du Rat et de la Souris, Granit (1941) a mis en évidence trois modulateurs chez le Rat (maxima à 600, 530 et 470 mµ).

Les Sciuridés constituent une famille à part, au sein des Rongeurs: ils ont des mœurs diurnes et leur rétine comporte surtout des cônes (cas de l'Ecureuil vulgaire), ou exclusivement ce type de récepteur (Marmotte, selon Rochon-Duvigneaud, 1943; Spermophile, selon Karli, 1951 et Vilter, 1954; Ecureuil gris, selon Arden & Tansley, 1955). Le sens chromatique de l'Ecureuil vulgaire vient d'être démontré récemment par des expériences de Meyer-Oehme (1957) qui a adapté à cette espèce la technique du jumping-apparatus de Lashley; l'Ecureuil vulgaire distingue bien quatre couleurs au moins: rouge, jaune, vert et bleu. Quant au Spermophile, nous savons seulement, d'après Kolosvary (1934) qu'il semble distinguer le bleu du rouge. Des expériences portant sur cette espèce sont actuellement en cours au Laboratoire de Psychologie animale de Strasbourg. Nous ignorons tout encore de la sensibilité chromatique de la Marmotte et de l'Ecureuil gris. L'intérêt de l'étude des Sciuridés est évidente, car ce sont les seuls Mammifères dont la rétine soit si riche en cônes, ce qui les rapprocherait des Reptiles et des Oiseaux. Mais, selon François & Verriest (1957) qui s'appuient sur le fait que, chez les Sciuridés, la sensibilité spectrale a son maximum vers 520 mµ,

'... les récepteurs des Sciuridés diurnes sont des bâtonnets modifiés, adaptés à la vision photopique, et non des cônes. Le maximum de sensibilité n'est pas situé vers 500 mµ, parce que le cristallin a une coloration jaunâtre'.

Des Insectivores, on ne sait que fort peu de choses. Herter (1933, 1934) a montré que le Hérisson (*Erinaceus e. europaeus*), dont la rétine contient quelques cônes, a une perception chromatique très pauvre; par dressage dans un appareil à choix double, Herter a toutefois montré que le Hérisson distingue le jaune de tous les gris.

Les Carnivores, animaux à activité nocturne prédominante, sont généralement considérés comme achromates, bien qu'ils possèdent une rétine mixte et que Granit ait mis en évidence, chez le Chat, l'existence de plusieurs modulateurs. D'ailleurs, chez le Chat, les données fondées sur le comportement ne sont pas univoques: en particulier, les résultats récents de Miles, Meyer & Ratoosh (1954), obtenus à l'aide d'une technique d'apprentissage dans un appareil à choix, sont absolument négatifs. Au contraire, les expériences de Buchholtz (1952) paraissent indiquer que la discrimination chromatique est bonne chez le Chat, puisque six couleurs sont sûrement distinguées entres elles et différenciés d'une gamme de 25 nuances de gris. La méthode de Bucholtz est fondée, non sur les tendances alimentaires, mais sur le jeu de prédation, qui constitue un élément très important du comportement du Chat, même en ce qui concerne la satisfaction de la faim. Bien qu'il soit difficile de trancher, nous inclinerions à accorder plus de crédit à ces résultats positifs qu'à ceux de Meyer, Miles et Ratoosh et des autres auteurs qui, avant eux, ont refusé toute vision des couleurs au Chat, sur la base d'expériences de dressage classiques.

Chez les Canidés, qui possèdent aussi une rétine mixte, plusieurs tentatives pour mettre en évidence un sens chromatique ont toutes échoué jusqu'à présent: notamment les expériences de Gregg et collaborateurs (1929) et celles de Grzimek (1952), les unes et les autres faites sur le Chien.

Sur les Ongulés, nos connaissances sont encore très restreintes. Nous savons qu'ils ont une rétine mixte, et Grzimek (1952) a prouvé, par des expériences de choix multiple, que les Chevaux peuvent être dressés à distinguer le rouge, le jaune, le vert et le bleu. Par la même méthode, Hoffmann (1952) a établi que le Zébu différencie des gris le rouge, l'orangé, le jaune, le bleu et le violet; mais le vert, le jaune et l'orangé constituent pour cette espèce une qualité chromatique unique.

Sur les Cétacés, rien n'est connu. Par contre, les données concernant les Primates abondent. Selon Bierens de Haan & Frima (1931), les Lémuriens n'auraient qu'une vision chromatique très fruste: par le dressage, *Lemur mongoz* n'a pu acquérir qu'une seule discrimination, celle du bleu et du gris. Au contraire, tous les Simiens présentent un sens chromatique plus ou moins bien développé. Les Platyrhiniens des genres *Cebus* et *Ateles*, en particulier, ont été étudiés par Malmö & Grether (1937) et par Grether (1939, 1940); ils ont une rétine riche en cônes et ils paraissent voir les couleurs comme un Homme protanope.

Ce n'est que chez les Catarhiniens que l'on observe une sensibilité chromatique voisine de celle de l'Homme normal: encore y-a-t-il lieu de noter un amoindrissement de la sensibilité au rouge chez le Babouin (Grether, 1939), chez le Macaque Rhesus (Trendelenburg & Schmidt, 1930) et même chez le Chimpanzé (Grether, 1940). En somme, la vision chromatique des Catarhiniens est intermédiaire entre celle des Platyrhiniens et celle de l'Homme normal; ils présentent encore une légère tendance à la protanopie.

Selon Trendelenburg & Schmidt (1930), le système trichromatique des Catarhiniens *Pithecus fascicularis* et *Macacus rhesus* est très voisin de celui de l'Homme, car la sensibilité différentielle chromatique présente deux maxima, à 589 et 490 mμ (585 et 495 chez l'Homme), et un minimum situé à 535 mμ (540 chez l'Homme). Le mélange des couleurs rouge et verte obéit à l'équation de Rayleigh valable pour l'Homme (617 mμ + 535 mμ = 589 mμ), et la radiation 589 mμ est confondue par ces Singes avec la couleur de mélange. Chez le Chimpanzé, selon Grether, l'équation de Rayleigh est à peu près la même, mais le mélange qui donne le blanc (610+495 mμ) exige plus de rouge que chez le sujet humain. Les valeurs de Δλ sont presque identiques à celles de l'Homme pour le bleu, le vert et le jaune, mais nettement plus élevées dans le rouge (9 à 12 mμ, au lieu de 4 à 7 chez l'Homme).

Enfin Rensch (1957) a étudié les préférences spontanées pour les couleurs chez un Capucin, un Cercopithèque et un jeune Chimpanzé: le bleu est dédaigné par les trois Singes, qui préfèrent le jaune et le blanc, et en général les couleurs vives aux gris. Les Singes s'intéressent aussi aux combinaisons de couleurs vives, ce qui tend à montrer que certains facteurs esthétiques sont en jeu dans le comportement de ces animaux, en réponse à des stimuli colorés.*

Comme nous l'avons indiqué plus haut, la vision chromatique s'est développée largement dans la classe des Mammifères et principalement chez les plus évolués d'entre eux, les Primates. Il est cependant vraisemblable que tous les Vertébrés possèdent au niveau rétinien un mécanisme de discrimination des couleurs. *Mais cela ne signifie pas forcément que tous voient les couleurs.* Ainsi que le disait à peu près Tansley, à propos des travaux de Granit, au Symposium de Cambridge, en 1949

> ' ... on ne peut attendre qu'un animal dont les organes terminaux répondent identiquement à toutes les longueurs d'onde puisse avoir une vision des couleurs. Mais l'inverse n'est pas vrai: il n'est pas sûr que tous les animaux qui présentent des différences rétiniennes de sensibilité aux longueurs d'onde voient nécessairement les couleurs.'

Autrement dit, il existe des conditions rétiniennes qui sont *nécessaires* pour que la vision chromatique puisse s'exercer, mais ces conditions ne sont pas *suffisantes*, et l'on doit prendre en considération le fonctionnement de 'l'analyseur visuel' dans son ensemble, pour reprendre un concept de Pavlov.

Pour conclure, rappelons encore, avec Walls, que la répartition du sens chromatique chez les Vertébrés est en relation étroite avec leur mode de vie; des animaux diurnes comme les Tortues et les Lézards, beaucoup d'Oiseaux, les Sciuridés, ont une vision des couleurs bien développée; au contraire, la plupart des petits Mammifères, animaux nocturnes, n'en ont pas. Il faut toutefois insister sur le fait que nos connaissances en la matière sont très incomplètes, et que des groupes zoologiques entiers n'ont encore fait l'objet d'aucune étude.

L'ensemble des données qui viennent d'être exposées sont récapitulées dans le tableau ci-après.

---

* Entre la présentation et la publication de ce rapport, nous avons eu connaissance des résultats de travaux encore inédits de l'école russe de Madame Ladyguina-Kohts. Une de ses élèves, V. S. Moukhina, a étudié les préférences chromatiques spontanées chez plusieurs Corvidés (Corbeau, Pie, Choucas, Corneille, Freux). Tous ces oiseaux préfèrent le noir au blanc, le rouge et le jaune au bleu. Il n'y a pas de préférence nette dans des choix jaune-rouge. En tout état de cause la technique employée ne permet pas de savoir s'il s'agit de préférences fondées sur le chroma ou sur la luminance des plages colorées.

A. I. Markhova a étudié les préférences chromatiques chez une douzaine de Singes inférieurs (Hamadryas et Macaques). Tous les animaux ont préféré les objets colorés à des objets gris, surtout dans le cas de colorations du domaine des courtes longueurs d'onde. Quand on ne leur présente que des objets colorés, les Singes préfèrent

Tableau récapitulatif des espèces animales qui ont paru dotées du sens chromatique

VERTÉBRÉS

MAMMIFÈRES	PRIMATES	Simiens	Catarhiniens	Chimpanzé (Grether, 1940; Jarvik, 1956) *Macaca mulatta, M. nemestrinus* (Grether, 1939) *M. rhesus, Pithecus fascicularis* (Trendelenburg & Schmidt, 1930) *Papio papio* (Grether, 1939) *Cercopithecus callitrichus* (Grether, 1939), *C. aethiops* (Rensch, 1957)
			Platyrhiniens	*Callicebus, Lagothrix, Ateles, Saimiri, Cebus apella, C. unicolor, C. capucinus* (Grether, 1939-40; Malmo & Grether, 1937) *Callithrix* (Miles, 1958)
		Lémuriens		
	CÉTACÉS			
	ONGULÉS			Cheval (Grzimek, 1952), Zébu (Hoffmann, 1952)
	CARNIVORES	Félidés		Chat? (Buchholtz, 1953)
		Canidés		
		Mustélidés		
	INSECTIVORES			Hérisson (Herter, 1933-34)
		Sciuridés		*Sciurus vulgaris* (Meyer-Oehme, 1957)
	RONGEURS	Myoxidés		
		Muridés		Rat albinos (Muenzinger & Reynolds, 1936; Walton & Bornemeier, 1939)
		Caviidés		Cobaye (Sgonina, 1937; Trincker & Berndt, 1957)
		Léporidés		
	MARSUPIAUX			
	MONOTRÈMES			

très généralement les couleurs du domaine des courtes longueurs d'onde (violet, bleu, vert) aux teintes à grandes longueurs d'onde (rouge, jaune). La brillance apparente des objets présentés n'influerait pas sur ces choix qui s'effectueraient seulement en fonction de la nuance chromatique. L'A. indique toutefois que les objets argentés ou brillants sont préférés à tous les objets colorés présentés en même temps.

Enfin, une volumineuse étude de Madame Kohts concerne la différenciation des couleurs d'objets chez le Chien et les variations inter-individuelles de ce type de discrimination. Les principaux résultats des 23.000 réactions de choix observées sont, en résumé, les suivants:

(1) le noir est moins bien discriminé des teintes chromatiques (58% de choix corrects) que des gris (80%);

(2) le rouge est assez mal discriminé de diverses nuances de gris (62,8% de choix corrects). Cette discrimination est abolie dès qu'on opère avec des nuances rouges peu saturées. Les discriminations 'rouge-autres teintes chromatiques' ne sont guère plus sûres (66,4% de choix corrects en moyenne);

(3) les résultats de la confrontation du bleu comme stimulus positif avec d'autres teintes, neutres ou chromatiques, ne sont pas plus nets que dans le cas du rouge;

(4) Les chiens seraient capables de discriminer à des degrés divers un rouge ou un bleu (stimuli positifs) de papiers gris de même luminosité, présentant ainsi une capacité de discrimination chromatique vraie, bien que faible.

(5) les variations inter-individuelles sont extrêmement considérables dans toutes ces expériences.

OISEAUX	CARINATES DIURNES		Grives: *Turdus ericetorum* (van Eck, 1939) Perruches: *Stilorynchus violaceus* (Morrison Scott, 1937) *Melopsittacus undulatus* (Plath, 1935) Poule (Lashley 1916; Revesz, 1921; von Törne, 1941) Faisan, Perdrix (von Törne, 1941) Pigeon (Hamilton & Coleman, 1933; von Törne, 1941) *Tetras urogallus* (Hoglund, 1956)
	RAPACES NOCTURNES RATITES		
REPTILES		Lacertiliens	*Ptychozoon homalocephalon* (Boschma, 1925) *Calotes, Agama* (Verrier, 1930) *Anolis carolinensis* (Musolff, 1955) *Lacerta agilis, L. viridis* (Wagner, 1933)
	SAUROPHIDIENS	Ophidiens	Caméléon (Boschma, 1925) Couleuvre *Natrix natrix* (Grodzinska, 1948)
	CHÉLONIENS		Tortues *Emys europaea, Clemmys caspica* (Wojtusiak, 1933)
	CROCODILIENS		
BATRACIENS	ANOURES		*Rana, Bufo, Hyla arborea* (Birukow, 1939, 1950) *Rana esculenta, R. pipiens, R. clamitans* (Thomas, 1955)
	URODÈLES		Salamandre, Tritons (Birukow, 1950)
POISSONS	TÉLÉOSTÉENS		Cyprin rouge (Hirose, 1922) Vairon (Burkamp, 1923; Schiemenz, 1924; v. Frisch, 1925; Wolff, 1926) Bouvière, Tanche (Burkamp, 1923) Goujon (v. Frisch, 1925) *Lepomis gibbosus* (Rochat, 1927); *L. macrochinus* (Hurst, 1953) *Betta splendens* (Lissmann, 1933) Épinoche *Gasterosteus aculeatus* (Tinbergen, 1940)
	DIPNEUSTES CHONDROSTÉENS CROSSOPTÉRYGIENS ÉLASMOBRANCHES AGNATHES OU CYCLOSTOMES		

INVERTÉBRÉS (moins les Insectes)

ARTHROPODES moins les Insectes	CRUSTACÉS	Malacostracés Décapodes	*Carcinus moenas* (v. Buddenbrock & Friedrich, 1933) *Crangon vulgaris* (Koller, 1927; Schlegtendal, 1934) *Leander* (= *Palaemon*) *adspersus* (Schlegtendal, 1934) Pagures: *Eupagurus anachoretus, Clibanarius misanthropus* (Koller, 1929)
		Amphipodes Isopodes Entomostracés	
	MYRIAPODES ARACHNOMORPHES XIPHOSURES		*Evarcha blancardi* (Kaestner, 1949)
MOLLUSQUES	CÉPHALOPODES		*Octopus* (Kühn, 1950), *Sepia officinalis* (Kühn, 1950; Boulet, 1958)
	LAMELLIBRANCHES GASTÉROPODES AMPHINEURES		
VERS ET VERMIDIENS	HIRUDINÉES OLIGOCHÈTES POLYCHÈTES NÉMATODES PLATODES ROTIFÈRES, etc.		

ÉCHINODERMES

COELENTÉRÉS

SPONGIAIRES

REFERENCES

ARDEN, G. & TANSLEY, K. (1955) *J. Physiol. London*, **127**, 592.
BAILEY, P. & RILEY, R. L. (1931) *Trans. Roy. Soc. Canada I.*, **18**, 47.
BIERENS DE HAAN, J. A. & FRIMA, M. J. (1930) *Z. vergleich. Physiol.*, **12**, 603.
BIRUKOW, G. (1939) *Z. vergleich. Physiol.*, **27**, 41 et 322.
BIRUKOW, G. (1950) *Z. vergleich. Physiol.*, **32**, 348.
BOSCHMA, H. (1925) *Biol. Bull.*, **48**, 446.
BOULET, P. (1958) *Mém. Mus. Nation. Hist. Nat.*, *nouvelle série, série A, Zoologie*, **17**, 1.
BUCHHOLTZ, C. (1953) *Z. Tierpsychol.*, **9**, 462.
VON BUDDENBROCK, W. (1929) *Zool. Anz.*, **84**, 189.
VON BUDDENBROCK, W. & FRIEDRICH, H. (1933) *Z. vergleich. Physiol.*, **19**, 747.
VON BUDDENBROCK, W. & MOLLER-RACKE, I. (1953) *Staz. Zool. Napoli Publ.*, **24**, 240.
BURGERS, A. C. J. (1952) *Physiol. comparata et Oecol.*, **2**, 272.
BURKAMP, W. (1923) *Z. Sinnenphysiol.*, **55**, 133.

CLARK, W. E. LE GROS (1940) *Nature*, **146**, 558.
CUENOT, L. (1940) *Rev. Sci.*, **78**, 222.
DENZER-MALBRANDT, U. (1935) *Zool. Jahrb.*, *Abt. allg. Zool. Physiol.*, **55**, 525.
DONNER, K. (1953) *J. Physiol. London*, **122**, 524.
VAN ECK, P. (1939) *Arch. néerl. zool.*, **3**, 450.
EWALD, W. F. (1914) *Z. Sinnenphysiol.*, **48**.
FRANÇOIS, J. & VERRIEST, G. (1957) *Ann. Oculist.*, **190**, 633.
VON FRISCH, K. (1923) *Naturw.*, **11**, 470.
VON FRISCH, K. (1925) *Z. vergleich. Physiol.*, **2**, 393.
VON FRISCH, K. & KUPELWIESER, H. (1913) *Biol. Zentr.*, **33**, 517.
GRANIT, R. (1941) *Acta physiol. Scand.*, **2**, 334.
GRANIT, R. (1942) *Acta physiol. Scand.*, **3**, 137.
GREGG, F. M., JAMISON, E., WILKIE, R. & RADINSKY, T. (1929) *J. Comp. Psychol.*, **9**, 379.
GRETHER, W. (1939) *Comp. Psychol. Monogr.*, **15/4**, 1.
GRETHER, W. (1940) *J. Comp. Psychol.*, **29**, 167, 179 et 187.
GRODZINSKA, M. (1948) *Bull. Acad. polon. Sci. Lettres*, **B**, 225.
GRZIMEK, B. (1952) *Z. Tierpsychol.*, **9**, 23.
HAMBURGER, V. (1926) *Z. wiss. Biol.*, **C/4**, 286.
HAMILTON, W. & COLEMAN, T. (1933) *J. Comp. Psychol.*, **15**, 183.
HEBERDEY, R. (1936) *Biol. Zentr.*, **56**, 207.
HERTER, K. (1933) *Z. vergleich. Physiol.*, **18**, 481.
HERTER, K. (1934) *Z. vergleich. Physiol.*, **21**, 450.
VON HESS, C. (1922) *Ergeb. Physiol.*, **20**, 1.
HIROSE, S. (1922) *Jahresvers. jap. ophtalm. Ges. Kyoto*, **4**, 2 et 3.
HOFFMANN, G. (1952) *Z. Tierpsychol.*, **9**, 470.
HOGLUND, N. H. (1956) *Viltrevy (Suède)*, **1**, 122.
HOPKINS, H. E. (1927) *Z. vergleich. Physiol.*, **6**, 299.
HOSOYA, Y., OKITA, T. & AKUNE, T. (1938) *Tôhoku J. Exp. Med.*, **34**, 532.
HURST, P. (1953) *J. Comp. and Physiol. Psychol.*, **46**, 442.
ILSE, D. (1937) *Nature*, **140**, 544.
JARVIK, M. E. (1956) *J. Comp. and Physiol. Psychol.*, **49**, 492.
KARLI, P. (1951) *Compt. rend. soc. biol.*, **145**, 1376.
KOEHLER, O. (1924) *Z. wiss. Biol.*, **C/1**, 84.
KOLLER, G. (1929) *Z. vergleich. Physiol.*, **8**, 337.
KOLOSVARY, G. A. (1934) *J. genet. Psychol.*, **44**, 473.
KÜHN, A. (1927) *Z. vergleich. Physiol.*, **5**, 762.
KÜHN, A. (1930) *Nachr. Ges. Wiss. Göttingen, Jahresber. Ges. Math. physik Kl*, **1**, 10.
KÜHN, A. (1950) *Z. vergleich. Physiol.*, **32**, 572.
LASHLEY, K. S. (1916) *Journal of Animal Behaviour*, **6**, 1.
LEMKE, G. (1935) *Z. vergleich. Physiol.*, **22**, 298.
LICHE, H. (1934) *Bull. Acad. polon. Sci. Lettres*, **B**, 233.
LISSMANN, H. W. (1933) *Z. vergleich. Physiol.*, **18**, 65.
MALMO, R. & GRETHER, W. (1947) *J. Comp. and Physiol. Psychol.*, **40**, 143.
MEYER, D. R., MILES, R. C. & RATOOSH, P. (1954) *J. Neurophysiol.*, **17**, 289.
MEYER-OEHME, D. (1957) *Z. Tierpsychol.*, **14**, 473.
MILES, R. C. (1958a) *J. Comp. and Physiol. Psychol.*, **51**, 152.
MILES, R. C. (1958b) *J. Comp. and Physiol. Psychol.*, **51**, 328.
MILES, R. C., RATOOSH, P. & MEYER, D. R. (1956) *J. Neurophysiol.*, **19**, 254.
MUENZINGER, K. F. & REYNOLDS, H. E. (1936) *J. genet. Psychol.*, **48**, 58.
MUSOLFF, W. (1955) *Zool. Beitr.*, N.F. **1**, 399.
O'DAY, K. (1947) *Nature*, **160**, 648.
PIÉRON, H. (1941) *Psychologie zoologique*. Paris.
PLATH, M. (1935) *Z. vergleich. Physiol.*, **22**, 691.
RENSCH, B. (1957) *Z. Tierpsychol.*, **14**, 71.
REVESZ, G. (1921) *Z. Psychol. Physiol. der Sinnesorgane*, **1/88**, 130.
ROCHAT, G. (1927) *Ned. Tijdschr. Geneesk.*, **71/1**, 2690.

ROCHON-DUVIGNEAUD, A. (1943) *Les yeux et la vision des Vertébrés.* Paris.
SCHEFFER, D., ROBERT, P. & MEDIONI, J. (1958) *Compt. rend. soc. biol.*, **152**, 100.
SCHIEMENZ, F. (1924) *Z. vergleich. Physiol.*, **1**, 175.
SCHLEGTENDAL, A. (1934) *Z. vergleich. Physiol.*, **20**, 545.
SGONINA, K. (1936) *Z. wiss. Zool.*, **148**, 350.
SMITH, F. E. & BAYLOR, E. R. (1953) *Am. Naturalist*, **87**, 49.
TANSLEY, K. (1950) *Symposia Soc. Exp. Biol. 4*, p. 19. Cambridge.
THOMAS, E. (1955) *Zool. Jahrb., Abt. allg. Zool. Physiol.*, **66**, 130.
TINBERGEN, N. (1940) *Z. Tierpsychol.*, **4**, 1.
VON TÖRNE, H. (1941) *Z. Tierpsychol.*, **4**, 347.
TRENDELENBURG, W. & SCHMIDT, I. (1930) *Z. vergleich. Physiol.*, **2**, 249.
TRINCKER, D. & BERNDT, P. (1957) *Z. vergleich. Physiol.*, **39**, 607.
VIAUD, G. (1938) *Recherches expérimentales sur le phototropisme des Daphnies*, Paris-Strasbourg.
VIAUD, G. (1940) *Bull. biol. France et Belg.*, **74**, 249.
VIAUD, G. (1949) *Behaviour*, **2**, 163.
VILTER, V. (1954) *Compt. rend. soc. biol.*, **148**, 1768.
WAGNER, H. (1933) *Z. vergleich. Physiol.*, **18**, 378.
WALLS, G. L. (1942) *The Vertebrate Eye*, Bloomfield Hills, Mich.
WALLS, G. L. (1953) *Univ. of Calif. Publ. in Physiol.*, **9**, 1.
WALTON, W. E. & BORNEMEIER, R. W. (1938) *J. Genet. Psychol.*, **52**, 155.
WALTON, W. E. & BORNEMEIER, R. W. (1939) *J. Comp. Psychol.*, **28**, 417.
WOJTUSIAK, R. J. (1933) *Z. vergleich. Physiol.*, **18**, 393.
WOLFF, H. (1926) *Z. vergleich. Physiol.*, **3**, 279.

E

DISCUSSION

PIÉRON

Y a-t-il des questions à poser? ou des objections? Dans cet inventaire, il y a, nous le savons, beaucoup de lacunes. D'autre part, nous savons aussi qu'il y a des discussions, qui restent encore très vives sur certains points, en particulier sur la capacité de discrimination chromatique de divers mammifères, et plus spécialement du Chat, déclaré achromatopsique, non seulement par Gregg et Miles,* mais encore par Gunter,† Cohn,‡ et, plus anciennement de Voss et Ganson (1929).§

VON FRISCH

Wenn ich Sie recht verstanden habe, meinen Sie, dass Daphnien wahrscheinlich farbenblind sind. Ich bin anderer Meinung, und zwar auf Grund einer Arbeit gemeinsam mit Dr. Kupelwieser aus dem Jahre 1913. Ein Aquarium mit Daphnien wurde in einer Dunkelkammer von einer Seite mit einer mässig starken Lampe belichtet. Die Daphnien adaptieren sich an diese Belichtung und sind gleichmässig im Gefäss verteilt. In diesem Zustand reagieren sie auf Verminderung der Lichtintensität durch Hinschwimmen zur Lichtquelle. Auf Vorschalten eines bestimmten *Blau*filters aber reagierten sie durch Wegschwimmen von der Lichtquelle, obwohl das Vorschalten des Filters zweifellos auch eine Verminderung der Intensität bedeutet. Auf Erhöhung der Intensität des weissen Lichtes reagieren sie durch Wegschwimmen vom Licht. Fügt man aber zu dem weissen Licht, an das sie adaptiert sind, *gelbes* Licht hinzu (durch einschalten einer zweiten Lampe mit Gelbfilter), so schwimmen sie zur Lichtquelle hin, obwohl das Hinzufügen des zweiten Lichtes zweifellos eine Erhöhung der Gesamtintensität für sie bedeutet.

Sie reagieren also auf die beiden Farben in qualitativ verschiedener Weise. Ihre positiv phototaktische Reaktion bei Steigerung der Lichtintensität durch Hinzufügen gelben Lichtes scheint mir als dermatoptische Reaktion nicht verständlich.

Es kommt hinzu, dass die Daphnien auf Belichtung des Auges durch bestimmte Augenbewegungen reagieren, die bei Steigerung und bei Herabsetzung der Intensität einander entgegengesetzt sind. Diese Augenbewegungen sind wahrscheinlich die primäre Reaktion, durch welche die phototaktischen Bewegungen gesteuert werden. Blaues Licht bewirkte die gleiche Augenbewegung wie Erhöhung der Lichtstärke bei weissem Licht, gelbes Licht bewirkte die entgegengesetzte Augendrehung, genau wie Verminderung der Intensität weissen Lichtes. Offenbar wird die spezifische Farbreaktion durch das Auge ausgelöst, und nicht auf dermatoptischem Wege.

* Gregg, F. A. (1929) *J. Comp. Psychol.*, **9**, 379.
† Gunter, R. (1954) *J. Comp. and Physiol. Psychol.*, **47**, 169.
‡ Cohn, R. (1956) *J. Neurophysiol.*, **19**, 416.
§ Voss, J. C. de & Ganson, R. (1915) *J. Animal Behaviour*, **5**, 115.

MEDIONI

Je voudrais présenter rapidement les résultats obtenus par M. Viaud, qui a repris récemment à Strasbourg l'expérience faite en 1913 par le Professeur von Frisch et son collaborateur Kupelwieser. Le dispositif expérimental employé est tout à fait comparable à celui du Professeur von Frisch (Fig. 1). Il est essentiellement constitué

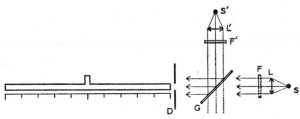

FIG. 1. Schéma de l'appareillage utilisé par Viaud pour reproduire l'expérience de von Frisch et Kupelwieser: S, source lumineuse principale; S′, source auxiliaire; L et L′, lentilles collimatrices; F, filtre bleu; F′, filtre jaune; G, glace transparente; D, diaphragme.

d'une cuve cylindrique en verre, de 1 mètre de long et 3 cm de diamètre, reposant horizontalement sur un banc d'optique. Au-dessous de la cuve se trouve une échelle centimétrique, permettant un repérage exact de la position des animaux, à l'aide de prises de vue photographiques en lumière rouge. La source S émet un faisceau lumineux parallèle, coaxial au tube et diaphragmé au diamètre de celui-ci. La source auxiliaire S′ permet d'ajouter de la lumière dans l'axe du tube.

L'expérience est conduite de la manière suivante: on introduit dans la cuve, à égale distance des deux extrémités, un lot de 50 Daphnies préalablement adaptées à l'obscurité totale pendant 30 minutes. La cuve étant éclairée par une lumière blanche de 260 lux (émise par la source S), on laisse les animaux évoluer librement, en repérant leur position de 5 en 5 minutes. Au bout d'une demi-heure, les Daphnies sont réparties dans toute l'étendue de la cuve, et l'expérience proprement dite commence. Elle peut prendre deux formes différentes:

(1) Interposition d'un filtre bleu dans le faisceau émis par la source S (lumière bleue, d'énergie moindre que la lumière d'adaptation).

(2) Adjonction de lumière jaune à la lumière blanche d'adaptation, par allumage de la source S′, devant laquelle un filtre jaune est placé (lumière jaune, d'intensité supérieure à celle de la lumière d'adaptation).

Les résultats obtenus sont représentés grahiquement dans la Fig. 2.

Celle-ci indique l'évolution dans le temps de la position moyenne du groupe, ce que M. Viaud a appelé son 'centre de gravité statistique' (le zéro de l'échelle des ordonnées correspond au point d'introduction des Daphnies dans la cuve, au milieu de celle-ci).

On constate que le centre de gravité statistique est assez fluctuant au cours des vingt premières minutes d'adaptation à la lumière blanche, mais qu'à la trentième minute, il est à peu près stabilisé, dans l'une comme dans l'autre expérience.

L'interposition d'un filtre bleu entre la source S et la cuve a provoqué, à notre surprise, non pas une fuite, une phase de répulsion phototropique, comme le signalent von Frisch et Kupelwieser, mais au contraire une *forte attraction*, le centre

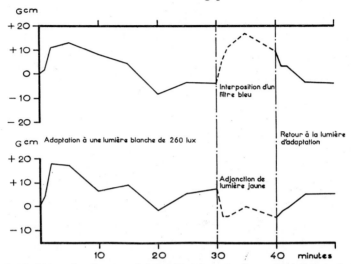

Fig. 2. Variations dans le temps de la position du centre de gravité statistique des lots de 50 Daphnies utilisés dans les deux expériences. L'interposition du filtre bleu dans le faisceau de lumière blanche d'adaptation cause une *attraction* des Daphnies vers la lumière. L'adjonction de lumière jaune à la lumière d'adaptation entraîne une répulsion phototropique.

de gravité statistique se déplaçant d'une quinzaine de centimètres vers la lumière au cours des 5 premières minutes en lumière bleue. Si, au bout de dix minutes, on revient à la lumière blanche d'adaptation, en ôtant le filtre bleu, la population de Daphnies recouvre graduellement sa position moyenne d'équilibre.

L'adjonction de lumière jaune à la lumière blanche d'adaptation cause le phénomène inverse: les animaux *s'éloignent* de la source lumineuse (au lieu de s'en approcher, comme le rapportent von Frisch et Kupelwieser). Cette répulsion phototropique dure aussi longtemps que l'exposition à la lumière jaune additionnelle. Quand on éteint la lumière jaune, le centre de gravité statistique revient graduellement à sa position initiale.

Les résultats de M. Viaud sont donc radicalement opposés à ceux du Professeur von Frisch; ils s'expliquent très simplement par la sensibilité des Daphnies à des variations de luminosité, sans qu'il soit besoin de faire appel à l'existence et à l'intervention d'une sensibilité chromatique qui reste hypothétique.

VON FRISCH

Auch wir hatten solche Daphnien, die nicht in der geschilderten Weise auf die Farben reagierten. Wir haben das in unserer Arbeit ausdrücklich besprochen. Die Reaktionen sind nicht bei allen Populationen gleich. In manchen Populationen verhalten sie sich so, wie Sie es sagen. An solchen Populationen lassen sich keine beweisenden Experimente über das Farbensehen ausführen. Das Verhalten dieser Tiere gibt aber auch kein Argument gegen einen Farbensinn.

Für die Experimente muss man Populationen suchen, die das geschilderte Verhalten zeigen. Solche haben wir wiederholt gefunden, und sie zeigten durch

Tage und Wochen in zahlreichen Versuchen die spezifischen Reaktionen. Für diese Tiere ist ein Farbensehen erwiesen und die Annahme ist berechtigt, dass ein Farbensinn allen Vertretern dieser Gattung zukommt, auch wenn nicht alle das spezifische phototaktische Verhalten zeigen.

Es würde mich freuen, Versuche an unseren Daphnien mit Ihnen zusammen zu machen, um Sie zu überzeugen.

PIÉRON

Ce sont là des questions délicates, évidemment.

Mais il faut bien se dire que les expériences pour démontrér la vision des couleurs sont difficiles — que l'on risque aussi bien de se tromper en niant, peut-être, quelquefois, la vision des couleurs, parce qu'on a eu un échec, qu'en sens inverse en affirmant la vision des couleurs d'après des données qui ne sont pas suffisamment probantes.

A cet égard, je voudrais rappeler les réserves que j'ai faites sur l'homochromie, et qui se sont consolidées lorsque j'ai vu un travail tout récent, qui vient de paraître à la Société zoologique, et où une zoologiste a prétendu que l'*Hippolyte* — elle a peut-être raison, d'ailleurs — que cette crevette avait la vision des couleurs.*

Mais sur quoi s'est-elle fondée? Sur l'homochromie, dans les conditions suivantes: Les *Hippolyte* vivent à Roscoff dans un habitat où il y a trois sortes d'algues: des algues rouges, des algues vertes et des algues brunes.

Les algues rouges ont une leucie moyenne; les algues vertes ont une très grande leucie; les algues brunes en ont une très faible.

Or, quels sont les pigments de l'*Hippolyte*? Là aussi, des pigments du même ordre: il y a des individus qui sont rouges, des individus verts, des individus marrons.

Les individus marrons se mettent de préférence sur les algues brunes, mais qui sont sombres; les individus verts, qui sont très clairs, se mettent sur des algues vertes mais qui sont très claires; et les individus rouges se placent sur des algues rouges, qui sont d'une leucie moyenne.

C'est-à-dire qu'il y a une adaptation certaine à l'albedo des surfaces.

Il est possible que ces crevettes — souvent étudiées déjà — voient les couleurs† mais en tout cas l'expérience ne peut pas le démontrer. C'est pour cela qu'il faut se méfier, dans ce cas-là, de vraisemblances qui ne sont pas des certitudes.

Il se peut très bien, n'est-ce pas, que des animaux n'ayant pas de vision des couleurs se mettent très exactement sur des algues correspondantes, d'ailleurs avec des proportions qui ne sont pas de 100 pour cent, bien entendu.

Le Dr. De Valois a demandé la parole.

DE VALOIS

I would like to take exception to the statement that the platyrrhine monkeys are protanopes.

In the first place, in only one of the several platyrrhine genera — the *Cebus* — is there any evidence of dichromacy. For instance, the data of Grether‡ and also that

* CHASSARD, C. (1936) *Bull. Soc. Zool.*, **81**, 413.

† C'est a qu'a affirmé SCHLIEPER; se fondant sur sa méthode optocinétique (1927) (*Z. vergleich. Physiol.*, **6**, 193).

‡ GRETHER, W. F. (1939) *Comp. Psychol. Monog.*, **15**, no. 4.

of ours from the one animal that we have studied indicate that the *Ateles*, another platyrrhine, is not only trichromatic, but is closer to man in spectral sensitivity than are the catarrhines.

We have some preliminary results from *Cebus* which might be of interest although the study is not yet complete. The colour discrimination and neutral point determination data from one female *Cebus* give no indication that it is a dichromat. In this regard it is of interest that the four monkeys Grether*† studied were all males and, as you know, human colour-blindness is almost exclusively a male disorder.

There is also some question as to whether the *Cebus* that are dichromats are protanopes. This has been questioned by Walls.‡ We have recorded ERGs from two male *Cebus* on which, unfortunately, we have no behavioural data. The ERGs showed X-waves to the long wavelengths as big as those from trichromatic macaques. Armington§ has shown that human protanopes are missing X-waves to red in their ERGs. Thus, if these animals are colour-blind, they may be deuteranopes rather than protanopes.

In summary then, all platyrrhines are not dichromats; even in the one dichromatic genus, the *Cebus*, all the individuals are apparently not dichromats; and the dichromacy may very well not be protanopia at all.

MONNIER

Voici quelques précisions sur le problème de la *perception chromatique chez les Rongeurs*. J'ai constaté que M. Viaud dans son beau rapport sur la discrimination chromatique chez les diverses espèces, a parlé du cobaye ou du rat, mais pas du lapin.

On sait que la rétine des Rongeurs, comme celle de la plupart des mammifères utilisés dans les laboratoires de physiologie, comme celle de l'homme aussi, est une rétine mixte à forte prédominance scotopique (bâtonnets). Cette prédominance est plus prononcée encore chez les rongeurs que chez les carnivores.

L'électrorétinogramme du cobaye après une courte latence à l'obscurité montre un bon développement de toutes les phases a, b, c, d (off effect).

Après *adaptation à l'obscurité*, nous voyons chez les rongeurs à vision scotopique prédominante, un bon développement des phases positives b et c, cependant que les phases négatives a et b sont discrètes, ainsi que l'off-effect (potentiel d) (Fig. 1*a*, A B).

Après *adaptation à la lumière*, un stimulus lumineux intense produit quelques réponses photopiques discrètes: Diminution de voltage de toutes les phases, notamment des phases positives. Le potentiel b devient très faible et le potentiel c tend à disparaître. Par contre les potentiels négatifs sont présents; la composante b négative est particulièrement prononcée (Fig. 1*a*, F C et D).

Cette phase b négative est caractéristique des rétines des rongeurs; on la retrouve également chez les carnivores et même chez l'homme, mais moins prononcée. L'existence de ces phases négatives ne permet donc pas de nier l'existence d'un appareil photopique chez le cobaye.

La réponse à la ré-illumination (Fig. 1*b*) se caractérise par un potentiel b très marqué qui se superpose au potentiel d, c'est à dire à l'off-effect. Ce phénomène signifie que la cessation de l'illumination est suivie chez le cobaye d'une inhibition

* GRETHER, W. F. (1939) *Comp. Psychol. Monog.*, **15**, no. 4.
† MALMO, R. B. & GRETHER, W. F. (1947) *J. Comp. and Physiol. Psychol.*, **40**, 143-7.
‡ WALLS, G. L. (1953) *Univ. Calif. Publ. Physiol.*, **9**, p. 66.
§ ARMINGTON, J. C. (1952) *J. Opt. Soc. Amer.*, **42**, 393-401.

post-excitatrice (Granit) qui n'est pas compensée par un 'off-mechanism'très actif. Les 'off-éléments' sont donc beaucoup moins abondants que les 'on-éléments', chez ce rongeur, ce qui prouve une fois de plus que sa rétine est pauvre en cônes.

Enfin, la fréquence de fusion est basse (Fig. 1*b*, E); elle ne dépasse guère 45 cycles par seconde (Dodt & Wirth, 1953). Le flicker est composé surtout de phases positives b-b-b.

Tous ces faits permettent de conclure que l'électrorétinogramme du cobaye présente tous les signes d'une *très forte prédominance de l'appareil scotopique* (type E de Granit), comme nous l'avions affirmé en 1944 (Boehm, Sigg & Monnier, 1944). Parmi les rongeurs, le cobaye représente par ailleurs le cas extrême; sa rétine a si peu de cônes qu'on a même de la peine à démontrer l'existence du dominateur photopique.

Les possibilités de discrimination chromatique paraissent donc très limitées, si non exclues, chez le cobaye.

Avec Bider, Huber et Koller nous avons examiné l'influence des stimuli lumineux sur la *rétine du lapin*. L'électrorétinogramme du lapin déclenché par des stimuli photiques se caractérise par un potentiel b positif d'amplitude variable suivant l'intensité (30 μV à 80 μV), suivi d'un potentiel b négatif. Les stimuli lumineux intenses et prolongés (1 sec.) accentuent le potentiel c et font apparaître un off-effect très discret, sous forme de potentiel d. Les réponses électriques de la rétine varient en fonction de l'intensité et de la surface du stimulus lumineux. Lorsque l'énergie du stimulus augmente on constate une augmentation du voltage du potentiel b, en même temps qu'une diminution de sa latence, de son temps de culmination et de la durée de sa phase ascendante. La durée de la première moitié de la phase ascendante est un paramètre simple et précis, qui nous renseigne sur la pente et sur les phases

TABLEAU I

Influence de la longueur d'onde sur l'ERG du lapin (surface d'illumination 20 mm²; stimulus de même énergie pour chaque couleur)

	Faible Intensité			Forte Intensité	
	Bleu	Vert	Rouge	Bleu	Vert
Lapin I					
Ampl. μV	28,5	28	27	80,5	82
Lat. b	41	39	46,5	35,5	35,5
Temps 1/2 culmination	65	67	77	62	60
Durée 1/2 phase ascendante	24,5	28	30	26,5	22
Lapin II					
Ampl. μV	26,5	27	26	106	107
Lat. b	47,5	44	42	32,7	30,5
Temps 1/2 culmination	68,3	69,5	75,5	59	57,5
Durée 1/2 phase ascendante	20,7	25	33	26	27

De ces observations, il ressort que la rétine du lapin en tant que représentant des rongeurs semble peu apte à la discrimination chromatique.

dont se compose la partie ascendante de la courbe (onde x de Motokawa p. ex.).
Il en va de même du temps de demi culmination, mesuré entre le début du stimulus
et la première moitié du potentiel b.

Nous n'avons pas observé de variations significatives des paramètres de l'électrorétinogramme en fonction de la *longueur d'onde* du stimulus. Nous avions utilisé à
cette fin des éclairages de longueurs d'onde différentes, mais de brillance égale
(filtre bleu avec maximum à 420 mμ, filtre vert avec maximum à 515 mμ et filtre
rouge avec maximum à 630 mμ). Dans ces différentes conditions de stimulation la
latence, le temps de culmination et le pente du potentiel b n'ont pas présenté de
variations significatives, tant que l'énergie totale du stimulus restait constante
(amplitude égale du potentiel b). Tout au plus a-t-on constaté parfois un allonge-
ment du temps de culmination et du temps de la phase ascendante dans les réponses
aux stimuli rouges de faible intensité (Tableau I).

VERRIEST

Le rapporteur conclut de son étude comparative que la vision colorée ne se
retrouve que dans les groupements zoologiques les plus 'évolués'.

Je crois que cette interprétation ne peut être adoptée sans réserves.*

Rappelons en premier lieu que les taxa (groupements zoologiques) 'primitifs'
n'ont généralement pas été examinés au point de vue de la différenciation chromatique; celle-ci n'est donc pas nécessairement absente chez eux.

Soulignons ensuite que la différenciation de l'épithélium sensoriel en deux types
principaux de récepteurs se rencontre dans toutes les classes de vertébrés, mais
qu'elle ne s'observe néanmoins pas dans tous les ordres, familles ou genres de
chaque classe. En effet, on ne trouve bien souvent qu'un seul type de récepteur, que
l'on classe alors soit comme cône, soit comme bâtonnet. Cette classification est
souvent assez arbitraire, quoique chacun des deux types présente des caractères plus
ou moins définis et constants.

Il nous semble probable que la présence de rétines mixtes à la fois chez certains
poissons, chez certains batraciens, chez certains reptiles, chez les oiseaux et chez
certains mammifères n'est pas due à une convergence multiple, mais bien à une
différenciation homologue. On doit alors admettre qu'un des deux types principaux
de récepteurs a été perdu dans quelques groupements zoologiques circonscrits.
Une transformation secondaire de type résiduel paraît avoir eu lieu chez des espèces
déterminées de Geckonidés, de serpents ou de rongeurs (Walls).

Comme la vision colorée paraît bien être une fonction des cônes (tout au moins
en principe et sous réserve d'exceptions), on peut supposer que le sens chromatique
peut être perdu quand les cônes n'existent plus. La différenciation chromatique ne
repose donc pas nécessairement sur des phénomènes de convergence, du moins en
ce qui concerne les vertébrés (Fig. 1).

A propos de la part de discusion de M. Monnier, je voudrais encore signaler que
Arden et Tansley† ont montré que, chez les Sciuridés uniquement pourvus de
'cônes', il existe, malgré l'unicité réceptorale, une dualité de la réponse électro-
rétinographique (onde *x* à l'état photopique, onde *b* à l'état scotopique).

D'autre part, nous avons pu mettre en évidence le même fait chez le lézard *Psammodromus algirus*, que ne possède également que des cônes. L'onde *b* est bien plus
touchée que l'onde *d* lors de l'adaptation à la lumière (Fig. 2).

* VERRIEST, G. (1957) *Biologisch Jaarboek*, **24**, 234.
† ARDEN, G. & TANSLEY, K. (1956) *J. Physiol. London*, **130**, 225.

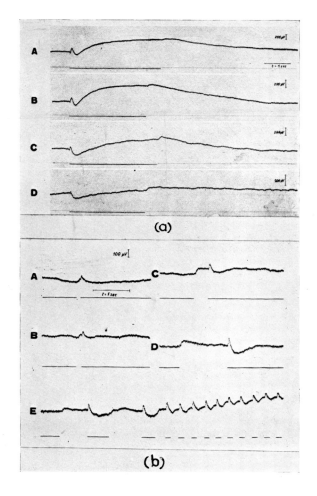

FIG. 1. (*a*) Action d'un stimulus lumineux de 3 sec. après adaptation à l'obscurité: A, pendant 300 sec.; B, pendant 60 sec.; C, pendant 10 sec.; D, action du même stimulus après adaptation à la lumière.
(*b*) Action de l'interruption du faisceau lumineux pendant des durées différentes sur la rétine adaptée à la lumière pendant 30 sec. (Boehm, Sigg & Monnier (1944), *Helv. Physiol. Acta*, **2**, 487 et 489.

On est donc en droit de conclure que la forme de l'électrorétinogramme est, du moins partiellement, due à certains facteurs qui sont tout à fait indépendants de la nature des récepteurs.

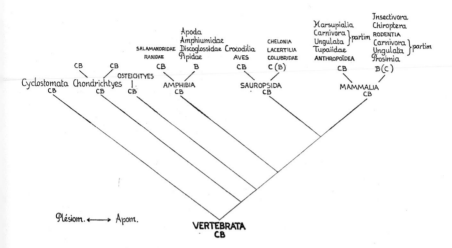

FIG. 1. On a constaté l'existence de rétines mixtes chez certains représentants de toutes les classes de vertébrés. Rien ne permet d'affirmer que cette différenciation extrêmement fréquente de l'épithélium sensoriel en deux types principaux de récepteurs ne soit pas un phénomène homologue! Si cette différenciation est un phénomène homologue, il est évident que la présence d'un seul type de récepteur est un caractère apomorphe (c. à. d. acquis plus tardivement). L'existence d'une discrimination chromatique est généralement liée à celle des cônes; la présence d'animaux nocturnes, dépourvus de cônes et achromates dans plusieurs classes *ne doit donc pas faire nécessairement conclure* à ce que la présence d'une vision colorée chez les représentants de certains autres groupes de vertébrés soit toujours dûe à des phénomènes de convergence.

Groupes en minuscules: discrimination chromatique non étudiée ou absente.

Groupes en majuscules: discrimination chromatique démontrée avec beaucoup de vraisemblance chez certaines espèces.

CB, rétines mixtes; B, rétines à bâtonnets (éventuellement quelques cônes); C, rétines à cônes.

Les listes de groupes zoologiques dans la partie supérieure la figure ne sont évidemment pas des subdivisions de la phylogénèse.

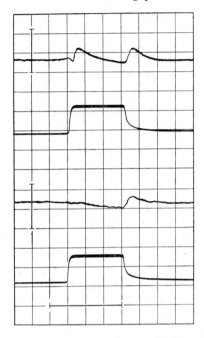

FIG. 2. *Psammodromus algirus.* En haut: adaptation à l'obscurité; en bas: adaptation à la lumière. Calibrage: 50 µV, 0,10 sec.

PIÉRON

Évidemment, là nous entrons dans le domaine de la neurophysiologie, puisqu'il s'agit de l'interprétation des électrorétinogrammes. Nous sortons un peu du domaine de l'exploration des animaux que nous avions aujourd'hui en sujet.

Demain, le problème neurophysiologique se posera. Pour ce problème physiologique, il est extrêmement intéressant de savoir qu'il y a trois espèces de mammifères qui ont des rétines à cônes pures et que, par conséquent, il est très désirable de s'adresser à ces espèces-là et de les bien connaître — ce qui n'est pas le cas puisque nous avons le spermophile, la marmotte et l'écureuil gris.

Ce sont des espèces, je crois, qui sont essentiellement destinées à des expériences neurophysiologiques fécondes, quand on n'a pas la gêne de l'ingérence des bâtonnets et de la vision scotopique dans les explorations neurophysiologiques que l'on fait.

NEUROPHYSIOLOGICAL PROBLEMS

I

AT THE RETINAL LEVEL

W. A. H. Rushton

Professor Piéron, Ladies and Gentlemen.

It is about a hundred and fifty years since Thomas Young first put forward the trichromatic theory of vision and in all that time the advances have been made almost entirely in the field of psychophysics.

If the psychophysicists feel that colour vision is their subject, they have a long and distinguished past to justify that view.

But the future will not sustain it. Though it is only about 20 years that the sciences of biochemistry and electrophysiology have been able to make useful contributions in the field of colour vision, it is certain that that is going to increase and it will no longer be possible to put forward a theory of colour vision simply by the economy of the hypotheses and the beautiful symmetry of the equations to which it leads.

It will be necessary for all of us to contribute together. This was of course clearly in the mind of Professor Piéron when he had this excellent idea of collecting us from many different disciplines, so that by marching together we could help each other in the very difficult territory of colour vision.

But I have sometimes thought that the psychophysicists have not been as enthusiastic as we could wish when some little advance has been made in electrophysiology.

This is not surprising. Electrophysiologists have taken from the psychophysicists freedom of imagination and the beauty of their symmetrical concepts and, in return, they have given them a very indigestible diet. Let us heal this divergence of opinion this morning.

First I would say to the psychophysicists: We *must* have the kind of basis that biochemistry and electrophysiology gives. It is beautiful to have economy of hypothesis but nature is not economical. In the forms of living things there is an almost infinite diversity.

The beauty of the flowers does not drop from the stars, it grows from the earth. If we would wish to get symmetrical blooms, we must dirty our fingers a little with the roots, which are far from symmetrical and never the same one with another. Let me ask you to descend with us into the earth and see what these roots are. Have some patience.

But my colleagues, the electrophysiologists, do not strain this patience too far!

If the psychophysicist is to look at the roots a little, he does not wish for us simply to give him mud; earth sterile or even putrid may be of value for us to analyse when we are alone, but today we are here in mixed session; let us be sure when we offer our electrophysiology that there are at least some little growing points which will eventually perhaps flower into the beautiful kinds of simplified relations which the psychophysicists enjoy.

I am aware that this is a very difficult thing for electrophysiologists to do. I am aware that I shall be the first to fail. But try to do better. And in the discussion, may I ask that we endeavour to keep the things we discuss near the centre field where everybody is interested in the answer. Let us not stray too far about some little detail of technique, interesting only to one small section.

And you, the psychophysicists, our friends, help us to do this and by your questions and your comments bring our subject into the domain which is of general interest.

Let me start with dark adaptation.

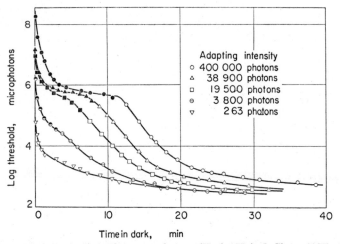

Fig. 1. Dark-adaptation curves in man (Hecht, Haig & Chase, 1937).

This study is very well known; I suppose everybody here has at some time or another obtained a dark-adaptation curve and we know from the original work of Kohlrausch and Hecht that there are two branches.

It is pretty certain that the upper one (black points, Fig. 1) is the cone branch because, on the fovea, this alone is present, and it is certain that in humans the lower one (white points) is the rod branch because it is not on the fovea and because the spectral sensitivity corresponds to the rhodopsin.

The first question I want to ask is why is the rod curve pushed so far to the right? The cone curve rises assymptotically to the vertical axis, but with strong adaptations the rod curve is displaced to the right and rises up as shown in Fig 1.

Is it the case that the rods cannot appear earlier because they are inhibited by the cones? I do not know the answer to this, but it is an exceedingly important question in the relation between electrophysiology and vision. And I want to raise this question because either from psychophysics or from electrophysiology you may have some answer. Let me give you one piece of evidence.

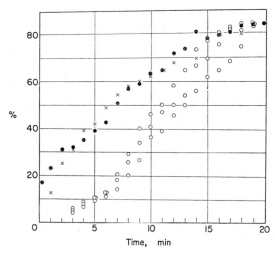

FIG. 2. Percentage regeneration in man of rhodopsin ($\times$), and of size of *b*-wave of ERG ($\bigcirc$) in normal, ($\bullet$) in rod monochromats (Elenius & Heck, 1957).

Fig. 2 is taken from Elenius and Heck (1957). It represents the *b*-wave of the human electroretinogram (ERG) measured during dark adaptation after a bright exposure, expressed as a percentage of the dark-adapted value.

The white circles give results for the normal eye, the black circles for a rod monochromat — the type of person who has only scotopic vision, photophobia and the rest of that syndrome. The crosses show the regeneration of rhodopsin measured physically in a fairly normal eye. In point of fact it is *my* eye, because Elenius took the published values that Campbell measured on my eye.

You see that in the absence of cones, there seems to be a good correspondence between the regeneration of rhodopsin and the return of the electroretinogram. It looks as though it was the presence of the cones which depressed the ERG from black circles to white. One is tempted to conclude that the rods themselves respond in accordance with their measured rhodopsin content, but that their electrical effect is inhibited by the cones. But there are difficulties.

In the first place we do not know the essential defect of the rod mono-chromat, the actual structure has never been worked out and, according to Walls, only one case has been studied histologically and that had *normal cones*. There are some histologists here who perhaps can comment on that.

But there is another point which we all know. It has been approximately verified many times that lights which appear equal by scotopic vision are equal in producing light adaptation of the rods. That is to say the second half of the dark-adaptation curve (the rod branch) will be the same, no matter what the colour of the adapting light, providing its intensity by *scotopic vision* always appears the same. If that is the case, this inhibition is equal for equal scotopic lights, not equal photopic lights. The thing that is causing the in-hibition of the rods is not due to the light on the cones; it is due to the light on the rods.

So if Elenius and Heck are correct in their conclusions and the rods are inhibited by the cones, it must be the rods which are telling the cones to inhibit them. That is not quite such a simple situation.

The best measurements we have of the rods are those of Aguilar and Stiles. They used conditions which enable rods to be measured by psychophysical methods at a much higher luminance than had commonly been done before, by ingenious methods which brought the rods out and which depressed the cones. They found that the rods would no longer function at a level of about 3000 scotopic trolands. Now it takes 40,000 trolands to bleach half the rhodopsin (Campbell & Rushton, 1955) so only about 7 per cent has been bleached at the level where rod function fails.

Clearly there is something which cuts off the rods at an intensity where very little of the rhodopsin is bleached away. As a matter of fact this intensity of 40,000 trolands also bleaches the cone pigment half away (Rushton, 1958), but in that condition we can see with the cones very well indeed. Our problem, then is as follows:

Bleaching half the pigment from the cones does not stop vision, but long, long before that the rods have ceased to function. Is this an inhibition and, if so, what is the inhibiting agent? And how is it that this agent receives its orders from the rods themselves?

I wish now to raise a question of a different kind, but also about rods and cones.

Are they both connected to the same optic nerve fibre? Or is there one set of fibres for the cones and one set of fibres for the rods? There are diffi-culties with both of these ideas and I want help from you in sorting them out.

Ever since Mueller, we have grown to accept as a matter of course that one class of nerve fibre conveys one class of sensation. We are all very familiar

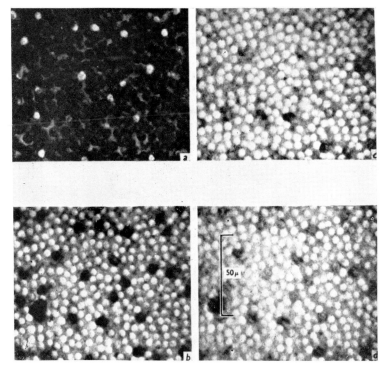

FIG. 5. Purple and green rods in one fresh frog's retina: *a*, *b*, photographed in green, and blue light before bleaching; *c*, *d*, the same after bleaching (Denton & Wyllie, 1955).

with the difference in sensation in photopic and scotopic vision. And we can ask: 'How is it possible that these very different sensations could be conveyed by nerve impulses travelling along the same nerve fibre?' Surely we must suppose that there is one set for the rods and one set for the cones. But how uneconomical that is!

We know from anatomy that the optic nerves are the bottleneck of the whole system. Down to the optic nerve there is convergence, enormous convergence in the human eye from more than a hundred million receptors to less than a million nerve fibres. And then at the other end, at the lateral geniculate body, there is divergence again, and a great deal of organization in the brain. The optic nerve is where there must be great economy in nerve fibres.

Gentlemen, what would you say if I told you I was going to start a telegraph company that would send day telegrams and night telegrams and, to avoid confusion, I was going to have an entirely different set of wires for the day telegrams, which would be idle all night, and another set for the night telegrams, which would be idle all day? I do not think that I should get money from any of you.

And can we suppose that this is what is done by the eye, that is so beautifully organized in so many ways? We have no records from optic nerves of the human eye, but there are by now a very great many records from the eyes of animals. In particular, Granit (1947), who has given us measurements from ganglion cells and optic nerve fibres from such a wide range of animals, has consistently found that, when leading from a single element in light adaptation and that same element in dark adaptation, he gets spectral sensitivity curves which are quite different. I do not remember that he has ever found a retina where one fibre is only sensitive in the light, and another only in the dark. In the light we get the photopic dominator and in the dark we get the scotopic dominator from the same ganglion. I think it would be safe to generalize that whenever an animal possesses both photopic and scotopic mechanisms, these converge on to a single ganglion cell, at least with the big ganglion cells which have generally been studied.

I would like to show you a repetition of Granit's work that was analysed a little bit further by Donner and myself 2 years ago but which, I am ashamed to say, is not yet published because of my negligence (now in press).

Fig. 3 is taken from a single ganglion cell in the common frog. It is an ordinary dark-adaptation curve, making use of a ganglion discharge as index of excitation. When the light was steady or, in the darkness, there was no discharge from this ganglion cell; we put a little flash of light, say 1 sec., on and off and measured the 'threshold' to obtain a ganglion spike.

The flash of light was of different wavelengths and in general for each colour we get the familiar branched curve. But now there is some difficulty.

F

If we accept the conventional conclusion that the upper branch is cones, the lower rods, which I believe to be correct for the human eye, we get into trouble.

We can take the spectral sensitivity at any stage of dark adaptation simply by measuring the curves of Fig. 3 at different times — a vertical line across the whole figure cutting the curves at levels which show the log sensitivity for each wavelength at that moment. The spectral log sensitivity curves so found

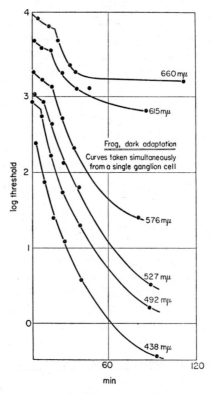

FIG. 3. Dark-adaptation curves in frog with test flashes at wavelengths shown. Single ganglion discharge used as index of excitation. Curves displaced vertically for clearness.

are plotted in Fig. 4. The photopic dominator (white circles) is present at first and, as dark adaptation proceeds, you see that there is something going on quite different from a simple change from cones to rods.

As Granit found 16 years ago, there is a great increase in the blue — right here in the blue — not rhodopsin. After about $1\frac{1}{2}$ hours of dark adaptation the sensitivity is given by the top curve (Fig. 4) which shows still a marked hump in the blue. If we wait a very long time that will disappear and we shall be left with nothing but a pure rhodopsin curve. What is going on here?

Now the first thing that you will think of is the observation already made by Boll & Kuehne in 1877 that the frog's retina contains more than one class of rod.

If you look at a frog's retina under the microscope (dissected out in the dark of course), you will see the beautiful mosaic (which is shown in Boll's first paper in 1877), a mosaic of purple rods and green rods. Of course there

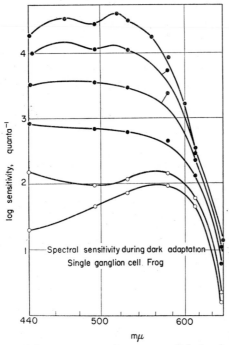

FIG. 4. Spectral sensitivity curves at various stages of dark adaptation, obtained from Fig. 3. Ordinates: log sensitivity (= −log quantum threshold). Abscissae: wavelengths plotted upon a uniform scale of wave frequencies.

will be a difference in the interpretation of the second half of the dark-adaptation curve if, instead of having one class of rods as in man, there are two classes of rods as in the frog.

Fig. 5 (facing p. 72) is from Dartnall (1957), taken from the actual photograph of Denton & Wyllie (1955). It shows the frog's retina photographed in a green light and in blue light before and after bleaching. All four frames show the same piece of retina and you can see very nicely the grass-green rods of Kuehne appearing transparent in green light (*a*) and opaque in blue light (*b*). Denton and Wyllie were able to show, moreover, that these rods were sensitive to blue wavelengths, and Dartnall (1957, p. 191) has been able to demonstrate in an extract of frog's rod pigments that there is a small component which is sensitive to blue light and has the appropriate difference spectrum. We might say then that the kink in the dark-adaptation curve represents a transition from cones to rods but that frog's rods are of two kinds, and the grass-green rods at mesopic levels of adaptation account for the high sensitivity in the blue. I am afraid it is not so simple as that.

I wish now to prove to you that in that part of the dark-adaptation curve which occurs after the kink there are also cones present, and for this I want to draw upon a new method for distinguishing rods and cones. It is, I think, an extremely valuable one and it is due to Flamant & Stiles (1948). As you all know, Stiles & Crawford (1933) showed with the human eye that when light enters the centre of the pupil and falls upon the fovea, it appears many times as bright as light which comes through the periphery of the eye and falls upon the same part of the retina — a retinal direction effect. The cones on the fovea are about three or four times as sensitive to light which is direct as light which falls a little oblique. How about the rods?

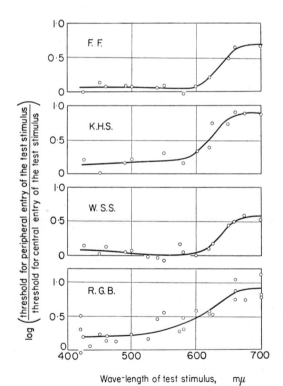

Wave-length of test stimulus, $m\mu$

FIG. 6. Stiles-Crawford effect 5° parafoveal. Ratio of thresholds for light entry through periphery or centre of the pupil: near unity for short wavelengths (rods) and rises to about 4 for long wavelengths (cones) (Flamant & Stiles, 1948).

Fig. 6 from the paper by Flamant & Stiles (1948) shows the results when light falls upon the retina 5° parafoveal where there is a mixture of rods with the still largely cone population. The figure gives for various wavelengths the ratio of the thresholds, for light coming through the centre and periphery of the pupil.

As you see (W. S. S., Fig. 6), in the case of Dr. Stiles—who is here to deny it — there is no difference between the central and the peripheral light if the wavelength is short, for it is stimulating the rods. But there is a big difference, 0.5 log units, when the wavelength is long. So that we expect that this phenomenon, first found on the fovea, is a property of the cones only and that the rods do not show it, or show it very little.

I jumped a little fast when I interpreted this as rods and cones.

Anyone who has read the paper of Flamant and Stiles will know that they

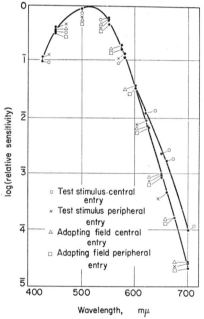

Fig. 7. Spectral sensitivity of 5° parafoveal region to light entering through centre or periphery of the pupil. Increment thresholds for all combinations of central and peripheral entry of flash and adaptation fields (Flamant & Stiles, 1948).

do not jump fast. And a very nice way of proving it, which I can't go into in detail, is the curve of Fig. 7. When the test flash enters through the periphery of the pupil the spectral sensitivity corresponds to the fully dark-adapted value — the rhodopsin-like rod sensitivity. When the flash enters centrally the spectral sensitivity still falls upon the same curve for short wavelengths, and shows that so long as rods are being stimulated there is no directional sensitivity. But at longer wavelengths the spectral sensitivity no longer coincides with rods; here cones are involved and exhibit a marked depression of excitability for rays which fall upon the retina obliquely.

But does this apply to the frog, which is the animal that we were talking about?

Donner and I (1956) repeated upon the frog the experiment of Flamant and Stiles, and obtained very much the same results.

The upper curve of Fig. 8 is the absorption curve of frog's rhodopsin

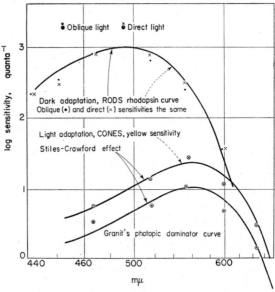

FIG. 8. Stiles-Crawford effect in the excised and opened frog's retina. Upper curve in dark adaptation, rhodopsin sensitivity, no S.-C. effect: ●, oblique light; ×, perpendicular. Lower curves in light adaptation, photopic dominator curve: ⊕ perpendicular light, is about three times as effective as ◯, the oblique light.

(Dartnall). Dots and crosses show the log spectral sensitivity when light fell obliquely or perpendicularly upon the retina, and, like Flamant and Stiles, we found that so long as we were on the rod curve there were no appreciable changes in 'threshold'.

But, in light adaptation, we get quite a different sensitivity curve. The lower curves are Granit's photopic dominator in the frog, which Wald has shown corresponds rather closely with the spectrum of iodopsin. And in this case, as you see, there is a big change in 'threshold', when changing from oblique light to direct. The vertical scale shows log sensitivity so direct light is about three times as effective as oblique light.

Now we have a method which we may apply to our dark-adaptation curve to see whether the humps attributed to green rods show the Stiles-Crawford effect or not.

Before dark adaptation (Fig. 9), we get, as before, the photopic dominator with a big Stiles-Crawford effect. The white circles are direct, the black circles oblique light.

After dark adaptation, the sensitivity by perpendicular light (circles) had a hump in the blue and one in the green above the rhodopsin curve shown.

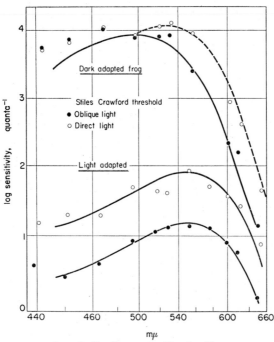

FIG. 9. Lower curves show S.-C. effect as in Fig. 8. Upper curves partly dark adapted and not giving full rhodopsin sensitivity. The hump in the green is direction sensitive and hence due to cones, that in the blue is not and hence due to the 'grass-green' rods.

When the light goes from direct to oblique, the green hump vanishes and the points (dots) coincide with the rhodopsin curve. It is exactly what Flamant and Stiles showed, in Fig. 7.

The blue hump on the other hand is independent of the obliquity of the light. We are therefore confirmed in the suggestion that this blue hump is due to the 'grass-green' rods, but it is equally clear that the long-wave hump is due to cones.

I see no escape from the conclusion that in the frog, after the kink in the curve, there are mixed together in the total excitability, green rods, rhodopsin rods, and at least one class of cone.

Now this situation gives us a very interesting possibility of seeing how these three classes of receptors interact, and the method that we have adopted to investigate that interaction is suddenly to substitute one light for another.

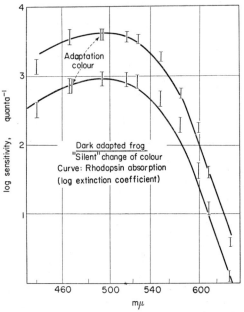

Fig. 10. Frog's eye adapted to wavelength and intensity shown by rectangles. This light was suddenly exchanged for another wavelength. If the new intensity lay upon the little vertical lines there was no discharge from the single ganglion recorded. At all other intensities there was. The curve shows the rhodopsin sensitivity. The upper curve was at a low level of adaptation.

Let me ask you to consider what we should expect if, instead of having this mixed population, we had simply a uniform population of rods. The upper curve (Fig. 10) is from a fairly dark-adapted eye. If we adapt to a rather weak light of wavelength about 500 mμ and suddenly increase that light a bit, we shall get a discharge when the new light falls outside the Fechner fraction, or if we decrease the light we will get a discharge again when it falls outside the Fechner fraction. I do not want to trouble you with the distinction of on-fibres and off-fibres, but our technique is always to change from the adaptation light to a new one and then change back again and see if there is a discharge. The vertical lines of Fig. 10 represent the extent of the 'silent interval' afforded by the Fechner fraction.

Now, instead of changing to a light of the same colour but of different intensity, we can go to a light of different colour. If we simply have rhodopsin rods, we should expect, provided that the light is increased in inverse proportions to the rhodopsin sensitivity, that we should get no ganglion discharge in going from any wavelength to any other.

The rhodopsin would not 'know' that the light had been changed if it was changed to a value which absorbed quanta at the same speed. And if the rhodopsin does not know the light has changed, clearly the receptor cannot know it. Now the upper curve of Fig. 10 represents rhodopsin sensitivity drawn through the adaptation point.

So we should expect three predictions with confidence.

(i) That we should get a silent change if we go to any other point on the curve.

(ii) The Fechner fraction expressed by the vertical line (on a logarithmic scale) should be of equal length at all points on the curve.

(iii) The shape of the curve should not be altered by changing the wavelength of the adaptation light, since the curve is always just the absorption spectrum of rhodopsin.

All these would be confidently expected, and all can be verified both on frogs and on men by this technique. And we have done so.

But it would not at all be expected that these things would happen if there was a mixed population of this rod and that rod, of this cone and perhaps that cone. To find *that* would be surprising. But that is what we have found.

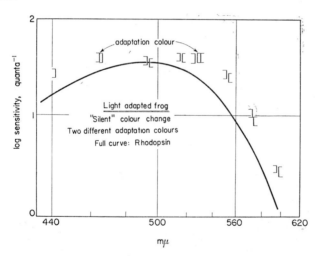

Fig. 11. Same as Fig. 10 but at higher adaptation level. As shown in Fig. 9 the hump in the green involves cones, that in the blue the 'grass-green' rods.

Fig. 11 shows an experiment of this kind. The eye is at about the level of adaptation shown in Fig. 9 and like Fig. 9 shows a hump in the blue due to green rods and a hump in the green due to cones. Yet we may adapt to a blue light and change silently to any other light within the small Fechner fraction shown. Or we may adapt to green and change silently to any colour upon the same curve as before. There is always a silent change possible, there is no differential adaptation, and the Fechner fraction is constant everywhere.

What are we to think of the neural organization which results in this unexpected simplicity?

Early in the retinal pathways, there must be some kind of pool of excitation into which receptors that are anatomically quite distinct, as distinct as rods and cones, can pour their excitation. It looks as though the level of excitation in this pool is the thing which triggers off, or does not trigger off, the ganglion discharge.

But it makes no difference to the discharge whether the pool level is altered by more rods and less cones, or the other way round. And, if the contributions from many different kinds of receptors is such that the pool level keeps constant, then there will be no discharge from the ganglion cells.

You may say:

'Well, this is a fancy notion. Surely no psychophysicist has suggested anything less like electrophysiology than this imaginary pool of excitation, in which things seem to have to add linearly in a way which we do not generally find them adding in electrophysiology.' One moment please. Let me end this Introduction by presenting to you some very beautiful records which Svaetichin & MacNichol (1958) have been good enough to send me, with permission to show them to you. The records are from fish in work done at Caracas in Venezuela.

The retina of the fish was taken out quickly and spread out on a flat slide in an atmosphere of moist oxygen. Then, from the receptor layer, a micropipette was pushed through until it reached some cells which showed results very different indeed from the ganglion cells.

This kind of work has also been done in Japan and it has been done by Dr. Gruesser (1957).

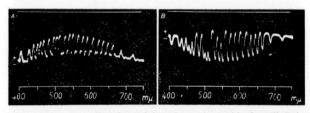

FIG. 12. Micropipette recording from fish retina: *A*, outside the cell; *B*, inside (with gain reduced ten times). Each wave represents the response to an equal energy (ergs) flash of indicated wavelength.

The records are obtained not (in the opinion of the authors) from the receptor cells themselves, and certainly not from the ganglion cells. We may call the cells 'luminosity intermediates' and 'colour intermediates' because the results are very different, depending upon the site of recording.

The record of Fig. 12 was obtained by putting flashes of light of different wavelengths upon the eye and reading off the potential developed.

Actually, as we shall see later, if the light was not a very brief flash, but was a continued light, then the excursion would be continued just like the output of a photo-electric cell.

In record *A* (Fig. 12) the electrode has not yet penetrated. There is no resting potential, but each flash gives a small excursion.

In record *B* they have tapped the table: that little vibration has pushed in the micro-electrode. There is now a resting potential of 20 millivolts, which has been balanced out so that it does not appear in the record. The amplification has been turned down to one-tenth of what it was in *A*, so that on that scale, you see, it would have come down to the floor. And the whole picture looks very much like a luminosity curve. It is hyperpolarization with the maximum at just about the wavelength you would expect for cone luminosity.

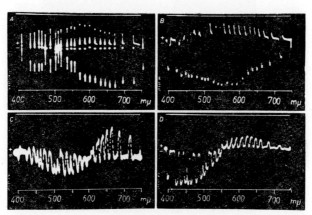

Fig. 13. Conditions as Fig. 12. Single retina, three localities: *B*, luminosity intermediate, all responses negative; *C*, R-G intermediate, red lights positive, green negative; *D*, Y-B intermediate yellow lights positive, blue negative. Retina from *mucilidae.*

Neglect record *A* (Fig. 13); *B*, *C* and *D* are from one retina, but with the electrode in different places. *B* they believe to be the horizontal cells and it is the luminosity intermediate just the same as in Fig. 12.

But look at this one! (Record *C*).

This is from a different place, a little further into the retina, that is to say nearer the vitreous, and red light depolarizes, green light hyperpolarizes.

And here another result (record *D*).   This time yellow light depolarizes and blue hyperpolarizes.

This fish is the only species which gives both a red-green and a yellow-blue response. Many people here will hope that it is a 'Herring', but it isn't! And I can't remember what it is — it is a Central American fish.

But you can see the beautiful results. At wavelength 600 mμ in record *C* there is just nothing coming from the receptor.

And here again in record *D*, there is a change-over point at about 540 mμ.

At each of these places, where there is nothing from the colour intermediate cell, there is a big discharge from the luminosity intermediate and one can say that — (Well, it's all obvious to you and it's very much the sort of thing that Hering's theory envisaged).

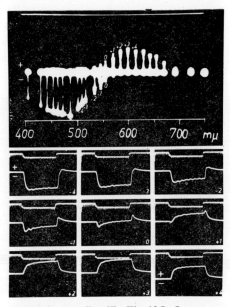

Fig. 14. Upper record Y-B intermediate like Fig. 13*D*. Lower records show the time course of the waves when the light flashes are as shown in the upper trace of each frame (time in 0.1 and 0.01 sec.).

The lower records of Fig. 14 give the time course. (The small divisions are hundredths of seconds.)

The labels —4, —3, ... on the lower frames represent the wavelengths so labelled on the upper record. Minus 4, you see, is about 500 mμ.

With this receptor there should be nearly no discharge at 0, but there is a little discharge there.

See what happens at 0 in the lower frame.

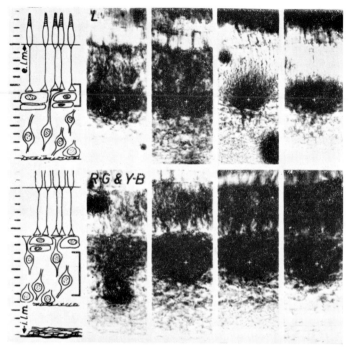

Fig. 15. Localization of L, and of R-G, Y-B intermediates by injection of dye from micropipette *in situ*. On left the formal histological picture to scale.

[W. A. H. Rushton]

[*facing page 84*

The positive and the negative processes do not have quite the same time constant. Those of us who have tried to balance out electrical artefacts with bridges are very familiar with this kind of thing. The two waves that we are trying to neutralize turn out not to have quite the same shape usually, and we nearly always are left with some little transients.

That is what seems to happen with this colour intermediate. And notice how the electric change is a steady one. So long as the light lasts, there is a constant deflection, very like a photo-electric cell.

Fig. 15 is an attempt to localize histologically where the electrodes are in these experiments — a matter so very important for interpretation.

These authors filled their micro-electrode with a dye, methyl-violet, and discharged this electrophoretically into the tissue and then obtained frozen sections. The dye shows that the luminosity intermediate is at a level which corresponds to the horizontal cells.

The colour intermediates are somewhat lower and may correspond to the bipolar cells. The formal picture at the side helps the identification.

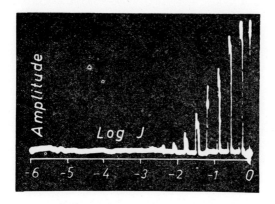

Fɪɢ. 16. Relation between amplitude of electric potential and log of light intensity *J*.

Fig. 16 shows the relation between log J (the light intensity) and the size of the depolarization or hyperpolarization of the cell. It is not all-or-none, as in most of the cells we study in electrophysiology, but the change is a linear function of the logarithm of the light. So that perhaps the Weber law and the ways in which the logarithm of the light enters into so many parameters of vision may be related to the fact that quite early in the electrophysiological process there is this logarithmic transformation and it is only after that, that the various interactions occur.

Monsieur Piéron, I have already overstayed my time. I must apologize to you and to the company. You will prefer that I do not end with concluding redundancies, but rather give place to all those here who are full of new ideas to help in the problems that I have raised. I thank you.

REFERENCES

AGUILAR, M. & STILES, W. S. (1954) *Optica Acta*, **1**, 59.
BOLL, F. (1877) *Arch. Anat. Physiol.*, 4.
CAMPBELL, F. W. & RUSHTON, W. A. H. (1955) *J. Physiol. London*, **130**, 131.
DARTNALL, H. J. A. (1957) *The Visual Pigments*, London.
DENTON, E. J. & WYLLIE, J. H. (1955) *J. Physiol. London*, **127**, 81.
DONNER, K. O. & RUSHTON, W. A. H. (1956) *J. Physiol. London*, **132**, 37P.
DONNER, K. O. & RUSHTON, W. A. H. (1959) *J. Physiol. London* (in press).
ELENIUS, V. & HECK, J. (1957) *Nature*, **180**, 810.
FLAMANT, F. & STILES, W. S. (1948) *J. Physiol. London*, **107**, 187.
GRANIT, R. (1947) *Sensory Mechanisms of the Retina*, Oxford.
GRÜSSER, O. J. (1957) *Naturw.*, **19**, 522.
HECHT, S., HAIG, C. & CHASE, A. M. (1937) *J. Gen. Physiol.*, **20**, 831.
MOTOKAWA, K., OIKAWA, T. & TASAKI, K. (1957) *J. Neurophysiol.*, **20**, 186.
RUSHTON, W. A. H. (1958) *Photoreception, Ann. N.Y. Acad. Sci.*, **74**, 291.
STILES, W. S. & CRAWFORD, B. H. (1933) *Proc. Roy. Soc.*, B, **112**, 428.
SVAETICHIN, G. & MACNICHOL, E. F. (1958) *Photoreception, Ann. N.Y. Acad. Sci.*, **74**, 385.
TOMITA, T. (1957) *Jap. J. Physiol. London*, **7**, 80.
WALLS, G. L. & HEATH, G. G. (1954) *Acta Ophthalmol.*, **32**, 253.

DISCUSSION

PIÉRON

Messieurs, vous avez certainement été enchantés de cet exposé qui est si nouveau, et qui nous montre évidemment combien sont importants ces phénomènes qui se passent au niveau de l'appareil récepteur — cet appareil oculaire qui est déjà un centre extraordinairement complexe — et nous y voyons ces interactions qui se produisent et qui nous donnent évidemment des résultats d'une complexité que l'ingéniosité du Prof. Rushton a permis de débrouiller dans un certain nombre de cas, ce qui est extrêmement précieux.

Mais il est certain que vous avez des questions à lui poser, et je vais donner la parole à ceux d'entre vous qui le désirent.

Les neurophysiologistes, ici, sont nombreux.

WEALE

I think that if the psychophysicists are to take part in the happy collaboration which the electrophysiologists wish on the subject, it is essential that we should clarify our terms.

Ever since Helmholtz, the psychophysicists have been perfectly aware of the difference between sensitivity and response.

I am not quite certain that the same is yet true of the electrophysiologists, and Dr. Rushton (Fig. 2, p. 71) raised, I believe unwittingly, a very interesting problem. But before I comment on that, I should like to refer to an earlier experiment performed, I believe, 12 years ago by Karpe and Tansley. In a series of very beautiful experiments they found that there is a parallel course between the ordinary dark-adaptation curve and the size of the b-wave as measured electroretinographically. The parallel is very impressive indeed. Now (I am quoting from memory) a few years later, Riggs and his collaborators showed that when you compare not the size of the b-wave, which for the sake of argument we may take to be a measure of the response, but the energy required to produce a b-wave of constant size which, I believe, may be a more comparable parameter, this parallel disappears.

Exactly the same thing turns up in Elenius's results. He compares the size of the b-wave, expressed as a percentage, with the amount of visual purple in the eye.

However, elementary photochemical theory shows, I think, that those quantities are not comparable. What should be compared is the amount of energy required to elicit a b-wave of constant size.

I don't know whether Elenius has obtained these results. I don't know whether anybody has. And I don't know what the comparison would be under those conditions; whether it would still hold.

I am intrigued, however, by Dr. Rushton's concluding remarks. Namely, that there is a fundamental relation between the response and the logarithm of the intensity, and I would be very glad if we could square these different correlations.

RUSHTON

I think, in justification of Dr. Tansley, who is here and probably somewhere where she can't get easily to the microphone, I should say that in the paper of Karpe and Tansley referred to, they did make a calibration curve relating energy with size of the *b*-wave. This curve may not agree entirely with the later work of Dr. Riggs, but they certainly cannot be accused of overlooking the point that Dr. Weale has just mentioned.

They did give the calibration curve from which the energy for a given size of *b*-wave could be obtained and the results seem to fit equally well on that basis. Isn't that right?

TANSLEY

Yes.

RIGGS

Since our work has been referred to, I think I may make one comment, and this is that there is no conflict between the use of (1) magnitude of response and (2) threshold of stimulation as criteria in simple systems. In *Limulus*, for example, that classic animal worked on so intensively by Hartline and his group, the relationship between size of response and sensitivity is a nearly parallel one, as dark adaptation proceeds. In other words, the dark adaptation of this simple eye is equally well described by (1) the increase in magnitude of response or (2) the decrease in stimulus threshold.

However, as Dr. Weale has remarked, we did feel very strongly that in a situation so complex as that of the human electroretinogram, where both rods and cones are represented, and where different states of adaptation are involved, it does become important to use a sensitivity criterion. That is, to give a quantitative description of dark adaptation by determining the minimum energy which is capable of exciting an approximately constant response in the eye, as dark adaptation proceeds. The reciprocal of this minimum energy defines the sensitivity of the eye.

Even this procedure is not completely defensible because one cannot always achieve equal responses in the light-adapted eye and in the dark-adapted by adjusting the energies of test flash. There are differences in wave form as well as in magnitude and latency of response. But I think the point is well taken that one should adopt some sort of response criterion in a situation of this kind and describe the experimental results in terms of the energy necessary for producing it.

VERRIEST

Je voudrais d'abord signaler quelques détails se rapportant aux courbes d'adaptation à l'obscurité.

Chez les achromates typiques, on constate très souvent une courbe biphasique et non une courbe monophasique (Fig. 1): sur ce point, nos observations coïncident tout à fait avec celles de Sloan.* Dans ces cas, on ne peut donc pas assimiler entièrement l'évolution du seuil subjectif à la courbe de regénération de la rhodopsine.

* SLOAN, L. (1954) *J. Opt. Soc. Amer.*, **44**, 117; FRANÇOIS, J., VERRIEST, G. & DE ROUCK, A. (1955) *Doc. Ophthalmol.*, **9**, 338.

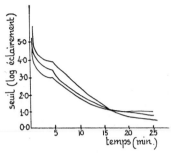

FIG. 1. Courbes d'adaptation à l'obscurité de 3 sujets atteints d'achromatopsie typique (achromatopsie congénitale complète avec amblyopie: rod-monochromatism). Seuils globaux après adaptation à 2.000 asb pendant 5 min. (température de couleur: 2750 °K). Points anguleux (coord. temps: env. 5 min.).

D'autre part, j'ai constaté que les courbes d'adaptation à l'obscurité des sujets trichromates normaux, déterminées avec la même technique (seuils globaux à 1 hertz), présentent plusieurs points anguleux, entre autres, un point anguleux assez apparent vers la 10 ème minute, c'est-à-dire en plein segment scotopique (Fig. 2). Achmatov* signale des points anguleux encore plus tardifs.

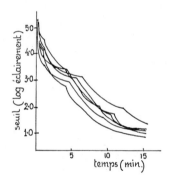

FIG. 2. Courbes d'adaptation à l'obscurité de 6 sujets trichromates normaux après adaptation à 2.000 asb pendant 5 min. (température de couleur: 2750 °K). Cette technique permet de mettre souvent en évidence 3 points anguleux pendant les 15 premières minutes de l'adaptation de l'obscurité. Le deuxième point anguleux (coord. temps: env. 5 min.) correspond à celui décrit par Kohlrausch.

Il est probable que ces points anguleux tardifs ne doivent pas être entièrement assimilés aux points anguleux précoces décrits par Auerbach, puisqu'il paraissent ne pas être dûs au passage du maximum de sensibilité d'un pigment à un autre, mais à l'organisation des neurones rétiniens. Nous pensons ici à l'hypothèse de Pirenne et Denton.†

Dans le cas de l'achromatopsie typique, une explications de ce type est beaucoup plus attrayante que celles qui font appel à des 'bâtonnets photopiques' (Hecht,

* ACHMATOV, A. (1927) *Pflügers Arch. ges Physiol.*, **215**, 10.
† PIRENNE, H. & DENTON, E. (1952) *Nature*, **170**, 1039.

Shlaer, Smith, Haig & Peskin, 1948)* ou à des 'cônes bleus' (Walls & Heath, 1954).† Melle Sloan (1958)‡ vient d'ailleurs de démontrer que la visibilité spectrale est semblable au niveau des deux segments de la courbe de l'achromate.

Un autre problème doit être mentionné dans le cadre de la revue générale des moyens d'investigation de la discrimination chromatique: il paraît en effet possible d'analyser l'électrorétinogramme en composantes qui peuvent être mises en rapport avec la vision colorée.

En ce qui concerne l'homme, il est d'ores et déjà certain qu'il existe des composantes photopiques et des composantes scotopiques; l'onde *b* scotopique est absente dans l'héméralopie essentielle; par contre, l'onde *x* photopique est absente dans l'achromatopsie typique.

Des recherches récentes de Heck et Rendahl§ indiquent qu'il est possible d'analyser l'onde photopique *x* en plusieurs composantes, dont certaines sont modifiées ou éliminées électivement dans des cas de dyschromatopsie.

Evidemment, il s'agit là d'un domaine de recherche plein de promesses.

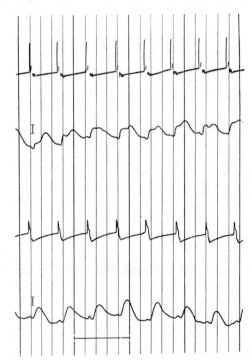

Fɪɢ. 3. Electrorétinogrammes (stimulation lumineuse à l'aide d'un stroboscope au néon). En haut: sujet trichromate normal; en bas: sujet protanope (mêmes conditions de stimulation et d'adaptation à l'obscurité). Pas d'individualisation de l'onde *x* chez le protanope. Calibrage: 50 µV, 0,50 sec.

* Hᴇᴄʜᴛ, S., Sʜʟᴀᴇʀ, S., Sᴍɪᴛʜ, E., Hᴀɪɢ, C. & Pᴇsᴋɪɴ, J. (1948) *J. gen. Physiol.*, **31**, 459.
† Wᴀʟʟs, G. & Hᴇᴀᴛʜ, G. (1954) *Acta ophthalmol., Kbh.*, **32**, 253.
‡ Sʟᴏᴀɴ, L. (1958) *Am. J. Ophthalmol.*, **46**, 1/II, 81.
§ Hᴇᴄᴋ, J. & Rᴇɴᴅᴀʜʟ, I. (1957) *Acta Physiol. Scand.*, **39**, 167.

Personnellement, nous n'avons encore pu mettre en évidence, comme un certain nombre d'autres auteurs, qu'une absence apparente d'individualisation de toute l'onde *x* dans l'achromatopsie typique, dans la protanopie et dans la protanomalie (Fig. 3).*

En ce qui concerne les dyschromatopsies protan, il ne s'agit dans doute pas d'une absence totale de l'onde *x*; il faut en effet tenir compte du fait que la sensibilité spectrale est très diminuée au niveau des longueurs d'onde longues.

PIÉRON

Il est certain — nous l'avons déjà dit — qu'il y aurait un très gros intérêt à ce que les anomalies que l'on rencontre chez l'homme soient utilisées encore plus complètement qu'elles ne l'ont été jusqu'à présent.

En particulier, les héméralopies, et surtout les héméralopies par avitaminose, qui éliminent l'intervention de la rhodopsine, pourraient rendre de grands services pour faciliter une analyse, car alors les cônes, éléments photopiques, sont seuls en jeu.

Il est certain, d'autre part, que si, chez la grenouille, on a trouvé ces récepteurs verts qui sont des bâtonnets et qui n'obéissent pas, par conséquent, à l'action directive que subissent les cônes, il serait fort important que les histologistes, systématiquement, passent en revue un certain nombre d'autres animaux de manière à voir s'il y a là une exception chez la grenouille, ou si l'on peut retrouver chez d'autres animaux des bâtonnets aussi différenciés les uns des autres.

Or, il est certain que les données histologiques actuelles, au point de vue comparatif, sont tout à fait insuffisantes.

Nous avons vu hier qu'il y avait beaucoup de lacunes au point de vue de l'inventaire zoologique, mais si nous envisageons le point de vue histologique, encore bien davantage: les données actuelles sont tout à fait insuffisantes.

Par conséquent, il y a là des nécessités de recherche et de travail, et je pense que nous pourrons peut-être, en fin de ces séances, déterminer quels sont les points les plus importants pour lesquels il serait désirable d'obtenir des données complémentaires.

M. Baumgardt n'a-t-il pas de question à poser?

BAUMGARDT

Le Dr. Rushton a montré que certains faits militent en faveur de l'hypothèse que cônes et bâtonnets fonctionnent bien ensemble de part et d'autre de la luminance à laquelle correspond le principal point de brisure (break) de la courbe d'adaptation.

Les travaux de Brown, Kuhns & Adler (1957) et de Brown & Woodward (1957) sur l'acuité visuelle nécessaire à la résolution d'une grille en fonction de l'état d'adaptation de l'œil fournissent un puissant apport à cette thèse. En effet, en adaptation à l'obscurité, une faible résolution requiert un minimum de luminance en lumière bleu-vert d'environ 500 mμ — prépondérance des bâtonnets. Mais lorsqu'on impose une résolution plus élevée, l'importance de la couleur baisse, ce qui traduit l'action des cônes.

Les branches 'cônes' et 'bâtonnets' sont réellement dûes en partie au fonctionnement simultané des bâtonnets et des cônes; la variation très importante avec la couleur du test, de la branche 'bâtonnets' en est une preuve irréfutable.

* FRANÇOIS, J., VERRIEST, G. & DE ROUCK, A. (1956) *Brit. J. Ophthalmol.*, **40**, 439.

Comment alors interpréter le point de brisure? J'incline à l'idée qu'il marque le passage d'un type de fonctionnement nerveux à un autre, sans que cela implique une variation brusque de la prépondérance de l'action des cônes ou des bâtonnets. Il pourrait s'agir du point où l'action des cellules ganglionnaires géantes commence à s'imposer; en fin d'adaptation, celles-ci fonctionneraient seules.

Le Dr. Rushton vient de commenter certains travaux de caractères divers ayant en commun le résultat suivant: les quantités mesurées varient selon une fonction liée à l'absorption de la rhodopsine, bien qu'on eût pu attendre une variation liée aux propriétés d'un pigment de cône.

Le Dr. Rushton a laissé échappér une publication importante qu'il convient d'ajouter à sa liste. Je parle de sa propre publication s'intitulant *Rhodopsine Density in the Human Rods* (1956). Il y analyse les résultats obtenus par d'autres chercheurs au moyen de méthodes d'extraction et autres et constate que la densité de la rhodopsine semble se situer entre 0,12 et 0,15. Ses propres mesures faites *in situ* fournissent la valeur 0,12, s'il admet que toute la surface rétinienne testée est occupée par les bâtonnets, et la valeur 0,15 s'il admet que ceux-ci n'occupent que 95 pour cent de cette surface (p. 37, *loc. cit.*). Or, on sait que les bâtonnets n'occupent environ que 70 pour cent des régions rétiniennes explorées par le Dr. Rushton. On ne peut donc échapper à l'alternative suivante:

(1) *Tous* les récepteurs réfléchissent la lumière comme s'ils contenaient de la rhodopsine, ou

(2) La densité en rhodopsine des bâtonnets est nettement supérieure à 1.

Puisque (2) ne peut être admis, dans l'état de nos connaissances actuelles, on ne peut échapper à la conclusion que le seul pigment présent dans l'état d'adaptation de l'expérience était bien la rhodopsine, et ceci dans les cônes comme dans les bâtonnets. Je me limiterai à cette remarque et espère que le Dr. Rushton voudra bien nous donner une explication sur ce point.

RUSHTON

Well, I don't think that I can give an explanation at this moment.

I wanted to listen to all that Dr. Baumgardt has to say and I do not do arithmetic in French very easily.

The calculation in my 1956 paper is quite complicated and it is quite possible that I have made a mistake, as Dr. Baumgardt suggests, but if so it would not embarrass me very much. It would, however, embarrass Dr. Dartnall.

In working out the density of rhodopsin in the rods, the value that I gave was a lower limit and I would be quite happy for my own measurements to have the limit raised about 50 per cent. But I would not be at all happy with this limit for Dr. Dartnall's measurements.

Everybody who has extracted rhodopsin from retinas has got values a good deal smaller than Dr. Baumgardt's suggestion and I gave what I thought was the highest value compatible with Dartnall's very careful work.

But you must excuse me from answering Dr. Baumgardt now. Perhaps we can leave the matter like this: I will examine the question and talk to him privately and, if with his help I find that I was quite mistaken, I will tell you before the session ends.

HURVICH

I should just like to comment on Dr. Rushton's expression of a hope that there would be a convergence of the fields of electrophysiology and of psychophysics. I think that the concept of the 'luminosity pool' for the frog is a beautiful example of this kind of convergence, because, through the years, the conclusion from many psychophysical experiments has been that there must be a separate luminosity mechanism in human vision.

Dr. Wright concluded on the basis of a long series of adaptation experiments that there would seem to be a general luminosity pool. Professor Piéron assumed that there would have to be a separate mechanism and, I believe, he postulated a luminosity cone containing different kinds of photosensitive substances. And the question has remained as to whether we are to conceive of a pooling of luminosity effects from different receptor elements, or whether, as Professor Piéron has suggested, there is a single element containing a multiplicity of photochemical substances. The results that Dr. Rushton has reported today for the frog, and I think probably the results of Granit on the dominator functions in the cat, indicate that the psychophysicists' concept of multiple photoreceptor activities leading to a specific brightness or whiteness mechanism is more likely from a physiological point of view. The work of the physiologist is certainly valuable to the psychophysicist. I think it also works the other way round, particularly since it was by using a technique derived from psychophysical studies, namely, the directional sensitivity test, that it was possible to analyse the elements that were being studied in the electrophysiological experiments on the frog.

RUSHTON

There is still one thing that remains to be done to complete the idea of Granit's photopic dominator being made up of a number of different receptors converging on to a pool.

It is that iodopsin should be found to be a mixture of the requisite cone pigments.

DEKKING

Since you want to separate rod and cone function, you might be interested in a substance with which it is possible to block cone action more or less, so that you turn yourself into a nocturnal animal. This drug is Tridione, and I reported about it at the International Ophthalmological Congress in London in 1950. Of course, nobody ever reads congress reports, and so it seems to be quite forgotten.

RUSHTON

May I ask you this? If you have a match made between two colours, a yellow and a green, or a yellow and a blue, under the influence of this drug, and then you dark adapt, does the match still remain good?

DEKKING

No, I have not. When I started taking Tridione, I did not know at all what to expect, and its effects took me completely by surprise. So I had no instruments available to do any precise colour measurements. In any case, the cone-blocking effect is only there at rather high levels of illumination, so I do not think one would find any particularities during dark adaptation.

AUTRUM

May I ask Prof. Rushton a question with reference to the experiments of Svaetichin?

Is it certain that Svaetichin has really inserted the micro-electrodes into the interior of the cones? One can judge the position of the micro-electrode tip only from the size of the resting potential. That is about 10-20 mV in Svaetichin's experiment; this value is relatively small, so that one might suspect that the micro-electrode was only in the vicinity of the cones, but not *in* the cone itself. If the micro-electrode lies outside the cone, however, one can draw no conclusions as to the sign of the potential change.

RUSHTON

I think the question that Professor Autrum has just raised is extremely important, but it cannot be answered at this date with certainty. Originally Svaetichin and Grüsser thought that they were recording from within the cones themselves, but the localization by dye injection has convinced MacNichol and Svaetichin that the cells are more centrally situated. Tomita, using a double pipette, has obtained good evidence that similar records may be obtained from spaces large compared with any cell seen under the microscope, and Tasaki has reached the same conclusion. But do you remember the first slide (Fig. 12) I showed? Record *A* gave positive waves; then they tapped the table (*B*), there was a change in resting potential, the waves suddenly reversed their sign and became negative waves of twenty times the amplitude. This looks very much like an electrode entering the cell responsible for the potential waves recorded.

When you say that 20 mV is small for an intracellular record, that is true for familiar all-or-none cells. But these intermediate cells are different. Their potential varies linearly with the log of the light, and I hardly know what we ought to expect about the size of wave for a given flash in that case.

BENOIT

Puisqu'on a discuté de la signification des enregistrements par microélectrodes dans la rétine, je voudrais signaler certains résultats non publiés que j'ai obtenus en 1956 avec Cornu et Gonella. En utilisant des électrodes de diamètre inférieur à 0,5 μ, nous avons réussi à recueillir des réponses hyperpolarisantes chez le Chat (en tous points analogues à celles qui ont été décrites depuis par Motokawa et collaborateurs)* et chez la Grenouille (voir Fig. 1). Bien que nous n'en ayions pas fait une étude détaillée, je puis apporter les précisions suivantes. Il s'agissait selon toute vraisemblance d'enregistrements élémentaires (quel que soit le type de cellules interrogées) et obtenus par voie intracellulaire. En effet, ces réponses à l'illumination ne se produisaient qu'après une soudaine déflection de la ligne de base dans le sens d'une négativation de la pointe de l'électrode, ce qui, jusqu'à plus ample informa-

---

* Motokawa, K., Oikawa, T. & Tasaki, K. (1957) *J. Neurophysiol.*, **20**, 186.

tion, reste pour le microphysiologiste le critère d'une pénétration. Ces faits montrent la généralité d'un type de réponses obtenues chez les Poissons par Svaetichin, et apportent, me semble-t-il, une confirmation du caractère intracellulaire de tels enregistrements.

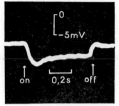

FIG. 1

PIÉRON

Si vous permettez — puisqu'on a parlé des dominateurs — je voudrais rappeler les données actuelles qui complètent ce qu'a déjà exposé M. Rushton, mais qui comprennent les derniers efforts pour obtenir des réponses dans la rétine, non plus seulement des cellules ganglionnaires, mais en prenant par l'autre pace du globe oculaire, en tâchant d'atteindre les récepteurs eux-mêmes.

Vous avez des données de Grüsser — il devait venir mais il n'est pas arrivé et je le regrette — qui ne concernent pas la vision chromatique, mais qui concernent tout de même les réponse de ce qu'il croyait être des 'cônes'. Et, il a trouvé, dans ce qu'il croyait être des cônes, des réponses à potentiel local et non plus des potentiels d'action; il a même enregistré simultanément les réponses de ganglionnaires, et pu montrer que la fréquence des réponses 'on' dans les ganglionnaires était commandée par l'amplitude du potentiel local qu'il avait obtenu dans la couche des récepteurs, en apparence, et plus probablement au niveau des bipolaires.

Evidemment, il a pu montrer que la même relation logarithmique que l'on trouve à la base, se rencontre au niveau des potentiels gradués initiaux, comme elle a été vérifiée pour la fréquence des réponses des cellules ganglionnaires et par conséquent, une donnée très solide montre qu'à la base des impressions lumineuses, il y a cette relation logarithmique fechnérienne qui, à l'heure actuelle, tend à ne plus être admise.

C'est un point extrêmement important.

Mais, on peut douter maintenant de la réalité d'une réponse du cône lui-même dans les expériences de Grüsser. Etant donné que Svaetichin croyait aussi avoir atteint ces réponses des cônes et que, c'est grâce au contrôle que Rushton nous a indiqué qu'on s'est aperçu que c'était au delà des récepteurs, au niveau des cellules horizontales ou des cellules bipolaires et amacrines que l'on trouvait ce potentiel lent.

C'est déjà cependant une donnée extrêmement importante puisque cela nous montre, que dans toute la transmission rétinienne — comme nous l'avons soutenu avec Galifret d'après nos expériences — il n'y a pas de potentiel d'action en déplacement entre les récepteurs et les ganglionnaires. Il y a là, seulement, des potentiels lents, qui ne répondent pas au 'tout-ou-rien', mais qui sont gradués et qui permettent donc des sommations entre des éléments récepteurs différents venant converger sur les cellules ganglionnaires.

Ceci, donc, a un extrême intérêt et une très grande valeur! Dans la bipolaire encore, et c'est ce que nous supposions, nous avons des potentiels lents. Ce n'est que dans la ganglionnaire que se fait la transformation des potentiels lents en une réponse répétitive qui donne les influx du nerf optique.

Voilà, par conséquent, une donnée toute récente, et les expériences de Svaetichin sont, à ce point de vue, d'un très gros intérêt.

Il y a naturellement cet intérêt général que, s'il a obtenu des effets d'hyperpolarisation ou de dépolarisation suivant les éléments nerveux interrogés, avec des longueurs d'onde différentes, cela semble indiquer que non pas peut-être au niveau des récepteurs — comme il le croyait — les effets directs de la lumière peuvent être d'hyperpolarisation ou de dépolarisation au niveau des éléments intermédiaires, des éléments transmetteurs, il peut donc s'exercer, à partir de l'excitation de certains récepteurs, des phénomènes soit inhibiteurs, soit excitateurs. Des récepteurs différents qui convergent vers ces éléments intermédiaires vont donc pouvoir exercer des effets opposés. Ces effets opposés évidemment, nous font songer tout de suite à la possibilité alors, du mécanisme de Hering et de couples complémentaire.

Mais à côté de ces éléments qui répondent de façon opposée aux longueurs d'onde, il y a toujours un très grand nombre d'éléments qui, eux, ne répondent que d'une seule manière, et qui paraissent être, en effet, l'équivalent du dominateur de Granit, dominateur de Granit déterminé, non plus au niveau de la ganglionnaire, mais au niveau des éléments intermédiaires.

Ces éléments dominateurs, Svaetichin les a seuls trouvés dans une rétine de poisson. Il y a donc un poisson pour lequel il n'y a que des dominateurs: la Brême (*Abramis brama*).

Dans ce cas-là, nous pouvons supposer naturellement qu'il n'y a pas de vision chromatique. C'est là que nous revenons au problème des inventaires zoologiques; il serait extrêmement important de connaître exactement, chez les différents poissons, ceux qui ont une vision chromatique et ceux qui n'en ont pas, pour que la neurophysiologie s'adressant à leur rétine puisse trouver ces correspondances et, montrer, comme c'est extrêmement probable, que c'est dans la mesure où l'on trouve des éléments qui répondent de façon différente suivant la longueur d'onde ou que, au contraire, tous les éléments intermédiaires répondent de la même manière, qu'il peut y avoir des discriminations chromatiques ou que ces discriminations chromatiques peuvent faire défaut, avec des systèmes qui, tout de même, peuvent être des systèmes purement photopiques.

C'est un point sur lequel j'avais insisté: il ne faut pas confondre la réalité de la réception photopique avec une capacité de discrimination chromatique, comme on l'a fait assez souvent.

Voilà les quelques remarques que je voulais faire, mais je n'empêche pas, bien entendu, que nous ayons encore à entendre des observations et des questions.

FESSARD

Je ne suis pas un spécialiste de la vision et je voudrais simplement poser quelques questions, en faisant allusion à quatre aspects qui me semblent avoir été un peu négligés.

Premier aspect: n'a-t-on pas étudié systématiquement les rapports biométriques entre le nombre des divers éléments rétiniens, récepteurs, bipolaires et ganglionnaires, en particulier chez un certain nombre de poissons? Je pense par exemple aux recherches de Vilter. Je serais heureux si, dans l'auditoire, quelqu'un ayant connaissance de ce genre de travaux, pouvait nous informer sur leur portée possible vis à vis de nos problèmes.

Deuxième point, toujours dans le domaine structural, je me demande si les recherches sur les ultrastructures, en particulier depuis l'utilisation de la microscopie électronique — et je pense aux beaux travaux de Sjöstrand en particulier — si ces travaux ne pourraient pas nous fournir des indications sur certaines propriétés différentielles des éléments rétiniens, en particulier des cônes. N'est-il pas possible, en effet, que ces facteurs de structure interviennent? Est-ce que le fait même que les cônes aient des propriétés directionnelles n'implique pas que des facteurs géométriques soient en jeu dans la réception chromatique? Encore une fois, je ne suis absolument pas compétent et, je demande au Professeur Rushton si l'on a fait une théorie pour expliquer cet effet directionnel? Est-ce que l'on a relié cet effet à la présence d'ultrastructures en couches superposées, car cela suggère évidemment que l'efficacité d'un rayon puisse ne pas être la même suivant son angle d'incidence.

Le troisième aspect sur lequel je veux attirer l'attention est d'ordre chimique. Les biochimistes sont évidemment à leur place quand on s'occupe de processus rétiniens, mais je ne pense pas ici à ceux qui ont étudié les pigments, mais à ceux qui, peut-être, auraient pu mettre en évidence dans la rétine, où il y a des phénomènes de transmission synaptique, des produits jouant le rôle de médiateurs? Je crois savoir que certains travaux ont été faits dans ce sens et, je pense en particulier à notre collègue belge Gerebtzoff, lequel, je crois bien, a mis en évidence par des méthodes histochimiques, des différenciations relatives à la présence de produits dérivant du métabolisme de l'adrénaline d'une part, de l'acétylcholine de l'autre. Il me semble que cette question présente une certaine importance. Si l'on compare les activités électriques de la rétine à celles de la cellule nerveuse, dans laquelle nous savons qu'il existe deux types de réactions suivant qu'il s'agit de phénomènes d'excitation ou d'inhibition, ces deux types étant accompagnés d'hypopolarisation ou d'hyperpolarisation — eh bien, nous pouvons penser que ces variations de polarisation sont liés à l'existence de phénomènes de médiation chimique. Il me semble peu probable que l'effet d'une stimulation sur un récepteur puisse être chose qu'une dépolarisation. Par contre, lorsqu'il s'agit d'un élément nerveux, il peut répondre soit par une hypopolarisation, soit par une hyperpolarisation à une action de médiateur. Alors, je pose encore la question à notre conférencier, lui est-il possible de nous donner quelques indications à ce point de vue?

Le quatrième aspect, dont il sera question cet après-midi, est d'ordre psychophysiologique. On a fait allusion plusieurs fois aux relations qui, tout en restant cordiales, sont quelquefois tendues entre les électrophysiologistes et les psychophysiciens. Eh bien, il ne faut pas oublier qu'entre la rétine et la réaction perceptive, il y a le cerveau. Les centres visuels ne sont pas des enregistreurs passifs de ce qui s'élabore dans la rétine. Dans quelle mesure interviennent-ils dans le mécanisme de la vision colorée? C'est un problème de première importance, dont la solution semble encore éloignée. M. Galifret doit nous en parler dans son rapport.

RUSHTON

It is not I who should answer your questions. There are many people, here in the hall, who can answer far better than I can.

PIÉRON

Je crois qu'en effet, les données des auteurs que vous avez rappelés, sont intéressantes non pas pour être immédiatement utilisées, d'autant qu'on voudrait évidemment les voir reprises et refaites, car jusqu'à présent elles ne l'ont pas été. Mais, Vilter a bien trouvé, par des numérations cellulaires, qu'il y avait, pour les régions fovéales un cône en relation, non pas avec une cellule bipolaire, mais avec trois cellules bipolaires et généralement deux cellules ganglionnaires au moins, chez l'Homme et le Spermophile. De telle sorte que, l'on peut comprendre qu'un récepteur puisse exercer des influences différentes en fonction des bipolaires qui le connectent à des ganglionnaires distinctes. Et on pourrait alors comprendre à la fois qu'il y ait juxtaposition d'une hyperpolarisation dans un certain circuit, et d'une dépolarisation dans un autre circuit.

En ce qui concerne alors le point de la possibilité d'un médiateur, vous avez certainement vu les hypothèses qu'a faites Grundfest récemment dans un article, où il dit qu'à son avis, au niveau des cônes ou des bâtonnets, il n'y a pas du tout de phénomènes électriques, il n'y aurait que des phénomènes chimiques dus à des médiateurs et ce n'est qu'au niveau intermédiaire que naîtraient les premiers phénomènes électriques, c'est-à-dire l'hyperpolarisation ou la dépolarisation.

Mais, naturellement, ceci reste purement hypothétique et il est difficile d'affirmer à l'heure actuelle que l'on ne trouvera pas, au niveau des récepteurs, des phénomènes électriques qui caractériseraient les phénomènes d'excitation initiale.

En tout cas, la question est posée. Jusqu'ici, on pouvait penser avec Grüsser et avec Svaetichin que, réellement, il y avait des phénomènes électriques au niveau des récepteurs, en particulier au niveau des cônes, plus volumineux, c'est-à-dire plus facilement accessibles aux microélectrodes, mais à l'heure actuelle, je crois que c'est un point sur lequel la question reste entièrement posée.

PIRENNE

Monsieur le Président, je voudrais poser une question au Dr. Rushton au sujet des expériences sur le changement silencieux dans la grenouille, et au sujet du 'pool'.

Si j'ai bien compris, on peut adapter la rétine à une certaine longueur d'onde, et il n'y a pas de changement dans la décharge tant l'intensité reste entre certaines limites. Maintenant, si on utilise une autre partie du spectre, on obtient quantitativement les mêmes limites. Or il a de bonnes raisons de croire que les recepteurs activés sont différents dans les deux cas. Supposons pour simplifier qu'il y ait seulement deux espèces de recepteurs, cônes et bâtonnets, qui doivent converger à un certain niveau. La question est de savoir si le fait que les limites sont les mêmes aux deux longueurs d'onde est une propriété des cônes et des bâtonnets, ou simplement une propriété du 'pool'.

On a l'impression que si c'étaient les récepteurs qui determinaient la valeur des limites, la fraction de Weber serait probablement différente pour des longueurs d'ondes différentes. Ceci se rapporte au problème de l'endroit — le 'pool'? — ou apparait la fonction logarithmique. Est-ce que le *delta* R, qui se rapporte à la variation de la réponse, est déterminé après le changement logarithmique — à supposer que son existence soit demontrée — ou avant?

RUSHTON

The distinction between the two possibilities lies in the Fechner fraction. As more types of element enter, the Fechner fraction gets smaller.

That would be expected if elements were added after the logarithmic transformation and not if they were added before it.

PIÉRON

Est-ce que vous voulez tirer la conclusion de votre rapport?

RUSHTON

No, I don't feel that we can come to any conclusion. But what I have enjoyed — and what perhaps we still have time to enjoy — is hearing the extraordinarily interesting and apposite communications which have come from such various aspects.

I have said already all that I want to say on this subject and I can see that the meeting has been able to overcome my deficiencies and understand it, because the questions have been very much to the point.

If we have five minutes more, let us have more questions and comments from the meeting.

LE GRAND

Je voudrais répondre à la question que le Prof. Fessard a posée tout à l'heure au sujet de l'effet Stiles-Crawford.

Dans les théories actuelles de cet effet, celles qui paraissent le plus vraisemblables sont du type de celle que Toraldo di Francia a proposée, c'est-à-dire sur le modèle d'un cône qui serait en somme un guide d'ondes, concentrant les radiations dans son axe de symétrie, par suite de la différence d'indices de réfraction entre le cône lui-même et la matière où il est plongé.

O'Brien, à Rochester, a fabriqué un énorme cône sur lequel, en envoyant des ondes décimétriques, il a pu montrer que cette explication rendait assez bien compte des phénomènes.

Quant à la structure feuilletée décrite par Sjöstrand, elle est la base d'une théorie de la vision des couleurs dont je dirai un mot dans le rapport que je dois faire mardi: la théorie proposée par Ingelstamm, où il suppose que cette structure feuilletée correspond également à des systèmes de résonance particulière des ondes.

Il est possible, néanmoins, que cette structure feuilletée, dans l'effet Stiles-Crawford, puisse tout de même intervenir et expliquer en particulier les variations de l'effet Stiles-Crawford avec la longueur d'onde et les changements apparents de couleurs que le Dr. Stiles a décrits dans l'effet Stiles-Crawford.

Quand la lumière arrive obliquement, non seulement son efficacité est modifiée, mais également la 'hue', la tonalité apparente de la lumière, change un peu.

Cet effet est peut-être en relation avec les structures feuilletées auxquelles le Prof. Fessard faisait allusion tout à l'heure.

STILES

As a postscript to Professor Le Grand's remarks on the theory of directional sensitivity, I would add that in one respect we should be very happy to find an explanation in terms of the intimate structure of the outer segments of the end-organs. Explanations which depend on light-trapping, focusing or other gross properties of the end-organs would be expected to be rather sensitive to the shape of the outer segment or of the whole end-organ. In the human eye, the foveal and extrafoveal cones show marked differences in form. But we observe directional effects of similar magnitude in the foveal and parafoveal cone systems. The recent electrophysiological work of Donner and Rushton demonstrating directional effects in the frog with, it seems, a difference between rods and cones analogous to that in man, leads one to hope that more evidence on the directional effect in different animals may be forthcoming with perhaps a possibility of relating the effect to differences of form or other gross properties of the end-organs.

AUERBACH

I would like to put a question to Dr. Rushton with respect to the term 'excitation pool'.

Some time ago we were able to isolate psychophysiologically a short-wave sensitive mechanism and hope, in a short while, to report about further results.

My question is: At what level are we dealing with these mechanisms? I think we can exclude as a matter of course that we are at the level of the retina alone. By using this method we are most definitely also at the level of the brain.

Where, then, does that pool take place? And how are you able under this point of view to bring together psychophysical with electroretinographical results which are sometimes amazingly similar?

RUSHTON

Perhaps we might restrict the term 'receptor' to the actual rods and cones. You then isolated not short-wave receptors but short-wave mechanisms such as Stiles's π mechanism, which may indeed be connected simply to blue cones but it may not be.

There must be a great difference between the specific colour mechanisms of the human eye, and the 'excitation pool' of the frog's eye which show no specific colour discrimination at all. If these pools correspond to anything in man it is more likely to be the mechanism underlying the sense of brightness. Prof. Piéron long ago proposed that all the pigments might be collected in a single luminosity cone. The pool suggestion would be simply a modification of this: instead of collecting the three pigments into one cone the signals from the three pigments are collected into one pool.

PIÉRON

Il me reste, je pense, à vous remercier.

Cette séance aura été très féconde et, en tout cas elle nous a apporté des données très intéressantes.

Je vous en félicite bien vivement, et je vous en remercie.

II

AU NIVEAU DES VOIES ET DES CENTRES

Y. Galifret

Les problèmes neurophysiologiques posés par les mécanismes de la discrimination chromatique relèvent essentiellement de l'expérimentation électrophysiologique mais les données de la pathologie chez l'Homme et les résultats du conditionnement après ablation de certains territoires chez le Singe ou tout autre animal doué de perception chromatique peuvent apporter à l'électrophysiologie des compléments de valeur.

Avant d'entrer dans le détail des résultats particuliers obtenus chez les différentes espèces animales nous examinerons la question sous son *aspect méthodologique.*

Concernant l'électrophysiologie nous envisagerons ici les nombreux travaux expérimentaux relatifs aux voies et aux centres optiques dans la mesure seulement où ils nous apportent d'utiles indications concernant les mécanismes de la *discrimination chromatique.* Cela nous conduira à ne faire qu'une part extrêmement réduite aux importantes recherches effectuées en utilisant comme stimulus le choc électrique et comme animal d'expérience le Chat. Nous réserverons de préférence notre attention aux travaux dans lesquels est enregistrée la réponse électrique à une *stimulation lumineuse de longueur d'onde variable,* la détection de cette réponse pouvant se faire soit par électrode de dimension notable soit par microélectrode (diamètre à l'extrémité de l'ordre du micron).

INVESTIGATIONS UTILISANT LA MACROÉLECTRODE

Il s'agit de mettre en relation avec un changement de *longueur d'onde* de la stimulation, des variations de *latence,* d'*amplitude* ou de *forme* de la réponse, dans le cas d'une stimulation brève (quelques millisecondes) et en outre les variations relatives de ces trois caractéristiques en 'on' et en 'off' dans le cas d'une stimulation durable (suffisamment durable pour qu'au moins l'effet 'on' n'exerce pas une perturbation sur l'effet 'off').

L'excitabilité du système variant avec son état d'adaptation il est nécessaire (et cette précaution est trop souvent négligée) d'espacer suffisamment les stimulations successives pour qu'une sorte de 'remise au zéro' ait le temps de s'effectuer.

Dans ce type d'expérimentation deux difficultés doivent être surmontées:

(1) Dissocier ce qui relève effectivement des effets de la variation de longueur d'onde de ce qui relève simplement des variations d'intensité.

Cette difficulté est résolue, en général, en déterminant pour chaque longueur d'onde stimulatrice le seuil d'efficacité. Il faut avouer que cette détermination, à partir d'une ligne de base où interviennent un certain nombre de fluctuations aléatoires, n'est pas aisée et comporte une certaine part d'arbitraire. Néanmoins, le seuil étant déterminé, on fait croître ensuite l'intensité stimulatrice, exprimée en multiples du seuil et l'on suit les variations de la réponse consécutives à l'accroissement du stimulus. On peut espérer mettre en évidence, de cette façon, des évolutions dans la morphologie de la réponse, différentes suivant les longueurs d'ondes.

(2) La difficulté majeure réside, en fait, dans la nécessité de dissocier, lorsqu'on s'adresse à des animaux à rétine mixte, ce qui relève, d'une part de l'activité des cônes et qui nous intéresse, et ce qui relève d'autre part de l'activité des bâtonnets et qui est à exclure.

Cette exclusion nous semble indispensable au point de vue méthodologique malgré la thèse d'auteurs comme Willmer (1955) pour lesquels les bâtonnets participeraient à la discrimination chromatique en jouant le rôle du troisième récepteur de la triade de Young. La réfutation de cette thèse a été faite avec suffisamment de succès par de nombreux auteurs pour que nous n'ayons pas à la reprendre ici (cf. en particulier Brindley, 1957).

Malheureusement la plupart des animaux de laboratoire utilisés ont des rétines mixtes avec une fovea (pas toujours) et une périphérie dans laquelle on rencontre bâtonnets et cônes. Dès lors il est extrêmement imprudent de prétendre que les variations, en fonction de la longueur d'onde, de la réponse globale à la stimulation d'une telle rétine, revèlent le jeu des mécanismes de la discrimination chromatique. Utilisant une stimulation de courte longueur d'onde on sollicite préférentiellement le système scotopique et, à l'inverse, utilisant une stimulation de grande longueur d'onde on sollicite le système photopique, des stimulations intermédiaires provoquant des participations simultanées variables des deux systèmes. Il n'est donc pas étonnant que l'on observe des variations dans la réponse électrique liées à la longueur d'onde de la stimulation, mais ces variations ne font que traduire le taux des participations photopique et scotopique et sont sans rapport avec la discrimination chromatique.

Cette difficulté, extrêmement importante, peut être tournée de différentes façons.

La plus simple consiste évidemment à utiliser des animaux dont les rétines ne contiennent que des cônes.

Un certain nombre de serpents, de lézards, remplissent cette condition, ainsi que des Mammifères tels que la Marmotte, le spermophile ou l'écureuil gris. Il faudrait toutefois que les zoopsychologues puissent nous garantir que ces animaux perçoivent les couleurs, car le fait qu'ils ont bien une courbe de visibilité photopique n'est pas une preuve suffisante de leur possibilité de discrimination chromatique.

On peut aussi — autre façon de tourner la difficulté — utiliser des animaux dont la fovéa est bien individualisée, et tenter, soit de stimuler exclusivement la fovéa — ce qui est assez difficile — soit de recueillir les réponses dans des territoires thalamiques ou corticaux dont on a la certitude qu'ils reçoivent exclusivement des afférences fovéales.

On pourrait également penser éliminer l'activité scotopique en soumettant la rétine à des niveaux d'adaptation élevés. Mais pour une élimination complète il faut atteindre des niveaux très élevés, et à ces niveaux, pour provoquer des réponses à partir du système photopique, il faut des énergies considérables qu'il est difficile d'obtenir si l'on travaille avec des bandes spectrales étroites.

INVESTIGATIONS UTILISANT LA MICROÉLECTRODE

Il s'agit d'entrer en contact avec des éléments (fibres ou cellules) qui répondent à la stimulation rétinienne avec des modalités qui différent selon la bande spectrale utilisée pour la stimulation. Dans le cas le plus simple le train d'influx a une fréquence et un nombre d'influx qui revèlent, pour différents éléments étudiés, des répartitions spectrales de sensibilité différentes. D'une manière plus générale la spécificité chromatique se manifestera par une variation systématique avec la longueur d'onde du 'pattern' de réponse.

Dans ce type d'expérience, le plus correct est d'utiliser des bandes spectrales stimulatrices suffisamment étroites et d'énergies quantiques égales. Les microélectrodes utilisées actuellement sont soit des microélectrodes de verre emplies de KCl 3 M soit des micro-électrodes de tungstène ou d'acier dont seule l'extrême pointe n'est pas recouverte d'un vernis isolant.

Une difficulté de cette méthode tient aux dimensions souvent très faibles des cellules à partir desquelles se fait la détection. Cette difficulté est résolue par des prouesses de technique (dont la littérature est de moins en moins avare).

L'autre difficulté peut être dite statistique. Elle est mineure dans le cas où l'on explore un tissu formé d'éléments à fonctions exclusivement photopiques (couches dorsales du G.L. du singe par exemple), les chances de rencontrer des unités à réponses spécifiques sont alors assez grandes. Elle devient considérable lorsqu'on explore un tractus dans lequel coexistent des éléments photopiques et des éléments scotopiques. Ces derniers risquant d'être plus nombreux et plus volumineux leur chance de détection devient très supérieure à celle des éléments photopiques.

Il est évident que l'expérimentation physiologique doit prendre appui sur une connaissance précise de l'anatomie et de l'histologie, le problème étant de lier aspects fonctionnels et structures. C'est dans cette perspective que nous passerons maintenant en revue les questions soulevées par les résultats acquis ou les opinions controversées concernant les mécanismes de la vision chromatique chez l'Homme, le Singe, le Chat, le Pigeon et accessoirement les Vertébrés inférieurs.

Homme — Le *nerf optique* de l'Homme compte de 800.000* à 1 million de fibres dont les trois quarts selon Chacko (1948) ont un diamètre inférieur ou égal à 2 µ (valeurs extrêmes 0,7 et 10 µ). Un des problèmes essentiels qui se pose ici et d'une façon générale pour toutes les espèces, est celui de la destinée des fibres en fonction de leur diamètre. Bishop & O'Leary (1940) ont montré que, chez le Chat, ce sont les grosses fibres qui se rendent aux corps genouillés latéraux, les fibres fines se rendant aux tubercules quadri-jumeaux antérieurs. Ce résultat, confirmé par Bishop & Clare (1955), peut-il être appliqué mécaniquement à tous les mammifères? Il est séduisant d'imaginer que, compte-tenu de la différence de diamètre des fibres les temps de trans-mission sont tels que le message visuel peut atteindre les corps genouillés puis le cortex et déclencher des influx dans la voie geniculo-tectale et dans la voie cortico-tectale qui atteindront les tubercules quadrijumeaux supérieurs avant que le message empruntant la voie rétino-tectale n'y soit parvenu. On peut aussi admettre que les fibres pupillaires dont Magoun & Ranson (1935) ont montré qu'elles se rendent dans la région prétectale ne sont pas les plus grosses, contrairement aux affirmations des vieux auteurs tels que Gudden ou Von Monakov. Il n'en reste pas moins que si l'on s'en tenait aux travaux des histologistes de la rétine, à Polyak (1941) en particulier, on serait amené à une conception diamétralement opposée à celle issue des travaux de Bishop. Les histologistes nous décrivent les ganglionnaires de la fovéa comme les plus petites (naines de Polyak). Or, en général, qui dit petit corps cellulaire dit petit diamètre de l'axone. Polyak décrit lui-même les axones des ganglion-naires comme étant de plus en plus gros à mesure que l'on s'éloigne vers la périphérie rétinienne. On serait donc tenté de conclure que les fibres fovéales — et si nous insistons c'est à cause de leur importance dans la perception chromatique — sont de petit diamètre. Des fibres de petit diamètre et d'une importance fontionnelle capitale n'iraient donc pas au tectum mais au cortex par le corps genouillé.

Les histologistes pourraient nous apporter là des éclaircissements. En les attendant, nous pouvons essayer de comprendre les contradictions apparentes entre les deux groupes de faits. Si Bishop et ses collaborateurs n'ont pas trouvé ces fibres de petit diamètre allant au corps genouillé latéral c'est peut-être parce que chez le Chat la fovéa est quasi inexistante. Même chez

---

* Nous donnons ici et pour les autres espèces les chiffres communément admis; il se peut que le microscope électronique nous révèle l'existence de fibres inférieures au micron beaucoup plus nombreuses que ce qui était apparu au microscope optique.

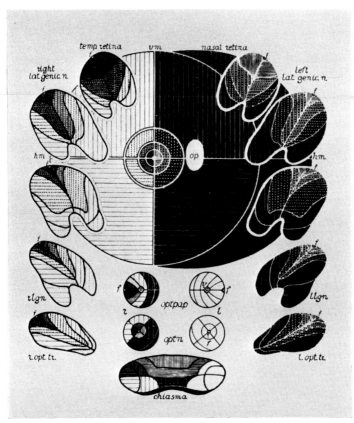

FIG. 1. Projection de la surface rétinienne de l'œil droit dans le nerf optique, les bandelettes et les corps genouillés latéraux chez le Macaque Rhésus (d'après Polyak, *The Vertebrate Visual System*). *f*, point de fixation; *hm*, méridien horizontal; *llgn*, corps genouillé latéral gauche; *l. opt. tr.*, bandelette optique gauche; *op*, papille optique; *opt. n.*, nerf optique; *opt. pap.*, papille optique; *rlgn*, corps genouillé latéral droit; *r. opt. tr.*, bandelette optique droite; *vm*, méridien vertical.

l'Homme ces fibres strictement fovéales si l'on compte une ganglionnaire pour une cellule réceptrice, ce qui semble exact, sont au nombre de 30 à 40.000, c'est à dire peu nombreuses. Il est vrai que, dans le cas de l'Homme où le faisceau des fibres issues de la macula* est bien localisé dans le tractus optique la recherche des fibres fovéales fines devrait être plus facile.

On pourrait également supposer que, contrairement aux indications de Polyak et à l'opinion couramment admise, les ganglionnaires connectées à la fovéa ont un axone de diamètre notable malgré les faibles dimensions de leur périkaryone. Mais ce ne sont là qu'hypothèses et c'est aux histologistes, redisons-le, de nous fournir les informations nécessaires.

Au niveau du *corps genouillé latéral* nous retrouvons une certaine imprécision concernant le rapport des fibres optiques afférentes et des cellules en rapport avec elles. Walls (1953) dans son important travail sur le corps genouillé latéral semble admettre, d'après les données de Balado & Franke (1937), une relation une à une entre fibres afférentes et cellules principales. Ceci est peut-être vrai pour la projection de la périphérie rétinienne mais il est peu probable que ce le soit pour la projection de la fovéa. D'ailleurs Glees & Le Gros Clark (1941) indiquent (chez le Singe, mais ceci est à plus forte raison vrai chez l'Homme) qu'une fibre venant de la rétine forme des boutons synaptiques sur cinq à six cellules du genouillé latéral. Le grand volume occupé par la projection maculaire dans le G.L. suggère cette possibilité d'expansion par divergence pour les éléments issus de la macula. Pour mémoire nous pouvons nous reporter au schéma de Polyak qui illustre parfaitement ce fait en ce qui concerne le Macaque Rhésus (Fig. 1).

Au niveau du *cortex occipital* la localisation de la vision des couleurs dans la couche 5 de Cajal (petites cellules étoilées) de l'aire 17 (Henschen, 1925) reste purement hypothétique. Les expériences de stimulation faradique des aires 17-18 et 19 par Foerster, par Penfield & Rasmussen (1952) ne permettent pas de préciser les fonctions respectives de ces aires — et à fortiori des différentes couches cellulaires — quand à la perception chromatique. Elles confirment toutefois, ce que la pathologie avait déjà montré: la nécessité de participation des aires 18 et 19.

L'enregistrement des potentiels électro-corticaux transcraniens relève de ce qui a été dit plus haut concernant la macro-réponse enregistrée dans un système mixte: on recueille un mélange de composantes photopiques et scotopiques, la grande distance de l'électrode aux foyers d'activité n'étant pas faite pour clarifier la situation.

---

* La *macula lutea* (diamètre de 1500 µ environ) comprend en son centre la *fovea centralis* (diamètre de 400 µ) et autour de celle-ci une mosaïque de cônes où quelques bâtonnets apparaissent déjà. On compte dans la macula environ 130.000 cônes au total.

H

Singe — Le système visuel du Macaque qui a été le plus étudié est très semblable à celui de l'Homme, les mêmes problèmes se posent donc là et en particulier celui du rôle fonctionnel des fibres de différent diamètre du nerf optique. Mais dans ce cas l'expérimentation est possible. Puisque nous avons le Dr. De Valois parmi nous je ne dirai rien ici de ses travaux sur le genouillé latéral car je pense qu'il voudra bien tout à l'heure nous exposer lui-même l'état de ses recherches sur l'enregistrement par micro-électrodes au niveau des différentes couches du genouillé latéral* et compléter ainsi les informations qu'il a publiées récemment dans une note pleine de promesses (De Valois *et al.*, 1958).

Au niveau cortical les enregistrements d'Adrian (1946) pris en même temps que l'ERG montrent comment la réponse globale à la même stimulation d'une rétine mixte, peut varier selon que l'on enregistre sur des structures où l'élement dominant (au point de vue volume, nombre de cellules) est scotopique ou photopique: lorsque la stimulation est bleue la réponse à l'électrorétinogramme est considérable, et lorsque la stimulation est rouge elle est très petite ou quasi inexistante; au contraire, au cortex, pour les mêmes stimulations la situation est complètement inversée, le bleu donne une réponse assez faible, alors que le rouge donne une réponse de grande amplitude.

Les expériences de conditionnement avec ablation n'ont pas encore apporté dans le domaine chromatique tout ce qu'on serait en droit d'en attendre. Klüver (1951) qui s'est beaucoup préoccupé des fonctions du lobe occipital a plus envisagé les phénomènes de perception complexe que la perception chromatique isolée. Quant aux résultats de Evarts (1952) ils sont difficiles à interpréter puisque l'ablation de l'aire 18 qu'il a pratiquée était, de son propre aveu, incomplète.

Chat — Les essais sérieux de conditionnement du Chat à la couleur ont échoué, ce qui semble indiquer que le Chat n'est pas l'animal de choix pour l'étude des mécanismes de la discrimination chromatique. Médioni nous a dit hier que ces échecs pouvaient s'expliquer par le fait que le Chat est un animal difficile à conditionner. Je veux le détromper. A l'Institut Marey, Buser a une 'équipe' de chats qui se conditionnent parfaitement et sont en géneral très coopératifs. L'un d'eux après avoir 'manipulé' un certain nombre de mécanismes dans l'expérience a même été capable d'inventer seul comment on pouvait ouvrir la cage et aller se promener. En conséquence on ne peut affirmer que seules peuvent donner des résultats démonstratifs des expériences de prédation avec petites souris barbouillées en rouge, en bleu ou en vert et tirées par des ficelles.

Par ailleurs, au point de vue neurophysiologique nous sommes obligés de

* Walls et également Chow (1955) puis De Valois (1958) ont fait justice de la théorie de Le Gros Clark (1949) concernant une localisation dans les différentes couches du G.L. des trois fondamentales de la théorie trichromatique.

constater que si le Chat perçoit les couleurs il a beaucoup de mérite à cela car son équipement chromatique est très défectueux.

Sa rétine contient relativement peu de cônes et si Kolmer (1930) signale une *area centralis* plus riche en cônes, Polyak une fovea rudimentaire, Cajal (1955) note qu'il ne s'agit pas d'une fovea véritable et Zürn (1902) pousse la restriction beaucoup plus loin.

En outre le nerf optique du Chat contient moins de 120.000 fibres (dix fois moins que chez le Macaque). On peut donc supposer une *forte convergence des récepteurs sur les ganglionnaires.* Barlow, Fitzhugh & Kuffler (1957) indiquent par ailleurs que tous les éléments ganglionnaires qu'ils ont isolés présentaient un effet Purkinje, preuve de la convergence sur la même ganglionnaire de cônes et de bâtonnets.

Si nous admettons les résultats de Bishop & Clare (1955) dont nous avons déjà parlé, le contingent des fibres fines (moins de 1 μ) allant au tectum et les fibres allant au genouillé latéral étant les plus grosses (8 à 12 μ) nous pouvons penser que ces grosses fibres, correspondent à des ganglionnaires de taille notable collectant sur une aire rétinienne étendue.

Au niveau du G.L., Glees (1941) trouve que chaque fibre afférente s'articule avec une dizaine de cellules principales, chaque cellule étant simultanément en rapport avec 40 fibres en moyenne. Cette nouvelle concentration (avec chevauchement), caractéristique des systèmes à grande sensibilité absolue, accentue encore le caractère scotopique de la vision du Chat.

Selon le Professeur Ingvar qui est ici présent et qui pourra développer ce point s'il est toujours d'accord avec ce qu'il écrivait (Ingvar, 1956), la rétine du Chat se comporte globalement comme la périphérie rétinienne de l'Homme. (Ce que Gunter (1954) a également établi par dressage). Les résultats ne montrent aucune trace de dualité rétinienne et contrairement à ce que trouve Adrian pour le Macaque les courbes de sensibilité spectrale établies à partir des réponses centrales coïncident souvent avec la courbe de l'ERG laquelle reproduit à peu près la courbe d'absorption du pourpre. Lorsqu'il y a divergence elle est dans le sens d'un accroissement de sensibilité au bleu et au vert comme si, au niveau central, le Chat était 'hyperscotopique'.

Il n'est donc pas étonnant que Cohn (1956) n'ait pu, à aucun niveau, mettre en évidence de réponses caractéristiques d'un effect spécifique de la longueur d'onde avec des stimulations bleue, verte et jaune.

Le Dr. Lennox avec Madsen, puis seule, a travaillé également sur le Chat (Lennox & Madsen, 1955; Madsen & Lennox, 1955; Lennox, 1956, 1958 a,b).

C'est, d'ailleurs, parce qu'elle est présente que je me suis permis de faire toutes les réserves que j'ai faites sur cet animal concernant le problème que nous étudions. Elle se fera, tout à l'heure, l'avocat du Chat, si elle le désire.

Il serait intéressant de discuter les résultats qu'elle a obtenus. Il me semble qu'il est difficile de les interpréter comme la manifestation d'effets chromatiques spécifiques. Il s'agit plus vraisemblablement du jeu de la dualité cônes-bâtonnets, la stimulation par les deux extrémités du spectre (1958) ne pouvant que favoriser un phénomène de ce genre.

A noter également que si, utilisant du rouge et du bleu on règle les intensités stimulatrices en se fondant sur l'amplitude de l'ERG, on donne au rouge une énergie de 100 à 300 fois plus forte que l'énergie du bleu. La comparaison entre les réponses corticales aux deux stimulations devient alors difficile à faire.

Je ne signalerai que pour mémoire les affirmations de Chang (1952) interprétant les trois pointes initiales du potentiel évoqué au niveau cortical par une stimulation électrique comme la manifestation de l'existence de trois voies à vitesse de conduction différente, chacune correspondant à une des fondamentales de Young. Si l'accord n'est pas réalisé entre les différents auteurs, concernant le nombre de groupes de fibres du nerf optique — quatre pour Bishop & Clare (1955) et pour Lennox (1958a), trois pour Chang (1951-1956), deux pour P. O. Bishop (1953) — tous sont d'accord avec Bremer & Stoupel (1956, 1957) et avec Malis & Kruger (1956) pour repousser l'interprétation de Chang. La mise en évidence de trois pointes initiales dans les aires auditives et somesthésiques (Bremer & Stoupel (1956); Landau & Clare (1956) achève de ruiner cette interprétation.

Pigeon — Le Pigeon a une fovéa bien formée comme la plupart des oiseaux (Cajal, Polyak, Rochon-Duvigneaud) et un grand nombre de fibres optiques, 988.000, selon Bruesch & Arey (1942). On sait par ailleurs qu'il possède une bonne vision chromatique (Hamilton & Coleman, 1933). En outre, le lobe optique (tubercule bijumeau) qui joue chez les oiseaux et les espèces inférieures un rôle très important (il reçoit la grande majorité des fibres optiques) est d'accès facile après enlèvement du télencéphale.

Comme il s'agit d'un animal à rétine mixte, la réponse dérivée par macroélectrode ne peut rien apporter de décisif, par contre l'exploration de la région juxta-tectale et du lobe optique par microélectrode permet d'isoler des éléments unitaires. La difficulté réside dans le fait, signalé plus haut, que les chances de rencontre d'éléments 'chromatiques' sont peu élevées. Elles ne sont pas négligeables cependant et nous pourrons revenir sur ce point plus tard.

Vertébrés inférieurs — Des nombreux reptiles possèdent des rétines à cônes purs ou à cônes prédominants, mais l'électrophysiologie s'est encore très peu intéressée au lobe optique de ces espèces.

Certains Poissons ont une fovéa bien formée (*Blennius*), beaucoup ont une rétine mixte riche en cônes. Seule la macro-réponse du lobe optique a été enregistrée (Buser, 1955), elle ne peut (rétine mixte) rien apporter de certain quant aux mécanismes spécifiquement chromatiques.

C'est donc l'exploration par microélectrode qui paraît devoir apporter les informations les plus précises tant au niveau rétinien qu'aux niveaux supérieurs.

Utilisant cette technique, l'expérimentateur doit se défendre contre une tendance simplificatrice qui le conduit plus ou moins consciemment à postuler l'isomorphisme des manisfestations électriques au niveau où il les enregistre et de la perception visuelle.

La découverte des effets 'on', 'off' et 'on-off' par Hartline a été vite 'digérée' par cette tendance à l'isomorphisme qui a attribué aux effets 'off' la responsabilité des phénomènes du genre contraste consécutifs.

Mais l'inventaire de Jung et collaborateurs (1955) des types de réponse au niveau des neurones du cortex optique, comme celui de Grüsser (1958 a,b) au niveau des ganglionnaires rétiniennes révèlent une diversité et une complexité des 'patterns' notablement plus grandes.

Les résultats de Kuffler (1953), de Barlow (1953), de Barlow, Fitzhugh & Kuffler (1957) indiquent par ailleurs que ces 'patterns' peuvent pour un même élément, varier suivant les interactions spatio-temporelles qu'il subit. Les mêmes auteurs ont trouvé que, chez le Chat non anesthésié, les éléments isolés présentent, même à l'obscurité totale, une activité spontanée importante, résultat confirmé chez le Pigeon. La stimulation aurait donc pour effet de moduler l'activité spontanée.

Si l'on ajoute à ces données la possibilité d'une restructuration du message au niveau du corps genouillé latéral (P. O. Bishop *et al.*, 1953), et le jeu, qu'on ne peut imaginer que complexe, de l'écorce visuelle, on voit que la conception d'un système linéaire à un petit nombre de chaînes quasi-indépendantes répondant coup pour coup à la stimulation est largement dépassée.

REFERENCES

ADRIAN, E. D. (1946) *J. Physiol. London*, **105**, 24.
BALADO, M. & FRANKE, E. (1937) *Monog. Gesamtgeb. d. Neurol. u. Psychiat. Fasc.*, **62**.
BARLOW, H. B. (1953a) *J. Physiol. London*, **119**, 58.
BARLOW, H. B. (1953b) *J. Physiol. London*, **119**, 69.
BARLOW, H. B., FITZHUGH, R. & KUFFLER, S. W. (1957) *J. Physiol. London*, **137**, 327.
BISHOP, G. H. & CLARE, M. H. (1955) *J. Comp. Neurol.*, **103**, 269.
BISHOP, G. H. & O'LEARY, J. L. (1940) *J. Neurophysiol.*, **3**, 308.
BISHOP, P. O., JEREMY, D. & MCLEOD, J. G. (1953) *J. Neurophysiol.*, **16**, 437.
BISHOP, P. O. & MCLEOD, J. G. (1954) *J. Neurophysiol.*, **17**, 387.
BONIN, G. V., CAROL, H. W. & MCCULLOCH, W. S. (1942) *Biol. Symposia*, **7**, 117.
BREMER, F. & STOUPEL, N. (1956) *Arch. intern. physiol.*, **64**, 234.
BREMER, F. & STOUPEL, N. (1957) *Arch. ital. biol.*, **95**, 3.
BRINDLEY, G. S. (1957) *Progr. Biophys. and Biophys. Chem.*, **8**, 50.
BRUESCH, S. R. & AREY, L. B. (1942) *J. Comp.Neurol.*, **77**, 631.
BUSER, P. (1955) Thèse, Paris.
CHACKO, L. W. (1948) *Brit. J. Ophthalmol.*, **32**, 457.
CHACKO, L. W. (1949) *Arch. Ophthalmol.*, **42**, 402.
CHANG, H. T. (1952) *J. Neurophysiol.*, **15**, 5.

Chow, K. L. (1955) *J. Comp. Neurol.*, **102**, 597.
Cohn, R. (1956) *J. Neurophysiol.*, **19**, 416.
de Valois, R. L., Smith, C. J., Kitai, S. T. & Karoly, A. J. (1958) *Science*, **127**, 238.
Evarts, E. V. (1952) *J. Neurophysiol.*, **15**,
Glees, P. (1941) *J. Anat.*, **75**, 434.
Glees, P. (1942) *J. Anat.*, **76**, 313.
Glees, P. & Le Gros Clark, W. E. (1941) *J. Anat.*, **75**, 295.
Granit, R. (1947) *Sensory Mechanisms of the Retina.*
Granit, R. (1955) *Receptors and Sensory Perception*, New Haven.
Grüsser, O. J. & Rabelo, C. (1958) *Pflügers. Arch. ges. Physiol.*, **265**, 501.
Grüsser, O. J. & Kapp, H. (1958) *Pflügers. Arch. ges. Physiol.*, **266**, 111.
Gunter, R. (1954) *J. Physiol. London*, **123**, 409.
Hamilton, W. F. & Coleman, T. B. (1933) *J. Comp. Psychol.*, **15**, 183.
Henschen, S. E. (1925) *Trav. Lab. Rech. Biol. Madrid*, **23**, 217.
Ingvar, D. H. (1956) *Congrès Int. Physiol.*, Bruxelles, 459.
Jung, R. & Baumgartner, G. (1955) *Pflügers. Arch. ges. Physiol.*, **261**, 434.
Kluver, H. (1942) *Biol. Symposia*, **7**, 301.
Kluver, H. (1951) in *Cerebral Mechanisms in Behavior*, p. 147.
Kolmer, W. (1930) *Albrecht von Graef's Arch. Ophthalmol.*, **124**, 668.
Kuffler, S. W. (1953) *J. Neurophysiol.*, **16**, 37.
Landau, W. M. & Clare, M. H. (1956) *EEG and Clin. Neurophysiol.*, **8**, 457.
Lashley, K. S. (1942) *Biol. Symposia*, **7**, 301.
Le Gros Clark, W. E. (1949) *Doc. Ophthalmol.*, **3**, 57.
Lennox, M. A. (1956) *J. Neurophysiol.*, **19**, 271.
Lennox, M. A. (1958a) *J. Neurophysiol.*, **21**, 62.
Lennox, M. A. (1958b) *J. Neurophysiol.*, **21**, 70.
Lennox, M. A. & Madsen, A. (1955) *J. Neurophysiol.*, **18**, 412.
Madsen, A. & Lennox, M. A. (1955) *J. Neurophysiol.*, **18**, 574.
Magoun, H. W. & Ranson, S. W. (1935) *Arch. Ophthalmol.*, **13**, 791.
Malis, L. I. & Kruger, L. (1956) *J. Neurophysiol.*, **19**, 172.
Marquis, D. G. (1935) *Arch. Neurol. Psychiat.*, **33**, 807.
Penfield, W., Evans, J. P. & MacMillan, J. A. (1935) *Arch. Neurol. Psychiat.*, **33**, 816.
Penfield, W. & Rasmussen, T. (1952) *The Cerebral Cortex of Man*, New York.
Piéron, H. (1955) *La Sensation*, Paris.
Polyak, S. (1941) *The Retina*, Chicago.
Polyak, S. (1957) *The Vertebrate Visual System*, Chicago.
Ramon y Cajal, S. *Histologie du Système Nerveux de l'Homme et des Vertébrés*, Paris 1909, Madrid 1955.
Rochon-Duvigneaud (1943) *Les yeux et la vision des Vertébrés*, Paris.
Rushton, W. A. H. (1953) *Brit. Med. Bull.*, **9**, 68.
Walls, G. L. (1953) *The Lateral Geniculate Nucleus and Visual Histophysiology*, Los Angeles.
Willmer (1955) *Doc. Ophthalmol.*, **9**, 235.
Zurn, J. (1902) *Arch. Anat. Entw.*, Suppl., 99.

DISCUSSION

PIÉRON

Je pense que le Dr. De Valois va pouvoir tout de suite nous donner des indications sur ses résultats concernant le corps genouillé.

DE VALOIS

I would like to say a few words about the studies my associates and I have been making of colour vision mechanisms in the monkey. The monkey is a singularly appropriate animal for such an investigation, for both its colour discrimination and the structure of its visual system are very similar to that of man.

We have approached this problem by recording from cells in the lateral geniculate nucleus, since we hoped that the break-up of the visual system here into different layers might give us some hint as to the nature of the organization of the system. In Fig. 1 is a photomicrograph of the lateral geniculate of a macaque. You can see that it consists of six layers of cells, three of which receive projections from one eye, and three from the other. Also to be seen is an electrode track, showing the angle at which one approaches the geniculate in the stereotaxic plane.

We found, in recording from single geniculate cells, as others had previously in other animals, that different cells respond with different patterns of response to light. Some cells fire during the light; others are inhibited by light and fire off-responses; still others fire at both the onset and offset of the light stimulation. Furthermore, we found that these different types of cells were segregated into different geniculate layers, with on-cells in the dorsal pair of layers, both on- and on-off-cells in the intermediate layers, and inhibit-off cells in the ventral pair. In Fig. 2 are records of the responses of two cells each to two different intensities of white light. The layer 6 (dorsal layer) cell fires an on-response to the light; the layer 1 (ventral layer) cell is inhibited by light and fires an off-response at the termination of stimulation. It is thus clear that the lamination of the lateral geniculate represents a functional split in the primate visual system. The responses of single cells in these various layers to monochromatic light have provided additional clues as to the nature of this functional split, and also interesting evidence as to the nature of the primate colour-vision system. Our preliminary results* have been confirmed and extended in experiments on a number of additional animals.

The central portion of the retina projects to the dorsolateral and caudal portion of the lateral geniculate nucleus, and it is from this region that we have made most of our recordings. The majority of the cells in the dorsal layers in this part of the LGN give responses to only selective parts of the spectrum. They are similar to the modulators described by Granit.† An example of one such cell — a 'red modulator' — is shown in Fig. 3. In this figure the responses of this cell to different monochromatic lights equated for equal physical energy are shown superimposed on each

* DE VALOIS, R. L., SMITH, C. J., KITAI, S. T. & KAROLY, A. J. (1958) Science, 127, 238-9.
† GRANIT, R. (1947) Sensory Mechanisms of the Retina, London.

111

other. It can be seen that the peak response is to 620 mμ. Other pure on-cells have been found in the dorsal layers which give peak responses at *c.* 580, 550, 510, and 440 mμ.

I would like to emphasize that these narrow-band 'modulator' curves remain the same regardless of the adaptation state of the animal. That is, one does not have to light adapt the animal in order to get a pure red modulator curve, as one has to do in the case of the cat and some other animals studied by Granit. It would appear that these cells are related only to colour receptors in the eye. On the other hand, with reference to what Rushton said this morning, in other portions of the dorsal layers, which receive projections from the peripheral portions of the retina, we find cells with multiple spectral sensitivity peaks which do give different responses depending upon the adaptation state of the eye.

In the dorsal pair of layers alone, then, we have found what appears to be a complete colour-vision system, with different elements being sensitive to various narrow wavelength bands across the spectrum. This is what might be called a Helmholtzian colour-vision system in the sense that the various types of elements operate independently rather than in complementary pairs.

In the intermediate layers, however, we have found cells which also appear to be concerned with colour vision, but which are of an entirely different type. These single cells give either on- or off-responses, depending on the wavelength of the stimulating light. One of these cells may respond at the onset of the light only if it is blue; considering the on-response alone it appears to be a 'blue' modulator. But the same cell also gives off-responses at the termination of stimulation, and these off-responses are given only to the complementary wavelength of the light that produced the on-response. In other words, this cell gives on-responses to blue light, and off-responses to yellow light. Records from two such elements are shown in Fig. 4.

It is readily apparent that we have here a type of colour-vision system very similar to that originally postulated by Hering, with the various colour-selective elements hooked up in opposing complementary pairs. Our data would thus strongly suggest that in the primate there are at least two different colour-vision systems operating, at least two different ways in which the information coming presumably from the same colour receptors are encoded in the retinal nervous system. It may well be that the long dispute between Helmholtz and Hering type theories may be resolved by finding that both types of systems exist side by side in the primate visual system.

Most of the ventral layer cells (which are inhibited by light and fire off-responses) have broad rather than narrow spectral sensitivity, and probably have their main role in some aspect of vision other than colour vision as such. However, certain of these cells have shown very interesting long-term after-effects of stimulation. In Fig. 5 is a plot of the responses of one such cell. The number of spikes per 200 millisec. has been counted for intervals before, during and after the light. As can be seen, this cell is inhibited by blue-green light (the responses to 480 and 500 mμ have been averaged here), and fires an off-response. Light from the long wavelength end of the spectrum does not affect the cell while it is on, but a small off-response is produced. Then, 2 to 4 sec. later, the cell is completely inhibited for a long period of time. Whether these alternating inhibitory and excitatory responses to a colour and to its complement are related to after-images or not is still an open question, but the time relations are roughly right for this.

In addition to these studies of the responses of single cells in the geniculate to

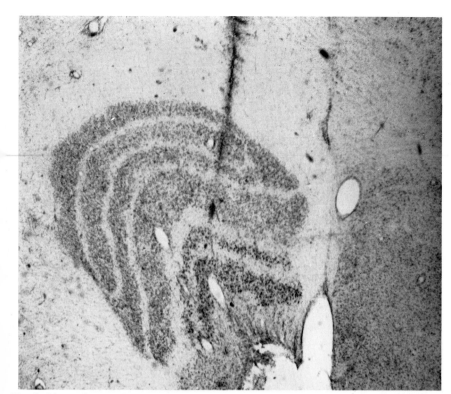

FIG. 1. Photomicrograph of a macaque lateral geniculate nucleus, with track of a micro-electrode.

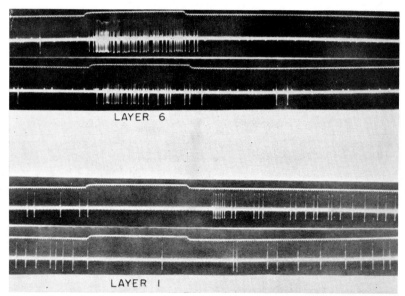

LAYER 6

LAYER 1

FIG. 2. Example of responses of dorsal layer (6) and ventral layer (1) LGN cells.
Bottom record in each case is one log unit lower intensity.

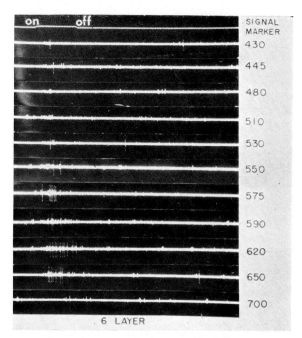

FIG. 3. Response of a dorsal layer cell to monochromatic lights adjusted to equal energy.

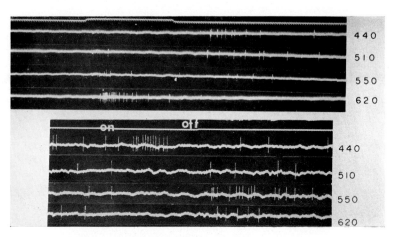

FIG. 4. Response of two intermediate layer cells to monochromatic lights adjusted to equal energy.

[*facing page 113*

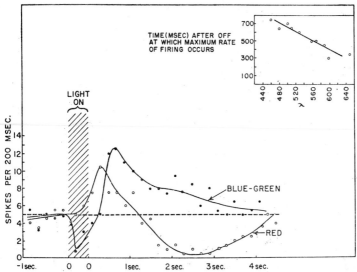

FIG. 5. Plot of the responses of a single inhibit-off cell which exhibits delayed
inhibition to the colour complementary to that which inhibits it at on.

monochromatic light, Dr. Smith and I have begun a study of the responses of
cortical cells in the monkey. The technical aspects of the problem — which are
much greater than with the cat — have not been completely overcome, and we have
but little to report.

Many cortical cells in the monkey visual cortex do not give any discernible
response to light. This same phenomenon has been reported for the cat by Jung.*
Among the cells that do respond to light, some are responsive only to light from the
ipsilateral eye, others to only contralateral stimulation, and still others fire to light

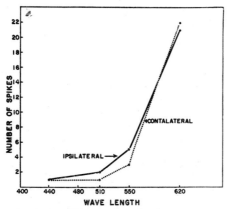

FIG. 6. Response of a single cell in monkey visual cortex to monochromatic light
stimuli adjusted to equal energy and presented to each eye in turn.

* JUNG, R. (1953) *EEG Clin. Neurophysiol.*, suppl. **4**, 57-71.

from either eye. The behaviour of one of these latter which we held long enough to collect some spectral sensitivity data is plotted in Fig. 6. It can be seen that this cell responded to light in the contralateral eye with a typical 'red modulator' type of response, giving twenty-one spikes to 620 in the red and virtually nothing to other wavelengths. When the ipsilateral eye was similarly illuminated with different monochromatic lights adjusted for equal energy, virtually the same spectral sensitivity curve was obtained. It is thus clear that a red modulator system from one eye, and one from the other eye, which project to different portions of the lateral geniculate nucleus, eventually come together on a single cell at the cortical level.

PIÉRON

Je veux remercier d'abord le Dr. De Valois qui montre la complexité des réponses, mais avec tout de même des spécificités intéressantes, qui établissent qu'il peut y avoir des électivités chromatiques, avec un pattern qui soustend ces réponses, susceptibles de grandes variabilités, avec des phénomènes d'excitation et d'inhibition.

Mais, je pense que Mrs. Lennox doit prendre la parole, si elle veut bien, et nous parler de ses expériences.

LENNOX

It has been a pleasure to hear these two fine presentations. I would like to show a single slide to illustrate a few additional features of cortical organization.

Fig. 1 shows micro-electrode recordings from the cortex of an anaesthetized monkey in the light-adapted state, that is with a background illumination on the eye. The responses of two single cells (*A* and *B*) are shown to light (left) and to electrical stimulation of the optic nerve (right). Three features of cortical organization are illustrated.

(1) I would like to point out first the response of the single cells to electrical stimulation. A single cell may respond with a single spike (*B*) or with at most two spikes (*A*) to electrical stimulation both at threshold and at high intensity stimulus. This indicates that a single cortical cell, even though not at the foveal area of representation, is connected by a single unit along the whole optic pathway to a single retinal ganglion cell. In such case there is no convergence on the single cortical cell and this is in agreement with the wide divergence from retina to cortex known to exist in the visual system. This must mean that Dr. De Valois* single cells in geniculate are projected directly to cortex. That is, the spectral sensitivity of a single unit in retina may be projected unchanged through the geniculate to single cortical cells.

(2) There appears to be no spatial organization with respect to colour as there is in the peripheral sensory system with its vertical columnar arrangement of separate modalities.† On the contrary, cells varying widely in their responsiveness to different colours are encountered with a micro-electrode traversing the cortex in a plane perpendicular to its surface. For example, the two single cells illustrated were encountered with the same micro-electrode. One responded to red only and one only to a green flash. There has been mention of how complicated cortical organization must be. As far as I can see, the organization at cortex must be extremely

---

* DE VALOIS, R. L., SMITH, C. J., KITAI, S. T. & KAROLY, A. J. (1958) *Science*, **127**, 238.
† MOUNTCASTLE, V. B. (1957) *J. Neurophysiol.*, **20**, 408.

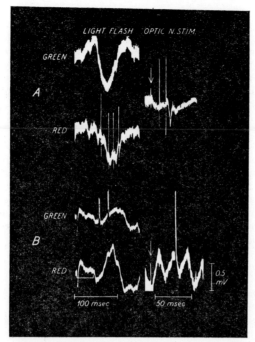

FIG. 1. Response of two single cells (*A* and *B*) in the cortex of a light-adapted monkey to light flash (left) and to electrical stimulation of the optic nerve (right). Positive is up.

simple and the organization at retina must be far more complicated. There is still considerable question, it seems to me, as to how these specific spectral sensitivities of single units can be recognized.

(3) The hypothesis of Le Gros Clark* has been rather summarily dismissed here. As you know, he recognized the difficulties in accounting for colour discrimination on the basis of spectral sensitivity alone and he postulated that there might be discrimination on the basis of conduction velocity. His cited histological evidence has proved misleading in this connection in view of Dr. de Valois's findings and those of others.

But his basic hypothesis that velocity of conduction may play a role in spectral discrimination has, as far as I can see, not been disproved on physiological evidence. It has in fact been established that the velocity of conduction in the central nervous system depends on the colour of the stimulating light in cat.† It is true that these findings have not yet been confirmed under conditions crucial for their interpretation in terms of colour vision, namely in the light-adapted monkey. One would, in advance, not expect that one could find differences in conduction velocity since all the fibres from the foveal area are small and one would not expect there to be a

---

* LE GROS CLARK, W. E. (1947) *Anatomical Pattern as the Essential Basis of Sensory Discrimination*, Oxford.
† LENNOX, M. A. (1958) *J. Neurophysiol.*, **21**, 70.

sufficient range of arrival times at cortex to allow such a method of discrimination. Actually, the range in arrival time at cortex is considerable. As it turns out, the small size of the fibres, the slow conduction velocity and the relatively long distance over which the impulses are conducted are all conditions favourable for a wide absolute variability in arrival time at cortex (as illustrated here at least between 15 and 35 millisec.) in the face of a small absolute variability in conduction velocity (between 7 and 3 millisec. respectively). Whether this code is utilized is yet to be shown in light-adapted monkeys, but it is in any case available.

DE VALOIS

I would like to make just one comment on Dr. Lennox's presentation. We have found in recording from the monkey visual cortex a number of cells which fire only once, no matter how intense the light. We have never seen this in the geniculate. I would think that this behaviour reflects complexity rather than simplicity; it is as if the intensity information has already been shunted somewhere else in the cortex and this cell is now carrying only part of the original information which was sent up on a single geniculate cell.

GALIFRET

Comme je le disais tout à l'heure le pigeon semble pouvoir être utilisé avec profit pour l'étude des mécanismes de la vision chromatique.

Après être arrivé à la conclusion que les recherches que j'effectuais sur le lobe optique de cet animal à l'aide de macro-électrodes ne pouvaient pas permettre l'étude fructueuse des mécanismes de la vision chromatique j'ai opté pour la technique de Hubel* des micro-électrodes de tungstène.

Les enregistrements ainsi obtenus ont été pris essentiellement à partir de la région prétectale et dans la partie antérieure du lobe optique.†

L'expérience étant faite après anesthésie locale, sans anesthésie générale, le premier fait qui frappe est l'activité spontanée parfois intense d'un grand nombre de cellules. La stimulation a pour effet de modifier cette activité spontanée de façon très diverse. A côté des 'patterns on-off' classiques (Fig. 1) on trouve un certain nombre d'autres types de réponses. Nous avons retenu celles qui semblent témoigner d'une certaine spécificité chromatique des éléments.

Cette spécificité se manifeste suivant différentes modalités.

(1) On voit (Fig. 2) les réponses de deux éléments qui se comportent différemment vis à vis des stimulations bleue, verte et rouge: en A on obtient une réponse notable pour le bleu et le vert et moindre pour le rouge. En B au contraire, les réponses sont celles d'un élément qui réagit très peu au bleu et au vert mais nettement au rouge.

A noter la configuration de la réponse: une volée initiale de quelques influx suivie plus tardivement d'un train à éléments plus espacés (qui se distingue de l'activité spontanée).

La volée initiale peut faire défaut comme on le voit pour 474 et 540 mμ en B où l'efficacité de la stimulation est moindre.

* HUBEL, D. H. (1957) *Science*, **125**, 549.

† A l'origine j'avais pensé que les potentiels recueillis étaient des potentiels de fibres; en fait il s'agit de potentiels de corps cellulaires recueillis dans le noyau genouillé latéral et les groupements cellulaires qui sont considérés comme faisant partie de la formation genouillée latérale (nucleus superficialis synencephali en particulier).

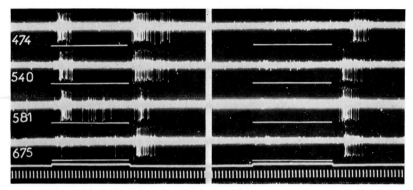

Fig. 1. Stimulations durables. Energies égales. Longueur d'onde en mμ indiquée sur les tracés. Tracés inférieurs: réponse de la photocellule à la stimulation et temps (1/50 sec.).
A droite, mêmes longueurs d'onde mais d'énergie réduite au 1/1000 de l'énergie utilisée pour les tracés de gauche. On voit que les réponses on et off n'ont pas le même seuil.

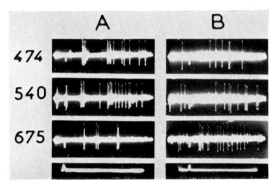

Fig. 2. Stimulations brèves (5 millisec.). (Position de la stimulation reportée sur la ligne de base). Energies égales. Longueur d'onde indiqué en mu. Durée totale du balayage, 350 millisec. Explication (voir texte).

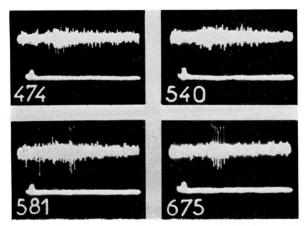

FIG. 3. Stimulations brèves. Energies égales. Durée totale du balayage: 250 millisec.

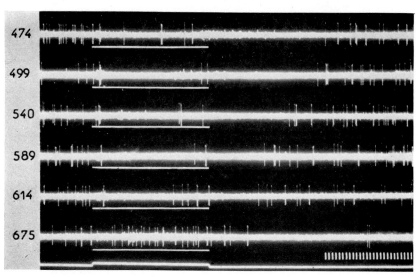

FIG. 4. Stimulations durables. Energies égales. Tracé inférieur: réponse de la photocellule à la stimulation et temps (1/50 sec.). Explication (voir texte).

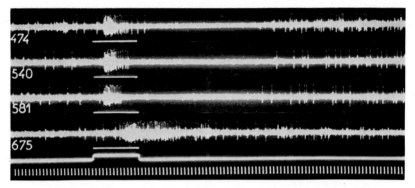

FIG. 5. Stimulations durables. Energies égales. Tracés inférieurs: réponse de la photocellule à la stimulation et temps (1/50 sec.). Explication (voir texte).

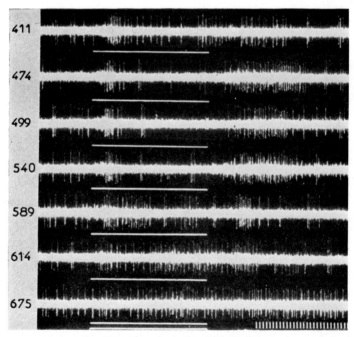

FIG. 6. Stimulations durables. Energies égales. Tracé inférieur: réponse de la photocellule à la stimulation et temps (1/50 sec.). Explication (voir texte).

[facing page 117

Voici (Fig. 3) la réponse d'un élément, nulle dans le bleu et le verte, faible dans le jaune, notable dans le rouge.

(2) A côté de cette modalité classique, absence ou présence de réponse il existe des modalités plus complexes. En voici un exemple (Fig. 4): notons d'abord la volée initiale, qui fait défaut pour le rouge extrême. C'est pour 540 mµ que la latence est la plus faible. De 474 à 614 mµ l'activité spontanée, bloquée complètement après la volée initiale, réapparaît avant que la stimulation ait cessé et est bloquée à nouveau à la cessation de la stimulation. Il est extrêmement intéressant de noter — et le fait se reproduit trés fréquemment — que ce blocage en 'off' est d'une durée qui diminue à mesure que la longueur d'onde augmente (de 474 à 614 mµ). Il s'agit bien d'un phénomène relevant des mécanismes chromatiques puisque les durées n'ont rien à voir avec l'efficience lumineuse des radiations. Si par ailleurs nous comparons le 'pattern' obtenu avec 675 mµ aux autres 'patterns' nous constatons: blocage en 'on' au lieu de volée initiale, puis accélération de l'activité spontanée au lieu du blocage provoqué par le maintien de la stimulation, puis absence de blocage en 'off' et enfin blocage tardif correspondant à la reprise de l'activité spontanée pour les longueurs d'onde plus courtes. La stimulation rouge extrême provoque donc dans cet élément des manifestations électriques systématiquement opposées à celles que provoquent les stimulation de plus courtes longueurs d'onde.

Nous retrouvons un phénomène assez analogue pour l'élément dont les réponses sont groupées dans la Fig. 5. On notera en outre dans ce cas la grande latence des phénomènes en 'on' et par ailleurs l'indifférence à la cessation du stimulus du train d'influx déclenché tardivement par la stimulation rouge.

La Fig. 6 enfin donne un exemple d'un ensemble de 'patterns' plus complexes encore. Dans ce cas c'est la stimulation 614 mµ dont les effets semblent le plus en opposition avec ceux de stimulations de courte longueur d'onde (499 mµ en particulier). La stimulation de 589 mµ réalisant un type hybride de 'pattern'.

On peut déjà entrevoir dans la complexité des réponses recueillies les lignes directrices suivant lesquelles on pourra les classer. Il reste à déterminer l'existence possible d'une relation entre certains types de réponse et les différents noyaux où se fait la détection et également à multiplier les enregistrements afin d'arriver à établir une statistique précise des différentes modalités par lesquelles se manifeste cette spécificité chromatique. Ainsi pourra-t-on apporter quelques éléments permettant de résoudre le problème du codage grâce auquel le système nerveux parvient à la discrimination des couleurs.

INGVAR

M. Galifret was kind enough to refer to a preliminary summary of my investigation of visual cortical responses to monochromatic flicker in the cat.* It would perhaps be appropriate in this discussion to summarize briefly the whole investigation which has now been carried to an end and which is in course of publication.†

The problem we have investigated is the following: Suppose we know the *retinal* spectral sensitivity curve in the cat. If we then use monochromatic light stimuli adapted energetically to this curve, the responses to all wavelengths in *cerebral* visual centres must be identical in amplitude, form and latency, if the retinal receptor mechanism is a homogeneous one, i.e. it depends upon only one photopigment with a single absorption maximum.

* INGVAR, D. H. (1956) *Acta Psychiat. and Neurol. Scand.*, **31**, 163-6; and (1956) *Intern. Physiol. Congr. Bruxelles*, pp. 459-60.

† INGVAR, D. H. (1959) *Acta Physiol. Scand.*, **46**, Suppl. 159.

When this hypothesis was tested experimentally in the dark-adapted cat two important observations were made. First, the retinal sensitivity curve, determined in dark adaptation with monochromatic flicker according to the 'resonance' method of Granit and Wirth* was not found to correspond to the visual purple absorption curve. The 'scotopic blue-shift' of Granit and Wirth was fully confirmed in all the

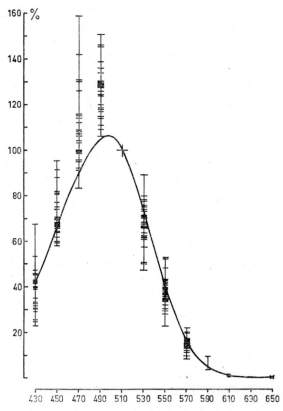

Fig. 1. Retinal spectral sensitivity measured by twenty-four determinations in fifteen experiments according to the resonance method of Granit & Wirth (1953). Flicker rate 5.1 per second. Conditions of dark adaptation. Line drawn in full represents rhodopsin absorption curve. *Reference point in this and subsequent spectral curves arbitrarily placed at* 510 mμ. The individual sensitivity values have been indicated as horizontal lines on a vertical bar at the respective wavelength. At 590, 610, 630 and 650 mμ only largest and smallest values have been indicated. Note 'blue-shift' of average sensitivity.

experiments (Fig. 1). Secondly, when stimuli were used which gave identical *b*-waves of the ERG (i.e. they were adapted energetically to the retinal sensitivity curve), the resulting responses from the visual cortex were fairly similar only, but never completely identical in the different wavelengths used (Fig. 3). Both these findings

* GRANIT, R. & WIRTH, A. (1953) *J. Physiol. London*, **122**, 386-98.

indicated that, even in the scotopic state, light reception may be dependent upon an heterogeneous mechanism. This problem was therefore further investigated in a larger series of experiments.

Fig. 2 gives a schematic diagram of the technique used. All the experiments were

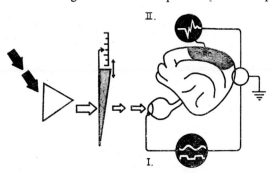

Fig. 2. Schematic diagram of experimental arrangements. White intermittent light from a tungsten filament lamp with calibrated emission passed a monochromator (Hitger-Tutton). A neutral grey wedge made intensity variations possible. The eye was dilated with atropine and diffusely illuminated. In each experiment measurements were made of the ERG (according to the resonance method of Granit & Wirth (1953)) and of evoked potentials in visual centres of the brain (unanaesthetized *cerveau isolé* preparations). All photographic records were made with a superimposition technique. A comparison was made of spectral sensitivity curves calculated from retinal and cerebral responses.

carried out in preparations of the *cerveau isolé* type. The fact that no anaesthetic was used has probably been of primary importance for the excitability conditions generally, as well as for the stability of the preparations during the long-lasting experiments. One eye was stimulated with monochromatic flicker (obtained by means of a monochromator and a rotating disc) of known energy at a constant rate of three (or five) per second.

For each wavelength tested, stimulation was started in the fully dark-adapted state with such low intensities of flicker that no colours were seen in the stimulating beam by the experimenter. The intensity was then increased stepwise and responses from cerebral visual structures (either visual cortex, lateral geniculate body, or superior colliculus) contralateral to the stimulated eye were recorded at each intensity step. In this way, cerebral visual responses to monochromatic light were studied as a function of light adaptation in flicker. Spectral sensitivity curves were calculated from energy reciprocals to responses in different wavelengths of equal amplitude or latency. Many such curves for subsequent steps of, for example, increasing amplitude, pictured changes in spectral sensitivity during increasing light adaptation. The range of flicker intensity was such that with the highest intensities the light-adapted state, the cone range, was reached. The series of spectral sensitivity curves obtained from cerebral visual centres at different levels of light adaptation were compared with the retinal control curve also obtained in each experiment. There were often large discrepancies between the simple retinal curve with a 'blue-shift' and the many different types of curves obtained in cerebral visual structures.

The heterogeneous nature of scotopic and photopic light reception mechanisms in the cat was also indicated by differences between wavelengths found in plots of gross

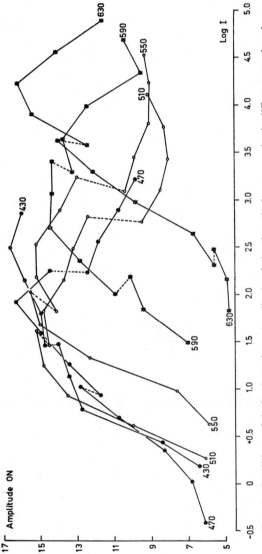

FIG. 4. Conditions of dark adaptation. Amplitude of visual cortical responses in six different wavelengths plotted against intensity of flicker. Shifts of main neutral filters indicated by dotted discontinuities. These were disregarded in the final analysis of curves. Note presence of up-going phase of amplitude with increasing intensity of flicker in all wavelengths. There is then (except for 430 mμ, which could not be followed longer due to limitations of the intensity available) a down-going phase, and, for 510, 550 and 590 mμ only, a final indication of a second up-going phase. When calculations of sensitivity curves were made, an ordinate level was chosen (i.e. equal amplitude), and the corresponding intensity values for the different wavelengths were read off. Sensitivity curves were calculated separately from both up-going and down-going phase. In similar curves the spectral sensitivity distribution was found to change pattern from the rising to the falling phase.

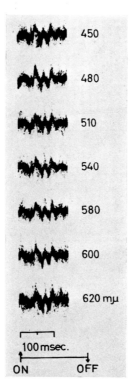

450

480

510

540

580

600

620 mμ

100 msec.

ON   OFF

FIG. 3. Superimposed records of (30-40) 'on' responses to monochromatic flicker in a point in the visual cortex. The intensity of the illumination with seven different wavelengths (450-620 mμ) was adapted to the spectral sensitivity curve of the stimulated eye as measured from the ERG. Note the gross similarity between the responses, but that smaller differences in the amplitude as well as latency are apparent on more detailed comparison. Width of original records was 60 mm.

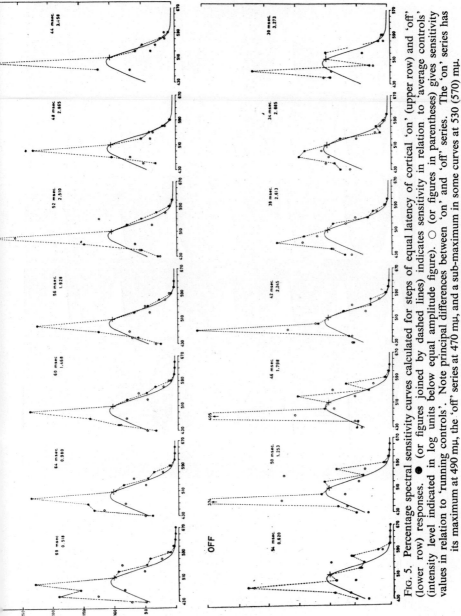

Fig. 5. Percentage spectral sensitivity curves calculated for steps of equal latency of cortical 'on' (upper row) and 'off' (lower row) responses. ● (or figures joined by dashed lines) indicates sensitivity in relation to 'average controls' (intensity level indicated in log units below equal amplitude figure). ○ (or figures in parentheses) gives sensitivity values in relation to 'running controls'. Note principal differences between 'on' and 'off' series. The 'on' series has its maximum at 490 mμ, the 'off' series at 470 mμ, and a sub-maximum in some curves at 530 (570) mμ.

122 *Neurophysiological Problems*

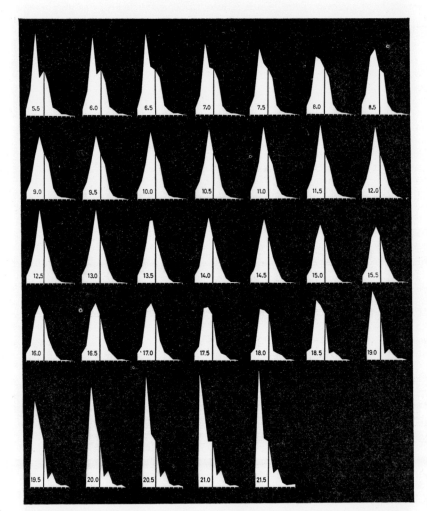

Fig. 6. Percentage spectral sensitivity curves calculated for narrow steps of increasing values of equal amplitude (indicated on each curve in arbitrary units). Every small curve is based upon a dotted line on which the dots indicate every 20th mμ from 430 to 650 mμ. The 100 per cent reference value at 510 mμ corresponds to the upper end of the black perpendicular bar in each small curve.

There is a gradual change of spectral sensitivity pattern expressed by small responses at low intensities to the patterns expressed by larger responses at higher intensities of flicker. Note change of initial maximum at 470 mμ (amplitude 5.5 to 8.0) to a maximum at 490 mμ (amplitudes 8.5 to 17.5). The final high-intensity pattern shows three humps, a large peak at 470 mμ and a definite sub-maximum at 550 mμ. There is also an indication of a hump at 610 mμ.

amplitude of cerebral visual responses as a function of intensity of illumination. Fig. 4 shows that there was no constant relationship between intensity and amplitude of response for six different wavelengths.

Calculations of spectral sensitivity curves for different visual centres in the brain were based upon plots similar to that in Fig. 4 from which energy reciprocals were obtained for responses in different wavelengths equal in amplitude (or latency). The resulting cerebral sensitivity curves demonstrated sometimes very large deviations from the retinal control curves, and, to a still larger extent, from the visual purple curve. Repeated determinations in the same and in different experiments showed, however, that the deviations were in some respects systematic and that mainly three types of spectral sensitivity curves could be differentiated in those calculated from the cerebral responses.

At low intensities, i.e. in sensitivity curves calculated from small responses of long latency, the deviations from the visual purple absorption curve were in general smaller than with higher intensities. Two principal forms of low-intensity curves were found, one had a single maximum at 490 mμ, and the other, two maxima at (450-) 470 mμ and at (510-) 530 mμ and a trough at 490 mμ. These two 'scotopic' patterns were sometimes recorded simultaneously, but differentially, in 'On' and 'Off' components of the same response (Fig. 5). Sometimes the two 'scoptic' patterns were found to 'compete' within the same response, predominating at different intensities, i.e. at different levels of light adaptation. Fig. 6 gives an example of this in an experiment in which many sensitivity curves were calculated for narrow steps of amplitude increase. The initial curves show two peaks with maxima at 470 and at 510 mμ. After a decrease these two peaks disappeared when the intensity was raised (i.e. at higher values of equal response amplitude) and a more simple form of curve was obtained (predominating from amplitude 8.5 to about 17.5 in Fig. 6), with a single maximum at 490 mμ.

The last eight sensitivity curves of Fig. 6 show a three-peaked pattern (maxima at 470, 550 and at 610 mμ). This pattern was encountered at high intensities of flicker when distinct colours could be seen by the experimenter in the stimulating beam. There is therefore every reason to assume that such intensities reached well into the cone range. The three-peaked pattern has been termed the 'photopic' one.

Fig. 7 summarizes the spectral patterns calculated from responses to monochromatic stimuli in visual centres of the cat's brain. The left half of the figure indicates the two 'scotopic' patterns (S1 and S2) in relation to the visual purple absorption curve (VP). The right diagram shows the 'photopic' pattern (Ph) and an S1 peak (490 mμ) which sometimes persisted even at high intensities.

The main patterns shown above were confirmed in a sufficient number of experiments to exclude that they were caused by random variations. It is further possible to exclude any significant contribution of preretinal absorption since this is negligible in the cat in the spectral range used.* Tapetal reflection must be taken into account in investigations like this. However, this factor cannot be made responsible for the systematic shifts found in the spectral patterns when light adaptation increased. Furthermore, it seems most unlikely that tapetal reflection could have influenced 'on' and 'off' components of the same response in a differential manner (Fig. 5).

The results shown above would seem to be at variance with all the numerous investigations which have demonstrated that the cat cannot distinguish colours. However, it should be emphasized that the method used probably is very sensitive,

* WEALE, R. A. (1954) *Nature*, **173**, 1049-50.

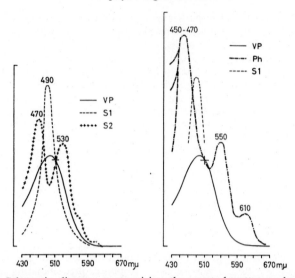

Fɪɢ. 7. Schematic diagram summarizing the spectral patterns obtained from responses to monochromatic flicker in cerebral visual structures. The three main patterns have been outlined in hypothetical, 'pure', forms in which the height of individual peaks is only grossly indicated. The *left* diagram summarizes the two main *low-intensity* patterns (called S1 and S2 here) and indicates their main spectral peaks in relation to the rhodopsin absorption curve (VP). The *right* diagram shows the main *high-intensity* pattern (called Ph) and indicates relation to the rhodopsin curve (VP). The persistence of the maximum at 490 mμ (probably S1) at high intensities has also been indicated as well as the very high sensitivity at 430 mμ or lower which was sometimes seen in the light-adapted state.

since the cerebral visual responses studied may represent only very small groups of retinal receptors. The sensitivity characteristics of such small groups may not necessarily reflect the 'average' sensitivity determining the animal's perception.* Furthermore, it seems possible that receptor systems may show comparatively small differences in spectral sensitivity (like those between the two scotopic patterns S1 and S2) without being engaged in colour vision *per se*. This view is supported by the finding that animals like the guinea-pig, which have pure rod retinae and which cannot distinguish colours, nevertheless have been found to have retinal receptors with different spectral sensitivity. It is of great interest that the guinea-pig retina contains elements which show mainly two types of sensitivity curves, one with a single maximum at 490 mμ and another with two maxima at about 470 and at 530 mμ.† The two rod systems in this animal show great principal similarities with the two 'scotopic' systems demonstrated above in the cat. They may also be related to the two morphologically different types of rods found by Sjöstrand.‡

As to the 'photopic' spectral sensitivity pattern found in the cat (Fig. 7, right half) one is inclined to interpret this as representing an 'asymetric' trichromatic colour

* Gʀᴀɴɪᴛ, R. (1955) *Receptors and Sensory Perception*, New Haven and London.
† Gʀᴀɴɪᴛ, R. (1941-1942) *Acta Physiol. Scand.*, **3**, 318-28.
‡ Sᴊösᴛʀᴀɴᴅ, F. S. (1953) *J. Cellular Comp. Physiol.*, **42**, 45-70.

differentiating mechanism in which only the blue and to a lesser extent also the green components have reached a higher degree of development. In contrast to the poorly represented red one, these two components would be able to affect the photopic sensitivity of the cat as determined by behavioural methods. As a matter of fact, Gunter* showed a blue and a green deviation in sensitivity from the visual purple curve in the light-adapted cat.

GALIFRET

Je pense qu'il faut d'abord rendre hommage à la longue patience du Professeur Ingvar car il est certain que les résultats qu'il a apportés n'ont pu se dégager avec certitude qu'après un grand nombre d'expériences. Peut-on interpréter ces pointes caractéristiques comme la résultante d'un 'pool' dans lequel la participation de bâtonnets et de cônes peu nombreux varie avec le niveau d'adaptation? Les deux pointes trouvées en état scotopique révèleraient-elles l'existence de deux types de bâtonnets? Il est difficile de répondre à cas questions. L'existence de ces pointes milite-t-elle en faveur de la possibilité d'une certaine discrimination chromatique chez le Chat? Je ne pais pas. En tout cas la neurophysiologie ne peut rien prouver dans ce domaine, elle ne peut qu'expliquer les résultats de la psychologie.

WEALE

I want to tell you as briefly as I can about a topic which, this afternoon, will not be very popular for two reasons.

In the first place, it contains a minimum of electronics and in the second place, it deals with the colour vision of man.

A few years ago I investigated various visual properties of cone monochromats, who are defined as people whose vision is normal in every way except that radiations of equal brightness appear alike to them in all respects. One of the properties which we studied was the spectral sensitivity (Fig. 1).

This illustration, in which the logarithm of the sensitivities is plotted along the ordinate and the wavelengths along the abscissa in the usual manner, shows a comparison of the principal types of colour vision, and the conemonochromatic data, the average of three, are shown with black circles. The normal sensitivity is shown with white circles. A point I want to draw your attention to is this:

It has been said, more by guessing than anything else, that the conemonochromats represent a system in which the blue and the red mechanisms are absent; i.e. that they present the one example in which only the green mechanism is present.

From that point of view, therefore, it is of interest to note that the conemonochromatic sensitivity in the red part of the spectrum lies systematically about 0.2-0.3 log units higher than that of the protanope.

There is no doubt that this difference is significant and, as you know, Dr. Rushton

* GUNTER, R. (1954) *J. Physiol. London,* **123,** 409-15.

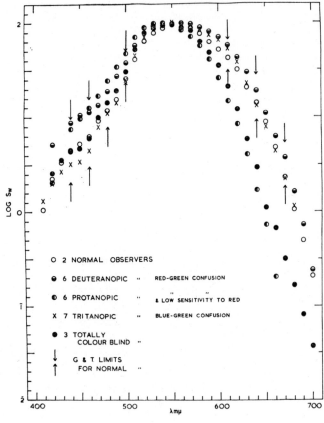

FIG. 1

has explained why the protanopic sensitivity is so low in the red. He has shown that it is impossible to detect the red-sensitive mechanism in the protanope although, of course, it can be detected in the normal and in the deuteranope.

I have also worked on normal observers and a conemonochromat, applying the opthalmoscopic method of examining retinal pigments, and have to tell you very briefly how the method works (Fig. 2a, facing p. 128).

As the result of quite a number of experiments on animals in which the same method was used, I reached the conclusion that the main thing to strive for is speed. These experiments have got to be done as quickly as one can. And that is the reason why we set up this arrangement, which dates back to 1953 and was really inspired by Grey-Walter's scanning of brain potentials. The source of light A is provided by an intense arc. B is a filter which cuts out the heat rays. The beam is collimated by the lens, L_1 and W represents a large wheel which carries twenty-six interference filters, covering the whole spectrum. Each filter is divided in two by two pieces of polaroid whose directions of transmission are at right angles to each other. When a filter crosses the beam, half the beam is transmitted by prism P_1 and the other half by prism P_2. The beams are intercepted by two other prisms, P_3 and P_4, which carry two more pieces of polaroid. And what happens is this:

As the wheel rotates, light passes either along the path α or the path β, but never simultaneously through both. Now, initially we used this method binocularly. We thought we were going to use one eye to act as a control for the other, but it got rather boring so we just use one eye (E_T) now and an artificial eye (E_C) as a control. The procedure is as follows:

The eye (E) under test is dark adapted and then the wheel is rotated. Light enters the eye, is reflected at the fundus, emerges at the pupil, is intercepted and thrown on to a photo-multiplier (P) and the photo-current is fed into a cathode-ray oscillo-graph.

The sort of trace which you can get on a film is shown in Fig. 2b. Each pair of

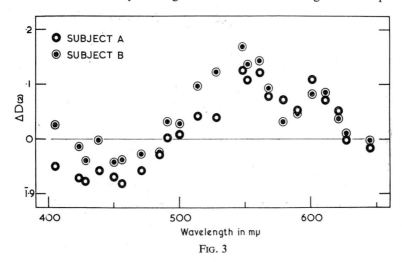

FIG. 3

excursions represents the light reflected from a human eye and from the artificial eye respectively; the latter serves as a check on the constancy of the light source and the recording gear.

When the eye is dark adapted you obtain a record of this sort. Then you bleach the eye and repeat the recording. You can get a spectrum trace in two-thirds of a second.

The apparatus is designed to give us fifty per second, but I think the electronic problems would be rather difficult at present. Two-thirds of a second will do for a beginning.

You can measure the height of each deflection and, by comparing the height before and after bleaching, obtain in the usual manner a measure of any substance which may have disappeared in the bleaching process. Examples of such experiments are shown in Fig. 3.

This shows the sort of difference which you get before and after bleaching, when the eye has been dark adapted. The $\Delta D_{(2)}$ means that we are dealing with double-transit. I think that the negative portion at short wavelengths must mean that a product of bleaching has accumulated.

The maximum change occurs at about 540 or 550 mμ and there is a second

distinct hump in the red part of the spectrum. There are only a handful of results in
Fig. 3 — here the scatter is rather great.

But, broadly speaking, I think the results are quite clear. This figure, incidentally,
shows results for 3 min. dark adaptation. The eye was bleached, left in the dark
for 3 min., a record was taken, then the eye was bleached again and another
record taken. Now, in Fig. 4, we have some results where dark adaptation proceeded for 12 min.

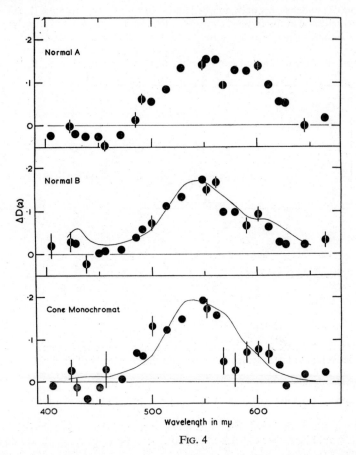

Fig. 4

The regeneration of the pigment in the fovea is complete, because you don't get
any increase after 12 min. You see that for subject A we have obtained a curve
significantly different from that obtained for subject B at long wavelengths, although
the colour vision of both subjects was normal. The amount of red-sensitive pigment
differs by a factor of two.

And here, this is the point of interest, we have the average of a few similar
measurements made on a conemonochromatic fovea. Now, as you know, the conemonochromat can distinguish no colours at all with foveal vision. It is of interest to
see, therefore, this distinct hump and if you bleach with red light and not with white

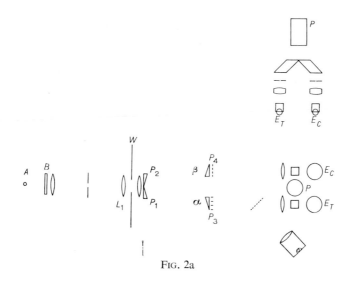

FIG. 2a

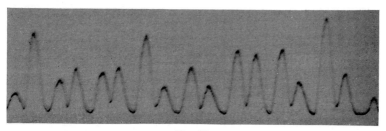

FIG. 2b

light then you can change this ratio of height at 550 to height at 600 mμ, which provides additional evidence for the view that this is an independent pigment. The curves in Fig. 5 represent the spectral sensitivities which were obtained for these observers on some other occasion and are corrected for the absorption of the lens of each of these observers.

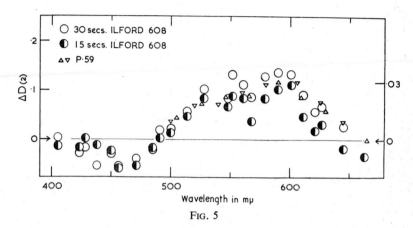

Fig. 5

A student of mine, Mr. Said, measured the spectral *in vivo* absorption of the crystalline lenses of the observers to whom these results refer. One has, therefore, no need to rely on average or dead material.

Well, summarizing then, I would draw your attention to this point of interest that the conemonochromat who behaves in all respects as though he had only one mechanism, has, in my opinion, at least two photosensitive foveal pigments. This must mean that some type of neural block exists at a centre higher than the outer limbs of his receptors and that is why I include this remark in this part of the symposium.

PIÉRON

Le Dr. Weale nous a donné une anticipation sur notre séance de demain matin en ce sens qu'il nous a montré, chez des achromates à vision fovéale des données fort intéressantes au point de vue des pigments et du rôle possible des pigments dans la vision chromatique plus, naturellement, qu'il ne nous a parlé des mécanismes neurophysiologiques qui peuvent être en jeu.

Nous retenons sa communication comme particulièrement intéressante en accord avec les données du Prof. Rushton sur les protanopes.

Mais le Prof. Bishop doit maintenant prendre la parole.

BISHOP

Two facts make it difficult for me to contribute directly to a symposium on colour vision.

In the first place, most of my work has been done with cats and cats have come under rather heavy fire today. And, in the second place, nearly all the work that I have done has been with electrical stimulation of the optic nerve rather than light stimulation of the eye. So these facts obviously preclude me from making any very direct contribution this afternoon.

However, in Sydney my colleagues and I have, for quite a number of years, been studying the properties of the central pathways and nuclei, so that I feel that I can make one or two useful comments about these properties.

Firstly, although I don't want to dwell on this, the question of fibre groups in the optic nerve has come under discussion. I'm a believer in two fibre groups.* The matter is, however, complicated by the fact that the conduction velocities of the respective groups are different in the two components in an optic tract — that is, the contralateral and ipsilateral components — and hence also in the optic nerve. A further complication is added by the marked topographical segregation of fibres according to size as the optic tract approaches the lateral geniculate body. It is particularly important that this last fact be taken into account when interpreting records obtained by stimulation of the optic tract *in situ*.

I don't think that these fibre groups are related in any direct way to colour vision. I do not know what their function is but the fact that they are both very widely distributed in their central connections argues that they are important for vision in a generalized sense rather than for colour vision. I am sure that both fibre groups go to the lateral geniculate body and also to the superior colliculus; there is no marked preferential distribution according to fibre size. As far as the lateral geniculate is concerned the large fibre projection predominates anteriorly and the small fibre posteriorly but there is always intermingling.

In the cat about four-fifths of the fibres in the optic nerve are of small diameter and yet I know of no good evidence that they relay to the cerebral cortex. In fact, the evidence that we have so far indicates that they do not relay, in any direct way, to the cortex and yet I feel that they must do so somehow or other.

The main comments I want to make are about the organization of the lateral geniculate body, its simplicity in one respect and, in another respect, its great complexity. Very recently we have been able to show† that the neurones in the lateral geniculate body are capable of being fired by a single optic nerve fibre. I don't think that this is an expression of the single 'bouton' per geniculate neurone that Glees and Le Gros Clark‡ have described. I think that a large number of nerve endings are probably necessary to make the cell fire, but these endings may all be the terminal branches of a single optic nerve fibre.

Our evidence that the cell may be discharged by a single optic nerve impulse is briefly as follows. We isolated a single cell with an extracellularly placed ultra micro-electrode and then turned down the strength of the electrical shock applied to the optic nerve until it was just threshold for that particular cell; that is, about half the time it fired and half the time it didn't. We then proceeded to take a large number of records without any further change in stimulus strength. We found that we got three different kinds of record, labelled *1*, *2* and *3* in Fig. 1.

As labelled, these are:

1 A spike discharge.

2 A local non-propagated synaptic potential.

3 No response.

* Bishop, P. O., Jeremy, D. & Lance, J. W. (1953) *J. Physiol. London*, **121**, 415.
† Bishop, P. O., Burke, W. & Davis, R. (1958) *Nature*, **182**, 728.
‡ Glees, P. & Le Gros Clark, W. E. (1941) *J. Anat.*, **75**, 295.

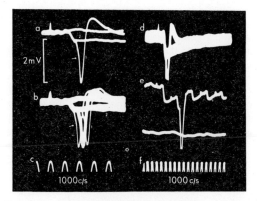

FIG. 1. Extracellular records from single lateral geniculate cell to electrical stimulation of ipsilateral optic nerve. (a) and (b) Stimulus of constant strength; (a) three and (b) many successive traces superimposed. Arrow indicates step on rising phase of spike potential. (d) Similar series later in the experiment. (e) Responses to a train of five stimuli at 300/sec. Time calibration (c) applies to (a) and (b), calibration (f) to (d) and (e). Voltage calibration applies to all records. Negativity upwards in all records. Spikes truncated in (d) and (e).

I do not think it appropriate here to give you the detailed evidence which we have for considering response (2) to be a synaptic potential (see Bishop *et al.*, 1958) but it displays all the properties which one normally associates with a synaptic potential. The latter is one that arises post-synaptically and forms an essential link between presynaptic impulse and postsynaptic propagated discharge. One property, for example, is that they may sum to cause a spike discharge as can be seen in Fig. 1e.

There are two curious features about these responses. One is that there should be three alternative states — a threshold is usually associated with two alternative states — and the other is that the local response, that is the synaptic potential, is always of the same amplitude. It appears to be all-or-none. We measured a large number and found this to be so — and if you superimpose a large number of traces (Fig. 1d) you can see that the width of the trace at the peak of the synaptic potential is no greater than that of the baseline before the stimulus artefact. In the case of some of the other cells from which we have obtained records we have been able to grade the synaptic potential to some extent by varying the strength of stimulation but this is always fairly critical.

Our explanation of these records is that the stimulus was critical for a particular optic nerve fibre. When this fibre was stimulated it produced a synaptic potential which was always of the same amplitude. It was all-or-none simply because it was produced by an all-or-none afferent impulse. This synaptic potential, in turn, was critical for the discharge of a propagated spike. There were two critical states — one was the stimulation of the optic nerve fibre and the other was the discharge of a spike from the geniculate neuron. The fact that in other cells it is usually difficult to grade the synaptic potential before it reaches the threshold for spike discharge indicates that a single optic nerve fibre normally makes a major contribution towards excitation of the cell.

If another optic nerve fibre was playing a part in the responses shown in Fig. 1 it must be producing a synaptic potential which for some reason we were not able to record. I think we can be fairly confident that if some other fibre was playing a part it must be a very minor one. Although the evidence indicates that a single optic nerve fibre can discharge a geniculate neuron, it is able to do so, I think, only because it breaks up into a large number of terminal branches and applies a large number of endings to a particular cell.

These results argue for a certain simplicity in the organization of the lateral geniculate body — a one-to-one kind of relay station. On the other hand we also have evidence for enormous complexity. About one in five of the units that we have recorded fired repetitively to a single afferent volley. Occasionally when recording from populations of cells the repetitive potential waves that may be obtained indicate that nearly all the cells in a particular region are firing repetitively.

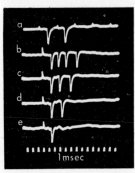

Fig. 2. Single unit (axon) records from lateral geniculate following stimulation of the contralateral optic nerve.   (a) Effect of repetitive stimulation at about 300/sec. (b) to (e) Effect of increasing strength of stimulation on the pattern of the repetitive discharge.

Fig. 2 shows records obtained from a single postsynaptic axon in or just above the lateral geniculate body. Records (b) to (e) show the effect of increasing afferent stimulation. At threshold (b) the unit fires four times and this is reduced to three, two and finally one as the strength of the shock applied to the nerve is increased. While this is the more usual effect of increasing stimulation on the pattern of the repetitive discharge the reverse may also occur. The interesting feature in the above records is that the stimulus strength required to produce a single postsynaptic spike was several times threshold and close to maximal for all the fibres in the optic nerve. We do not know what the mechanism is for this inhibitory effect but it indicates that a large number of optic nerve fibres scattered throughout the whole range of fibre diameters can influence a single cell in the lateral geniculate. In other words there is a considerable convergence, largely of an inhibitory kind, on the geniculate cells.

Recently we have been working on the problem of binocular interaction using unit recording and here also we have evidence of considerable convergence.   We have now recorded from nearly two hundred single cells and of these about 10 per cent are directly fired by impulses in either optic nerve. There is evidence, however, of a very much more widespread influence, at the geniculate level, of the impulses in the one optic nerve on the firing of the cells and the repetitive discharge that results from impulses in the other optic nerve. A very large number of the cells discharged by one optic nerve are indirectly affected by stimulation of the other optic nerve.

It is obvious that the lateral geniculate cannot be simply a relay station — indeed the evidence is to the contrary and argues a very considerable degree of organizational complexity. Now this is in the cat and we don't know whether cats have colour vision or not but I would think that in the primates, which are known to have colour vision, the lateral geniculate is likely to be even more complicated than this.

MEDIONI

Je désire revenir encore sur la question de la vision chromatique du Chat, car ce que M. Galifret nous en a dit illustre bien, à mon avis, la différence des points de vue du physiologiste et du zoopsychologue.

Au point de vue de la physiologie, il paraît évident, après tout ce que vous en avez dit, que le Chat n'est pas un matériel biologique de choix pour l'étude des mécanismes physiologiques de la discrimination chromatique chez les animaux. Aussi bien n'ai-je jamais prétendu cela.

J'ai seulement dit qu'il me paraissait possible que le Chat perçoive les couleurs. Et c'est justement ce problème de la présence ou de l'absence d'un sens chromatique même relativement fruste chez une espèce nocturne qui me paraît intéressant, en relation avec un problème spécifiquement biologique, et non pas physiologique: celui de la coaptation entre le mode de vie — diurne ou nocturne — des animaux et l'existence de la vision des couleurs.

Nous savons bien, évidemment, que le mode vie des animaux, et en particulier celui des Carnivores, n'est pas toujours facile à caractériser avec rigueur, mais il me paraît y avoir là un problème biologique qui a son importance.

Je pense donc que de ce point de vue biologique, ainsi que du point de vue de l'étude du comportement des animaux, la question de savoir si (oui ou non) le Chat voit les couleurs mérite d'être approfondie.

GALIFRET

Vous parlez des conditions biologiques. Je pense que ce que font les zoopsychologues en peignant les souris en rouge, en jaune et en bleu ne nous rapproche pas des conditions biologiques réelles. Les souris qui intéressent les chats sont grises ...

MEDIONI

Je n'ai pas parlé de conditions biologiques. J'ai parlé d'un problème biologique.

GALIFRET

Mais oui! C'est précisément le problème intéressant, celui du mode de vie. Or Rochon-Duvigneaud, qui fut un excellent observateur des mœurs animales en même temps qu'un passionné de l'histologie rétinienne, a noté que l'univers visuel du Chat était assez pauvre. Dans le domaine visuel le Chat réagit surtout aux mouvements des objets. Il a une mauvaise acuité. Et une mauvaise acuité va en général de pair avec une mauvaise vision chromatique. Etant donné les proies qu'il chappe, la vision chromatique ne lui apporterait guère d'informations supplémentaires utiles, contrairement à ce qui se passe chez l'Abeille par exemple, qui identifie les fleurs par leurs caractéristiques chromatiques, ou chez les oiseaux diurnes.

PIÉRON

Maintenant, il y a l'indifférence et l'impossibilité de percevoir les couleurs. Il y a là une nuance qui peut expliquer des divergences expérimentales, évidemment.

Il y a possibilité de dressage discriminatif chez les animaux chez lesquels la couleur joue un rôle important, qui sont très facilement conditionnés aux couleurs. L'on pourrait dire que ceux pour lesquels la couleur est tout à fait négligée rendent plus difficile un tel dressage. Entre l'impossibilité complète de percevoir les couleurs et une indifférence tenant à ce que, dans le comportement normal des animaux, les couleurs ne jouent à peu près aucun rôle, il y a évidemment une nuance qui est importante.

Il est possible qu'il soit très difficile de conditionner des chats aux couleurs, parce que, pour eux, les couleurs ne comptent habituellement pas.

Cependant, si vraiment on conditionne des chats à des stimuli électriques douloureux un assez grand nombre de fois, il serait extraordinaire, s'ils n'étaient pas complètement aveugles aux couleurs, qu'une liaison ne s'établisse pas.

Par conséquent, je crois que, tout de même, il y a des expériences cruciales que l'on peut faire pour savoir si c'est simplement une indifférence habituelle aux couleurs, ou si c'est réellement une impossibilité de les percevoir.

GALIFRET

Avec contrôle physique rigoureux.

PIÉRON

Ah! bien entendu, dans des conditions expérimentales rigoureuses. Ce n'est pas, évidemment, en barbouillant des souris avec du rouge ou du vert!

Eh bien, je pense qu'il y a encore des observations à faire. Est-ce que, du côté de la physiologie générale du système nerveux, M. Fessard n'a rien à dire? Avec son expérience des centres nerveux et de l'exploration des centres. Que pense-t-il de la possibilité de mettre en évidence des discriminations de sélectivité dans les éléments supérieurs?

FESSARD

J'ai bien peu à dire, sinon que je pense que les méthodes d'exploration actuelles ne sont pas encore exploitées à fond, et que l'on peut espérer de meilleurs résultats dans l'avenir. Je suppose que ces résultats — si l'on peut, toutefois, prévoir quelque chose dans ce domaine — montreront de plus en plus une distribution en mosaïque, une distribution qui ne sera pas en territoires fonctionnellement différenciés. C'est donc la microphysiologie, l'exploration par microélectrodes, qu'il faut développer, comme l'a bien rappelé Galifret.

Tout ce que je pourrais dire, je crois que Galifret l'a déjà dit. Espérons simplement que ces méthodes électrophysiologiques ne nous décevront pas et permettront au physiologiste de se rapprocher davantage du psychophysicien.

PIÉRON

Il est un point sur lequel je voudrais vous poser une question.

Il y a quelque chose d'assez frappant: c'est, dans les derniers travaux, en particulier de Jung, de Grüsser, son collaborateur, la présence, dans les cellules de projection corticale, d'éléments qui, les uns sont des éléments 'on', et d'autres des éléments 'off', comme dans les cellules ganglionnaires de la rétine, et il y a là déjà un point particulier — qu'on puisse avoir, au niveau cortical, une certaine correspondance, et d'autre part — ce qui est plus surprenant — c'est l'existence d'un très grand nombre de cellules dont on n'obtient jamais de réponses avec les stimulations visuelles, avec les stimulations lumineuses, qui restent toujours silencieuses, qui ne sont ni 'on' ni 'off' ni encore moins 'on-et-off' — qui ne sont rien du tout.

Eh bien, cela est un peu surprenant, n'est-ce pas?

On peut penser que, dans la zone de projection, les cellules interviennent quand il y a des stimulations lumineuses globales.

Qu'il y ait un grand nombre de ces cellules chez lesquelles on ne puisse déceler aucune modalité de réponse, au premier abord cela paraît curieux.

On peut se demander si ce sont des éléments qui ne joueraient qu'en relation avec des excitations et des mises en service d'autres éléments situés aux environs, de telle sorte que celles-là ne seraient pas en correspondance directe avec les phénomènes qui se produisent au niveau rétinien.

Mais, en tout cas, c'est un problème qui pourrait peut-être se poser: est-ce que ces réponses s'obtiendraient si l'on trouvait la clé, c'est-à-dire si l'on obtenait d'autres éléments du cortex qui, ceux-là, seraient en mesure de les éveiller, puisque l'on ne les éveille pas avec le nerf périphérique?

Voilà le problème qui me paraît se poser et sur lequel on n'a jamais discuté une possibilité de réponse, à ma connaissance.

FESSARD

Je pense qu'il faut être très prudent dans les interprétations. Vous voulez parler des cellules muettes du type A de Jung, qui sont dans une proportion d'environ 50 pour cent, je crois.

Eh bien, j'ai rencontré le Professeur Jung il n'y a pas très longtemps. Il admet qu'on a exagéré la proportion des cellules qui ne répondent pas. Celles qui ne répondent pas sont peut-être en effet des cellules en mauvais état. Les conditions physiologiques dans lesquelles nous opérons mettent l'animal dans des conditions qui ne sont pas absolument normales. Il est possible que l'introduction des micro-électrodes dans le cortex puisse produire des micro-lésions, des micro-compressions surtout, qui font que, lorsqu'on ne prend pas certaines précautions, on peut déclarer 'silencieuses', 'muettes', des cellules qui, en réalité, ne le seraient pas si on ne les avait pas abîmées.

Je crois que, justement, dans d'autres domaines, celui de la somesthésie, par exemple, il y a eu des travaux (Mountcastle) qui ont montré que l'on avait des réponses déjà dès les premières couches, alors que d'autres auteurs ne les avaient pas trouvées, probablement pour n'avoir pas pris les mêmes précautions contre les traumatismes possibles par des électrodes insuffisamment fines.

Il y a donc là des résultats qui doivent être discutés entre spécialistes, et pour lesquels il faut être extrêmement prudent au moment de faire la jonction avec la manifestation psychologique.

Je crois que c'est notre devoir, à nous, neurophysiologistes, de rappeler aux psychologues que nous avons nos défauts, nos difficultés, qui ne sont pas minces; et qu'il ne faut pas toujours prendre à la lettre certaines affirmations rencontrées dans la littérature.

PIÉRON

Un autre point, encore, c'est celui-ci: à l'inverse des cellules qui ne répondent jamais, il y a des cellules qui travaillent tout le temps.

Alors, là, on a pu se demander si ce n'était pas, justement, les irritations des micro-électrodes qui pouvaient intervenir pour réaliser une excitation qui, celle-là, se produisait du fait même qu'on les explorait et qui ne serait pas, donc, en rapport avec une activité réellement spontanée, telle qu'on peut l'attendre de cellules qui répondent, par exemple, par une inhibition et par 'off' parce qu'elles ont une activité spontanée qui se trouve interrompue.

Est-ce qu'il y a des cellules et quelle en est la fréquence — c'est là un problème général — qui se manifesteraient vraiment d'une façon spontanée avec une activité répétitive?

FESSARD

Eh bien, là, au contraire, je peux vous rassurer. Les décharges produites par des traumatismes, les 'injury discharges', sont des faits très réels que nous connaissons bien. Mais, en général, elles ne durent pas et elles ont des configurations qui ne ressemblent pas aux décharges continues. J'ai fait moi-même beaucoup d'expériences de ce type. J'ai fait faire par des chercheurs des expériences dans lesquelles on piquait une cellule avec des microélectrodes. Certaines de ces cellules présentment des activités rythmiques. Je parle, par exemple, des cellules de ganglions de mollusques, qui sont particulièrement accessibles. Dans certaines de ces cellules, qui sont très grosses il est possible de piquer deux microélectrodes, successivement. On peut se rendre compte ainsi du dommage causé par l'introduction de la deuxième électrode. Eh bien, dès qu'on a des électrodes inférieures à deux microns on n'observe en général aucun trouble sur le tracé d'activité autorythmique.

Je crois sincèrement que la capacité pour les neurones — pour beaucoup de neurones — du système nerveux central de fonctionner sur le type autorythmique est une des clés du fonctionnement nerveux central. Il en résulte une grande richesse de *patterns* spatio-temporels possibles, qui doit expliquer la richesse des modalités de réponse à la stimulation lumineuse.

PIÉRON

Ne pourrait-on, alors, demander aux neurophysiologistes de nous donner, par exemple, une idée, au point de vue statistique, de la fréquence relative des éléments autorythmiques dans la zone de projection visuelle?

Est-ce qu'on pourrait avoir une idée sur le point de savoir s'il y en a et combien, qui marchent spontanément dans la zone de projection visuelle?

GALIFRET

Je crois que Barlow, Fitzhugh et Kuffler ont très bien posé le problème dans la publication dont j'ai déjà parlé: la plupart des auteurs ont travaillé précédemment sous anesthésie profonde, qui fait disparaître complètement l'activité spontanée.

Si l'on fait une décérébration à l'éther et que l'on attende suffisamment longtemps — par exemple deux ou trois heures — alors l'activité spontanée se manifeste abondamment.

Chez les pigeons, que j'utilise et qui ont simplement subi une anesthésie locale, à peu prés les trois-quarts des éléments présentent une activité spontanée, souvent irrégulière avec une fréquence plus ou moins grande et plus ou moins variable mais présentent une activité spontanée.

PIÉRON

Alors, je repose la question de fréquence, mais au niveau du cortex — d'un chimpanzé, par exemple.

Est-ce que, dans un cas où l'anesthésie ne nuit pas à l'activité fonctionnelle, on pourrait savoir, à peu près, quelle est la proportion des cellules des zones de projection activées et silencieuses?

GALIFRET

Je crois que le Dr. De Valois et le Dr. Lennox peuvent nous renseigner à ce sujet.

DE VALOIS

I would like to make a couple of points with regard to the original question of the cells in the visual cortex which don't respond to light.

K

One is that it has been well known from ablation experiments that the visual cortex has other than just visual functions. Removal of the visual cortex leads to decrements in behaviour even in the case of blind animals. So it should not be particularly surprising to find that there would be some cells which have no particular visual function.

The other point I would like to make is that both Jung and we have presented only very simple visual stimuli to the eye: just a large area of white or monochromatic light with no patterning at all. Somewhere along the line the visual system must have elements which respond only to complicated forms or to movement. It might well be that the simple stimuli we have used would have no effect on these types of cells.

LENNOX

No one seems to have mentioned the incidence of the specifically light-responsive cells according to the depth below the cortical surface. Practically all the cells I have encountered up to about 0.5 mm. from the surface do not respond in any way to light, nor to optic nerve stimulation. Almost all or very many of those between 0.5 and 0.9 mm. respond to light. And from 1.2 to about 1.7 mm. virtually all respond to light. Presumably this fact accounts for the ten-fold increase in the amplitude of the summed response as a tungsten wire micro-electrode is advanced perpendicularly from the cortical surface to 2 mm. below it, the greatest increase occurring between 0.5 and 1.5 mm.

KRUGER

I have little to say on this subject which comes from my own experience, but having had the privilege of seeing a number of experiments with micro-electrodes in the cortex and in the thalamus, a few things have occurred to me from watching such experiments, and particularly from published papers, which may be relevant.

The first concern the question of whether there are units in the cortex which do not drive to a peripheral stimulus. This remains an open question I should think, because although a curarized animal can indeed be in a state such that unit driving is poor, Mountcastle has pointed out recently that deep or prolonged curare anaesthesia, for example, produces a condition in which driving is extremely poor and he has used a system of alternating light pentothal with curare anaesthesia. Under very light anaesthesia, a more ideal circumstance, it is relatively rarer to encounter a unit which does not drive. The remark that Dr. Lennox made might indicate an exception in the striate cortex if we consider the recent work of Erulkar, Rose and Davies on the auditory cortex and the work of Mountcastle, Davies and Berman on the somatic cortex. I think here the problem may very well be one of the status of the surface of the cortex, at least in part. It is extremely difficult to open the pia-arachnoid without producing any bleeding. This requires working at high magnification and opening it very carefully. It is extremely easy to produce damage in the upper few 100 microns and perhaps it is not rare (they are easily damaged) to find that it is difficult to find drivable units in the upper layers.

The work that Mountcastle *et. al.* recently published shows that there is indeed a fairly uniform distribution of drivable units from the top of the second layer down to the bottom of the sixth layer and the earlier work in the auditory cortex of Erulkar, Rose and Davies followed the same pattern.

Another problem which occurred to me is the position of stimulation on the retina. The recent experiments of Wiesel and Brown showed that you can get an on-response, an off-response, or any mixture in between, not by necessarily moving the point of maximal stimulation but by changing its characteristics, let's say, to an annulus, or changing the stimulus area. This may very well be one of the problems that one has to deal with — the kind of stimuli one is presenting to the eye broadly as well as what happens if you move the coloured stimulus just a little bit.

One of the things that may be even more bothersome is the problem of intensity itself. There have been a number of representations of what happens with variation of the wavelength of light and one is curious to know what happens in these circumstances and under their particular states of anaesthesia with a variation of intensity of illuminatory stimulus. In particular, one is interested in knowing, should we present a given single constant stimulus, say ten or twenty times, what is the probability of finding so many spikes at a given latency and so on. I think this is not a matter of attaining statistical sophistication — it is a matter of necessity, because the variation is not inconsiderable from what I have seen from other people's experiments and from the published results. In particular, I would refer to the work on the tactile thalamus of Rose and Mountcastle, which gave the most stable results in terms of variation of response in single units under deep nembutal anaesthesia. Even there it is not sufficiently inconsiderable to be ignored and therefore I think it is something that must be considered in comparing spectral stimuli. One must have an intensity series comparable to the spectral series so that the comparison has some meaning in terms of something other than just a luminosity function.

The final point that comes to mind is really another question; that is, what happens to the fibres in the visual system projecting to the cortex?

Dr. de Valois has just pointed out something extremely fascinating, namely that the two lower layers in the monkey lateral geniculate — the large layers which presumably do not degenerate (from what little information we have on the subject) after cortical lesions — are scotopic in their sensitivity curve. This is a bit puzzling and it is quite fascinating because it would suggest that perhaps the scotopic system may by-pass a direct cortical projection and there are a number of things that have to be explained if the smallest fibres do indeed come from the fovea. They presumably might not go to the largest cell layer in the lateral geniculate, but do they go to the cortex? Dr. Bishop raised the issue about whether both groups 1 and 2 of the two fibre groups, which are certainly present, go to the cortex. If only the first does, what happens to the small fibre group? It is hard to believe that about 80 per cent of the optic nerve is not really going to excite the cortex and it is rather peculiar that the 'scotopic' cells in the lateral geniculate are those in which it is difficult to find degeneration when one removes the visual cortex.

INGVAR

I had a short comment on what Dr. Kruger was just saying about the 'splitting up' of the optical message to the cortex on the one side, and to the brain system on the other.

In the experiments I was referring to a minute ago, we investigated whether there was any difference between spectral messages delivered to the superior colliculi and those to the visual cortex. In some experiments collicular responses to monochromatic stimulation were studied several months after ablation of the visual cortex when the principal cells of the lateral geniculate nucleus had degenerated completely. There were no differences in spectral sensitivity pattern between the two regions.

MONNIER

Avec Bider, Huber et Koller nous avons examiné les variations de la *réponse du centre visuel cortical* aux diverses modalités de stimulation lumineuse (Fig. 1). La

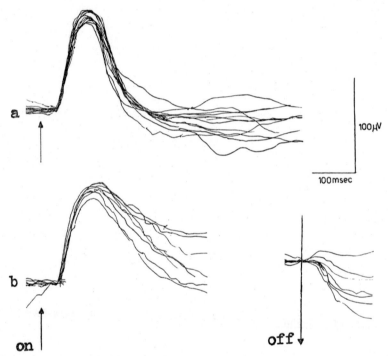

FIG. 1. (a) ERG du lapin en réponse à un stimulus de lumière bleue de faible intensité et de brève durée (40 millisec).
(b) ERG du lapin en réponse à une stimulation de lumière bleue prolongée pendant une seconde et de même intensité.
          Les phases a, c et d sont très peu prononcées.

réponse du centre visuel cortical débute après un temps rétino-cortical variable selon l'emplacement antérieur, central ou postérieur de la dérivation à l'intérieur de ce centre. Elle se caractérise par une déflexion surface-positive (potentiel b), dont l'amplitude varie suivant l'intensité du stimulus lumineux appliqué sur la rétine. La phase positive atteint son point de culmination après 70 à 90 millisec. Le plateau du sommet est entrecoupé très souvent d'une petite déflexion négative, avant le retour à la ligne isoélectrique. Les divers paramètres de cette réponse corticale (amplitude, latence, temps de culmination, durée de la pente) varient, comme ceux de l'ERG en fonction de l'énergie du stimulus lumineux (intensité ou surface d'illumination).

On a constaté une variation intéressante de la réponse en fonction du point de dérivation à l'intérieur du centre visuel cortical. Ainsi, le temps rétino-cortical est toujours plus court dans la région antérieure (7-14 millisec) que dans la région centrale (11-20 millisec) ou postérieure (21-35 millisec) lorsqu'on utilise des stimuli d'une certaine intensité. Si l'on utilise des stimuli de grande surface, la différence des temps de latence de la région antérieure et de la région postérieure est moins

TABLEAU II

Influence de la longueur d'onde, de la surface d'illumination et du lieu de dérivation sur la riposte du centre visuel cortical

A. Forte intensité

		Région					
		Antérieure		Centrale		Postérieure	
		10 mm²	20 mm²	10 mm²	20 mm²	10 mm²	20 mm³
Latence (millisec)	bleu	42	47	48	52,5	64,5	63
	vert	46,2	47	58	55	65	65
Temps culmination	bleu	71,2	74,5	73	83	91	86,0
	vert	71,0	67,2	90,5	86	92	87
Durée phase ascend.	bleu	29,2	28,5	25	30	19	22,5
	vert	24,7	20,3	31,5	31	26,5	22
Temps rétino-cortical	bleu	10	14	14	19	32,5	30,5
	vert	12	16,5	24	24,5	30,5	34,2

B. Faible intensité

		Région		
		Antérieure	Centrale	Postérieure
		20 mm²	20 mm²	20 mm²
Latence (millisec)	bleu	90	91	88
	vert	89	83	92
	rouge	71,5	70	84
Temps culmination	bleu	111	109	111
	vert	93	93	102
	rouge	86	82	92
Durée phase ascend.	bleu	18	18	23
	vert	8	11	9
	rouge	15	14	8,5
Temps rétino-cortical	bleu	51	49	47
	vert	51	47	53,5
	rouge	25	21	38

prononcée que si l'on utilise de petites surfaces d'illumination. Ce fait est dû vraisemblablement à un processus de sommation et de facilitation.

L'application de stimuli chromatiques ne provoque pas de variations significatives des divers paramètres en fonction de la longueur d'onde (latence, temps rétino-cortical, temps de culmination et durée de la phase initiale positive = pente) lorsque l'énergie du stimulus est égale pour chaque couleur (Tableau II).

S'il est vrai que la riposte corticale ne varie pas de façon significative en fonction de la longueur d'onde, il est toutefois intéressant de relever que certaine composantes de cette réponse apparaissent plus nettement dans certaines conditions topiques et chromatiques combinées. Ainsi l'utilisation de stimuli de longueurs d'ondes différentes a fait apparaître, dans certaines conditions, une petite déflexion négative secondaire au cours de la phase positive descendante du potentiel b. Cette composante est particulièrement nette dans la région centrale du centre cortical visuel

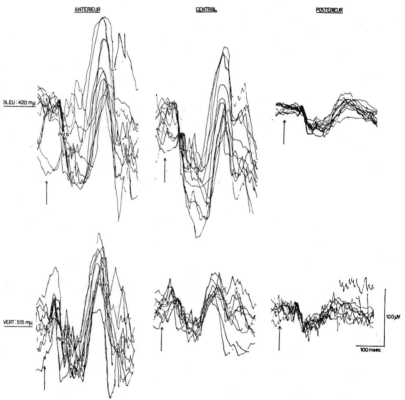

FIG. 2. Superposition de dix ripostes du centre visuel cortical (région antérieure centrale et postérieure), à des stimuli lumineux répétés chez le lapin. La superposition met en évidence la déflexion surface positive spécifique (potentiel b). Le stimulus de lumière bleue fait apparaître une petite déflexion négative secondaire à l'intérieur de la phase positive du potentiel b; cette composante est particulièrement nette dans la région centrale. A noter également une composante négative dans la région postérieure après le sommet de la riposte positive.

lorsqu'on utilise un stimulus bleu, ou dans la région centrale et postérieure lorsqu'on utilise un stimulus vert de grande surface d'illumination (Fig. 2).

Il n'est donc pas exclu que le facteur chromatique soit couplé dans une certaine mesure au facteur topique spatial du centre visuel cortical et peut-être même, dans une moindre mesure aussi, à la surface d'illumination.

PIÉRON

Quelqu'un a-t-il encore quelques observations à faire, quelques données à apporter à cette contribution qui nous montre évidemment la grande complexité des phénomènes, mais nous permet d'espérer qu'elle s'éclaircira?

Non.

Alors, nous allons lever la séance pour aujourd'hui et vous donner rendez-vous lundi matin, où se posera alors le 'Problème Biochimique', le problème des pigments qui peuvent entrer en jeu dans la vision chromatique.

BIOCHEMICAL PROBLEMS

VISUAL PIGMENTS OF COLOUR VISION

H. J. A. Dartnall

Professor Piéron, Ladies and Gentlemen:

When some months ago I received your kind invitation to take part in this programme, I accepted with alacrity, for Paris is always alluring and the symposium then lay ahead in a comfortably distant future. As the months became weeks, I began to realize with growing apprehension that I had committed myself to discuss the visual pigments of colour vision. Although I made a belated attempt to change my subject to one on which I would have felt happier to talk, it was to no avail. Your secretary was adamant, and I surrendered. And so I stand before you now to talk about the difficulties, the frustrations and the speculations associated with this subject.

THE ELUSIVENESS OF CONE PIGMENTS

It is a sobering thought that even today no one can say with complete certainty that he has ever had a cone pigment in a test tube. The most convincing candidate for this distinction is Wald, who discovered iodopsin, a photosensitive pigment with λ_{max} at 562 mµ, in the chicken retina (Wald, 1937; Bliss, 1945; Wald, Brown & Smith, 1955). The pigment was found in admixture with a rhodopsin, and, since the chicken retina contains both rods and cones, it seems reasonable to assign the rhodopsin to the rods, and the iodopsin to the cones. This conclusion is strengthened by the approximate agreement between the rhodopsin and iodopsin curves and Honigmann's data for the scotopic and photopic sensitivity respectively for the chicken (Wald, Brown & Smith, 1955, Fig. 22).

The agreement is about as good as can be expected, considering that Honigmann's (1921) data were obtained by behavioural experiments with living chickens, and hence include absorption by the pre-retinal media. In an attempt to carry the comparison further, Wald, Brown & Smith (1955) have considered the data of Granit (1942b) and of Donner (1943) on the closely similar retina of the pigeon. These data were obtained by inserting the micro-electrode into the retina after removal of the lens and cornea. Consequently, there is no complication due to pre-retinal absorption. Wald, Brown & Smith (1955, Fig. 23) showed that there is a close agreement between the scotopic curve and rhodopsin, but that the photopic curve is displaced from that of iodopsin by about 20 mμ. A reasonable explanation for this discrepancy is the filtering effect of the brightly coloured oil globules present in the cones of the chicken, the pigeon, and indeed of most birds. Wald, Brown & Smith (1955) observe that the photopic sensitivity of the chicken 'represents the resultant of the spectral sensitivities of at least three groups of cones concerned with colour vision'. The inference seems to be that colour vision in the chicken (and pigeon) is achieved by a single pigment, iodopsin, through the mediation of oil droplets acting as colour filters.

Wald, Brown & Smith (1955, Fig. 24) have also pointed out that there is a reasonable agreement between the iodopsin curve and the photopic sensitivities of the frog, the grass snake and the cat, as measured by Granit (1942a, 1943a, b). None of these species has oil droplets in its cones. Does this mean, therefore, that these animals have only one cone pigment and no colour vision? We do not know.

The other presumptive cone pigment is cyanopsin. This substance has not yet been detected in any retina, but was prepared by Wald, Brown & Smith (1953) in the following way. A digitonin extract of dark-adapted chicken retinae, i.e. a mixture of rhodopsin and iodopsin, was exposed to a deep red light. This bleached predominantly the iodopsin to a mixture of retinene$_1$ and cone opsin. A small amount of a certain isomer of retinene$_2$ was then added, and the mixture left in darkness for a few minutes. After this time, exposure of the mixture to deep red light resulted in bleaching maximal at about 620 mμ. According to Wald, Brown & Smith, this was due to the bleaching of a new substance, cyanopsin, which had been formed in solution by the interaction of the protein of iodopsin with retinene$_2$.

The claim of cyanopsin to be a cone pigment rests on two facts. In the first place it is related to iodopsin in possessing the same protein, but coupled to retinene$_2$ instead of retinene$_1$. In the second place, as shown by Wald, Brown & Smith (1953), its absorption spectrum is in approximate agreement with the photopic sensitivities of both the tortoise and the tench, as measured by Granit. Moreover, the tench retina is a vitamin A$_2$ retina, and, although we have no data on the tortoise, Wald, Brown & Smith (1953) state that the all-cone retinae of the related American turtles, *Pseudemys scripta* and *P. mobilensis*, contain vitamin A$_2$.

Are iodopsin and cyanopsin cone pigments? Do they have anything to do with colour vision? In an attempt to answer these questions, or at least to formulate them more precisely, let us consider the experiences of different workers who have attempted to extract photosensitive pigments from retinae which contain only cones. These experiences are quite simply stated. Wald, Brown & Smith (1953) were unable to extract light-sensitive pigments from the all-cone retinae of the two American turtles just mentioned; my colleague, Bridges, has so far failed to extract light-sensitive pigment from the all-cone retina of the grass snake, and I have so far failed to extract light-sensitive pigment from the all-cone retina of the grey squirrel. These are the facts so far as all-cone retinae are concerned. What of the mixed retinae, i.e. those containing both cones and rods?

Consider, for example, the retina of the frog. As previously mentioned, there is an approximate agreement between the photopic sensitivity curve for this animal and the curve for iodopsin. From this it would seem reasonable to infer that the frog's retina contains iodopsin. But no one has succeeded in extracting iodopsin from it. I have tried extracting retinae in red, yellow,

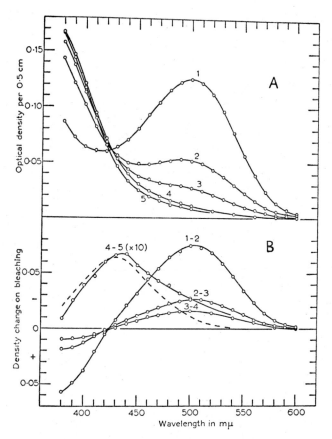

Fig. 1. Evidence for a blue-sensitive pigment in a retinal extract of *Rana esculenta*. A, curve 1, density spectrum of unexposed extract; A, curves 2, 3 and 4, density spectra of the extract after 2, 4 and 5 hours' exposure, respectively, to yellow light (570 mμ) which removes most of the pigment 502 (rhodopsin); A, curve 5, after exposure to white light. B, difference spectra constructed from the A-curves. The dashed curve (obtained by correcting 4-5 for the contribution of residual pigment 502) is the density spectrum of the blue-sensitive pigment (Dartnall. 1957).

green and violet light, but always with the same result. I have used as extracting agents the substances digitonin, saponin, cetyl trimethylammonium bromide and sodium desoxycholate, and other workers have used as many more different ones, but with the same result. I once even extracted the retinae of light-adapted frogs, on the supposition that photopic pigments might not be present in a dark-adapted eye. Whatever one does, it seems, one gets the same result — the photosensitive pigment known as rhodopsin, or visual purple.

If the retinal extract of the frog is subjected to careful analysis by the method of partial bleaching, it is possible to show the presence of a small amount of another photosensitive pigment besides the predominating visual purple (Dartnall, 1957). This is illustrated in Fig. 1. Curve 1 is the density spectrum of an unbleached extract; curve 2, the same after bleaching with light of 570 mμ wavelength; curves 3 and 4, after further successive exposures to the same yellow light; and finally, curve 5, after exposure to white light. The difference spectra between each curve and the next one are given in the lower part of the figure. They show that the changes from curve 1 to curve 4 are substantially the same in form and represent the bleaching of the main pigment, visual purple or rhodopsin. However, the final exposure to white light resulted in small density losses maximal not at 500 mμ but at 430-440 mμ. They are shown multiplied tenfold by the curve labelled '4-5'. The dashed curve was obtained by correcting '4-5' for the contribution of residual visual purple. Partial bleaching experiments which I have carried out in past years on frog extracts, using bleaching lights drawn from all parts of the visible spectrum, have so far failed to disclose any other pigments but these. It thus appears that extracts of frog retinae contain about 94 per cent of visual purple and 6 per cent of a pigment with maximum at 430 mμ. Denton & Wyllie (1955) have found that the frog's retina contains two kinds of rods; red rods amounting to 92 per cent of the total, and green rods forming the remaining 8 per cent. Denton and Wyllie found that the green rods absorbed strongly in the blue and moderately in the yellow and red, these characteristics accounting for their green colour. After bleaching they lost their absorption in the blue but retained it in the yellow and red. From this Denton and Wyllie inferred that the green rods would act as blue-sensitive receptors, and that the absorption in the yellow and red was due to the presence of a light-stable pigment in these rods.

It appears, then, that the 430 mμ pigment belongs to the green rods and the visual purple to the red rods. In other words, only rod pigments have been extracted from the frog's retina.

A similar situation exists *vis à vis* the tench retina. In 1952 I found that extracts of the tench retina contained predominantly the pigment 533. The absorption characteristics of this pigment are in good agreement with the scotopic sensitivity of the tench as measured by Granit (1941) (Dartnall, 1953). Partial bleaching experiments showed, however, that the extracts contained, in addition to pigment 533, another photosensitive pigment, with maximum at 467 mμ, to which, at present, we can assign no visual function. Is the pigment 467 a cone pigment? I doubt this. I think it may bear a similar relation to the main scotopic pigment (533), as does the green-rod pigment of the frog to visual purple. I have so far been unable to find cyanopsin in the tench retina even though some extracts have been made in blue-violet light.

Sometimes, the application of the method of partial bleaching leads to an *embarras de richesses*. A good example of this is the results I obtained with retinal extracts of the bleak, a common fresh-water fish (Dartnall, 1955). At first sight it seemed probable that the extracts contained only a single pigment, for the overall absorption characteristics were very similar to that

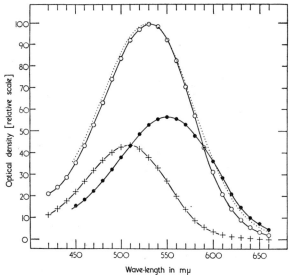

FIG. 2. Density spectra of the three photosensitive pigments of the bleak (*Alburnus lucidus*) retina in the proportions they were present in an extract. × — pigment 510; ○ — pigment 533; ● — pigment 550. The dotted curve is the sum of these three curves brought, for comparison, to the same maximum (100) as that for pigment 533 (Dartnall, 1955).

for pigment 533, well known for its presence in the retinae of other fish. On analysis by partial bleaching, however, it was found that although pigment 533 was the principal pigment, there were also present two other pigments with maxima at about 510 and 550 mμ respectively. The absorption data for these three pigments, scaled to the amounts in which they were present, are shown in Fig. 2. Their totalled absorption is shown by the dotted curve, which has been brought for comparison to the same scale as that for the pigment 533.

The fortuitous agreement between this totalled absorption curve and that for one of the components of the mixture points the moral that all retinal extracts should have their homogeneity tested even when the overall absorption appears to fall in line with expectations.

Since the bleak retina contains pigment 533, the same pigment as is present in tench, it seems reasonable to suppose that it mediates the scotopic sensitivity of the bleak as well as of the tench. What, then, of the 510 and 550 mμ pigments? Are these cone pigments? Again I doubt this. If the bleak and tench have similar scotopic sensitivities, should they not have similar photopic sensitivities also? Might one have hoped, then, to obtain the pigment cyanopsin from the bleak?

Ladies and gentlemen, I make no apology for laying so much stress on the failures of our search for cone pigments. I could, in fact, go on much longer; and I am sure that if we workers in this field were in the habit of publishing our disappointments as well as our successes, I should have enough material to last all day. It is almost as though the criterion of whether a pigment is a cone or rod pigment is whether one can extract it from the retina. If one can, then it is a rod pigment! If one can't, then it is a cone pigment! On this basis, the claim of the synthetic cyanopsin to be considered as a cone pigment is strengthened, for nobody so far has been able to extract it!

Are there 'Narrow-band' Pigments?

Let us, partly for guidance, and partly in desperation, now turn our attention to the results obtained by Granit in his micro-electrode survey of animal retinae (Granit, 1947).

Granit found that most animals yielded several sensitivity curves, according to the state of adaptation of their retinae, and the position of the exploring micro-electrode. Only one type of response, the scotopic dominator, could be elicited from the dark-adapted retinae, whatever the position of the electrode. Light-adapted retinae, on the other hand, produced two kinds of response: photopic dominators, and several modulators operative in different spectral regions.

Granit considers that the function of a dominator, which is a sensory mechanism having a broad spectral sensitivity curve, is to make a 'large range of wavelengths available for vision'. To the modulators, which have narrow sensitivity curves, he assigned the mediation of wavelength discrimination. Thus, both dark- and light-adapted retinae have their separate 'luminosity' mechanisms (the dominators), while light-adapted retinae possess, in addition, modulator mechanisms which may act as the peripheral mediators of colour vision.

Ought we perhaps to regard iodopsin and cyanopsin as cone pigments of a special kind? Namely, as *dominator* pigments? Their absorption characteristics certainly agree well with the sensitivity curves for the two main types of photopic dominators found by Granit. Have iodopsin and cyanopsin, therefore, the function of mediating *luminosity*? Have they nothing at all to do with *colour* vision?

Some years ago I suggested that the absorption spectra of the visual pigments which were then known had the same shape when plotted with frequency abscissae. This observation was based on similarities observed between the difference spectra of pigment 467 of the tench, pigment 502, the rhodopsin of the frog, pigment 533 of certain fish, and pigment 562, the iodopsin of the chicken (Dartnall, 1952, 1953). Since that time many new pigments have been extracted from retinae and revealed by the method of partial bleaching. They range from pigment 430, the green-rod pigment of the frog, through the golden coloured 'chrysopsins' of certain marine fish, as observed by Denton & Warren (1956, 1957) in England and Munz (1957, 1958) in America, through rhodopsins of fish, mammals and amphibia with λ_{max} around 500 mμ, to Crescitelli's group of gecko rhodopsins with λ_{max} from 518 to 524 mμ (Crescitelli, 1956). The yield in the 'A$_2$' series has not so far been so great, but includes 523 and 550 pigments. All these pigments, including the synthetic cyanopsin, have spectra which agree, though not exactly, then at least approximately, in shape with that for pigment 502 when all are plotted to a frequency scale. It is only their position in the spectrum which varies.

The spectral sensitivity curves for Granit's modulators, on the other hand, are much narrower than this common pattern.

Now, if the modulators reflect the absorption characteristics of a new type of 'narrow-band' visual pigment, and if, as Granit's Dominator-Modulator theory implies, they are the mediators of colour vision, then it would seem that none of the visual pigments so far considered has anything to do with colour vision. If this is so, then it is high time that I reached the subject-matter of my talk!

Let us, therefore, consider what evidence we have for the existence of visual pigments of modulator-like properties. At one time I though that there existed such a pigment in the retina of the clawed toad, *Xenopus laevis* (Dartnall, 1954). Although experiments showed that retinal extracts from this animal consisted principally of a pigment with λ_{max} at about 519 mμ, there were slight variations in the different spectra, obtained by partial bleaching, which suggested the presence of a small amount of a second pigment. These variations were such as to suggest that the additional pigment had λ_{max} at about 570 mμ, and possessed an extremely narrow absorption spectrum. This conclusion seemed to be supported by Denton and Pirenne's earlier measurements of the spectral sensitivity of this animal, which had a peak also at 560-570 mμ (Denton & Pirenne, 1951, 1954). In a later investigation suggested by Wald (1955), however, I was able to show that the *Xenopus* retina really

L

contained pigment 523 plus a small amount of pigment 502 in the approximate ratio of 92 to 8 respectively (Dartnall, 1956). In my earlier work these two pigments had not been clearly 'separated' and the minor variations which had been observed in the difference spectra had arisen, not because of the presence of a 570 mμ narrow-band pigment, but because of slight differences in the 523 and 502 compositions of the spectra. The '570 narrow-band pigment' was, in fact, merely a function of the difference between the absorption spectra of the 523 and 502 pigments. It seems possible that the modulator-like peak of sensitivity in the *Xenopus* curve may likewise be due to a mechanism depending on a *difference* in activity between two 'normal' pigments (Dartnall, 1956).

There is another claim still standing in the literature for a narrow-band pigment. This is the 535 'narrow-band' pigment which Arden found in the frog's retina. Arden's work (Arden, 1954a, b, c) differs from all that so far considered in that he used suspensions of visual cells. The outer segments of visual cells can be suspended in a 35-40 per cent sucrose solution. Advantage of this property is taken in a widely used procedure for obtaining outer limbs free from other retinal tissues (Saito, 1938). By diluting such a suspension, and then centrifuging, the outer limbs can be obtained in a compact mass which is then treated with extractants in the usual manner. My pupil Arden, however, had the idea of using the actual suspensions of visual cells as his working material. This offered a means of studying the visual pigments under conditions which more nearly approached their natural environment.

These suspensions scatter light very strongly, and in consequence have a milky appearance in which, however, can be seen the colour due to the visual pigment. Because of scattering, only a very small proportion of the incident light is transmitted, and consequently the suspensions have very high apparent optical densities when measured with respect to a clear control solution. Arden, however, measured the densities of his suspensions with reference to other samples of the same suspensions. When one of a pair was exposed to light, and the measurements repeated, only the changes due to the bleaching of the visual pigment were obtained.

By using these procedures, Arden at once discovered an interesting difference in properties between those suspensions which had been stored for a few days, and those which had been worked on immediately after preparation. When an aged suspension was bleached, a stable product of bleaching, which Arden identified as retinene, was formed. The difference spectrum for the bleaching had λ_{max} at 510-515 mμ. A fresh suspension also bleached to retinene, but in this case the retinene was unstable and rapidly faded to vitamin A, the λ_{max} of the overall change (visual pigment — vitamin A) being at 505-510 mμ.

The λ_{max} of the difference spectra of both aged and fresh suspensions are surprisingly high. For example, vitamin A does not absorb appreciably in the mid-visible spectrum, and therefore one might have expected that the difference spectrum for the conversion of rhodopsin to vitamin A (which occurs on bleaching a fresh suspension) would have λ_{max} the same as that for pure rhodopsin in solution, i.e. at 502 mμ. The fact that it was found to be at 505-510 mμ led Arden to consider whether suspension, might contain an additional pigment which, because it was destroyed by digitonin, had not been observed in extracts of rhodopsin.

Support for this hypothesis was obtained by Arden, who found minor variations in the difference spectra of his suspensions in apparent conformity with the wavelength of the bleaching light employed. He interpreted these differences as due to the presence (in suspensions) of a 535 mμ pigment having an extremely narrow absorption spectrum. He also correlated the absorption properties of this hypothetical pigment with one of the modulators detected by Granit in the retina of the light-adapted frog.

Some time ago I commenced an investigation of these suspensions with the object of gaining more information about the new 'narrow-band' pigment. I shall not deal on this occasion with the various experiments which were carried out using Arden's techniques, for they are being published elsewhere (Dartnall, 1959), but the conclusion reached was that the photosensitive contents of an unbleached suspension in no way differed from those of an unbleached extract. The unexpectedly high λ_{max} for the difference spectra of suspensions arises, not because they contain a narrow-band 535 pigment but because of the formation on bleaching of a stable orange product *in addition* to those photoproducts observed by Arden.

Behaviour of Visual Pigment in the Visual Cell

As already mentioned, most of the light incident upon a suspension of retinal outer limbs is scattered in all directions, and only a fraction is transmitted to the photocell. Since the proportion lost by scattering is progressively greater as the short-wave end of the spectrum is approached, the apparent density spectrum of a pigment suspension (when measured with respect to a control solution of the clear suspending medium) is distorted so that peaks of true absorption are shifted to shorter wavelengths.

In Fig. 3, curve A is the apparent density spectrum of a suspension of frog outer limbs measured in this way. The influence of scattering is shown by the overall height of the curve and by the density maximum at 484 mμ, well below that for frog rhodopsin.

If, now, a diffusing plate (e.g. of opal glass) is placed immediately behind the optical cell containing the suspension, a small but *representative* sample of the light transmitted and scattered forwards is collected and strikes the photocell (see Shibata, 1956; Latimer, 1957). Although less light strikes the photocell when the opal glass is in position (so that measurements have to be made with a more intense spectrum) the opal glass may, in a sense, be regarded as a gatherer of scattered light. This is because all (or practically all) of the light which the suspension scatters forwards (and which, for the most part, would otherwise miss the photocell altogether) is rescattered by the opal glass and adds its quota to that received by the photocell. The light transmitted by the

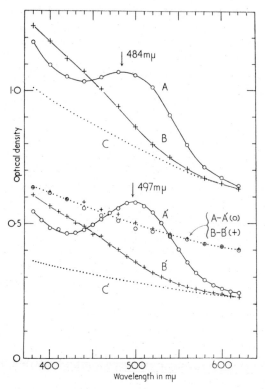

Fig. 3. Illustration of the 'opal-glass technique' for studying suspensions of retinal outer limbs. Curve A, the apparent density of an aged suspension when measured directly with respect to a 35 per cent sucrose solution control; curve A', the same but with an opal diffusing plate behind the suspension and control cells. After bleaching the suspension, the measurements were repeated with (curve B') and without (curve B) the opal diffuser in position. Curves C and C' (derived from the curve through A-A' and B-B' by scaling it to the 620 mμ values for the after-bleaching curves B and B') represent the effective density contributions to the measurements caused by lost scattered light (see text).

control solution, on the other hand, is still in a parallel beam and consequently the effect of the opal glass is similar to that of a neutral filter. In short, the attenuation parallel to the optic axis caused by the opal glass is less for light from the highly scattering suspension than it is for light from the non-scattering control solution.

The improved results with this technique are shown in Fig. 3, curve A′ by the shift of λ_{max} to 497 mμ and the lowering in overall height. Curves B and B′ represent the corresponding results obtained after the rhodopsin had been bleached by exposing the suspension to white light.

Of course, this technique does not take account of the light which is scattered backwards (i.e. reflected) by the suspension and consequently the curves A′ and B′ in Fig. 3 still include a considerable scattering component.

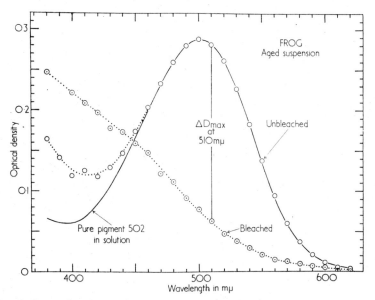

FIG. 4. Comparison between the light-absorbing properties of frog (*Rana temporaria*) rhodopsin *in situ* and in solution. ⊙ — the true density spectrum of an *aged* suspension calculated from the data of Fig. 3, viz. by subtracting the base line C′ from the data A′ (A minus C gives precisely similar results). ○ — the true density spectrum of the bleached suspension calculated in the same way (B′-C′ or B-C in Fig. 3). Continuous curve, the density spectrum of pure rhodopsin in solution.

Fortunately it seems legitimate to allow for the remaining scatter in the following way. The differences between the curves A and A′ for the un-bleached suspension are shown by the circles through which the dotted line in the middle of Fig. 3 is drawn. The differences between the curves B and B′ for the bleached suspension are shown by the crosses. They are the same within experimental error as those between curves A and A′. This result suggests (*a*) that the effect of scattering is the same in both unbleached and bleached suspensions and (*b*) that the contribution of scattering to the apparent density may be handled for purposes of calculation as though it were a true density curve. If, for the moment, we assume that the light scattered *backwards* by the suspension varies with wavelength in the same way as that scattered forwards, we may scale the scattering curve to the data in order to obtain the 'base-lines' C and C′ in Fig. 3. With these base-lines we may then calculate, if our arguments are justified, the true absorption of the pigment in suspension.

This has been done in Fig. 4. The empty circles give the true density of the total unbleached pigment in the suspension, calculated in this way from the data of Fig. 3. Similarly, the circles with centre points give the calculated true density of the total pigment after bleaching.

The full-line curve in Fig. 4 is an accepted density spectrum of 'pure' frog rhodopsin* in solution (e.g. see Dartnall, 1953). It is in close agreement with the suspension data from 620 mμ to 470 mμ. Moreover, the divergence below 470 mμ is probably due, not to real differences between the light-absorbing properties of *in situ* and extracted rhodopsin, but to the presence in the suspension of yellow 'impurities' such as lipid in the rods, and adventitious material of retinal origin. Digitonin extracts of rods which have been precipitated out of suspension (but not treated with petroleum ether to extract the lipid) commonly give density spectra in complete agreement with the present suspension data, even down to 400 mμ. The data in Fig. 3 for the bleached suspension should therefore be corrected for lipid, etc., in order to obtain the true densities of pigment and photoproduct, though for our present purpose this is not necessary.

Arden (1954a, b) considered that the final product on bleaching an aged suspension was retinene ($\lambda_{max} = 385$ mμ) but, as is clear from Fig. 4 (and as I mentioned earlier) another chromophore, absorbing in the blue, is present as well. This is more clearly brought out when the foregoing experiment is repeated with a fresh suspension for, according to Arden, the retinene formed on bleaching is then quickly reduced to the nearly colourless vitamin A. Such thermal decomposition in a bleached fresh suspension is shown by the dotted curves in Fig. 5. When the reaction is complete, however, the bleached suspension still contains a strongly absorbing chromophore with λ_{max} in the region 470-480 mμ. This chromophore is quite stable.

We may tentatively summarize the stages in the bleaching of a suspension of frog visual cells as follows. The *initial* product of bleaching absorbs strongly in the blue. About two-thirds of this initial photoproduct (like the 'transient orange' of solutions) is thermally unstable and rapidly decomposes, first to Arden's retinene and then, if the suspension is a fresh one, to vitamin

---

* It is possible that this curve, like all published curves for 'frog rhodopsin' includes the (small) contribution of the 430 mμ green-rod pigment. Since this pigment occurs in suspensions and extracts alike, however, it should not affect the present comparison.

A. The remaining one-third is either stable anyway or changes into the stable 470-480 mμ chromophore already described (Fig. 5). The presence of the latter in fully bleached suspensions is the cause of the unexpectedly high λ_{max} for the difference spectra (505 mμ for fresh, and 510 mμ for aged suspensions).

It is comforting to find that the absorption properties of a visual pigment (frog rhodopsin) are apparently identical *in situ* and in solution. It is less comforting that the products of bleaching are different in the two states.

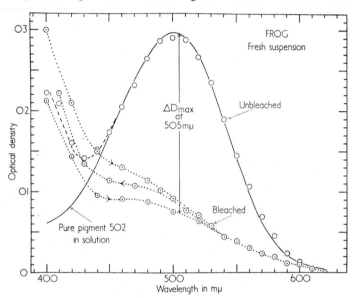

FIG. 5. As Fig. 4, but for a *fresh* suspension (*Rana temporaria*). The arrows in the bleached curves show the 'direction' of taking observations. The lowest of the bleached curves was measured about 2 hours after the bleaching and by then the thermal changes had ceased.

These preliminary experiments with the opal-glass technique suggest that we shall need to know much more about the *in situ* behaviour of visual pigments in various species before we can confidently interpret the difference spectra obtained in living animals. The results also suggest that it may be dangerous to assume (for example) that the true absorption of human rhodopsin in rods can be found by measuring the difference spectrum of a suspension of them (see Wald & Brown, 1958).

A Speculation

The visual pigments have been classified into the scotopsins and the photopsins, according as they are rod or cone pigments (Wald, 1953; Wald,

Brown & Smith, 1953). Now, the difference between rhodopsin ($\lambda_{max} = 500$ mμ) and iodopsin ($\lambda_{max} = 562$ mμ), on which this generalization is based, may seem large enough to justify such a qualitative distinction. But we should not forget what a wide variety of pigments might legitimately be described as 'rhodopsins'. They range from the 430 mμ pigment of the frog, through the 467 mμ tench pigment, and the 485-490 mμ 'chrysopsins' of deep-sea fish, up to the 'respectable' 502 mμ rhodopsins of amphibia, and beyond to the gecko rhodopsins of Crescitelli (1956), having λ_{max} to 524 mμ. This is a range of nearly 100 mμ.

It seems to me preferable to think of a visual pigment as potentially capable of being a rod pigment in one case and a cone pigment in another; possibly, even serving both functions in a single retina. In such an event, once the pigment had been obtained in solution, the clues to its different origins would be lost. In a suspension, however, the immediate environments of the pigment would be preserved. It might then be possible to ascertain its origin by observing the behaviour on bleaching (assuming this to be different in a cone and a rod). Thus the peculiar behaviour of rhodopsin in frog visual cells in bleaching to an initial photoproduct, two-thirds of which is unstable (decomposing first to retinene and then to vitamin A) and one-third of which is stable, *might* be due to the rhodopsin being present on the one hand in rods, and on the other hand in cones.

A fair question at this stage might well be: What is the point of having the same pigment, both in a rod and in a cone? Would they not have exactly the same spectral distribution of sensitivity?

I do not know the answer to this but I must confess that I am intrigued by the fact that the *difference* between the absorption spectra of rhodopsin and that of its stable orange photoproduct agrees in shape and spectral position with the 535 mμ modulator which Granit (1942a, 1947) found in the frog; it also agrees with the cone pigment found by Weale in the living squirrel (Weale, 1955), and, incidentally, is a pretty good fit also to one of the pigments found by Rushton in the living human fovea (Rushton, 1957). Could it be in all three cases, the frog, the squirrel and man, that these retinae possess some cones containing the pigment rhodopsin which bleaches only as far as an orange product?

And might other modulator mechanisms (which, on the Dominator-Modulator theory, mediate hue) similarly owe their 'narrow-bandedness' to interaction of some kind between 'normal' visual pigments and their 'abnormal' photoproducts? This is just a speculative thought which I leave with you. I had really spoken my last word at the beginning when I said 'even today no one can say with complete certainty that he has ever had a cone pigment in a test tube'.

REFERENCES

ARDEN, G. B. (1954a) *J. Physiol. London*, **123**, 377.
ARDEN, G. B. (1954b) *J. Physiol. London*, **123**, 386.
ARDEN, G. B. (1954c) *J. Physiol. London*, **123**, 396.
BLISS, A. F. (1946) *J. Gen. Physiol.*, **29**, 277.
CRESCITELLI, F. (1956) *J. Gen. Physiol.*, **40**, 217.
DARTNALL, H. J. A. (1952) *J. Physiol. London*, **116**, 257.
DARTNALL, H. J. A. (1953) *Brit. Med. Bull.*, **9**, 24.
DARTNALL, H. J. A. (1954) *J. Physiol. London*, **125**, 25.
DARTNALL, H. J. A. (1955) *J. Physiol. London*, **128**, 131.
DARTNALL, H. J. A. (1956) *J. Physiol. London*, **134**, 327.
DARTNALL, H. J. A. (1957) *The Visual Pigments*, London: New York.
DARTNALL, H. J. A. (1959) *J. Physiol. London*, **145**, 630.
DENTON, E. J. & PIRENNE, M. H. (1951) *J. Physiol. London*, **115**, 66P.
DENTON, E. J. & PIRENNE, M. H. (1954) *J. Physiol. London*, **125**, 181.
DENTON, E. J. & WARREN, F. J. (1956) *Nature*, **178**, 1059.
DENTON, E. J. & WARREN, F. J. (1957) *J. Mar. Biol. Assoc., U.K.*, **36**, 651.
DENTON, E. J. & WYLLIE, J. H. (1955) *J. Physiol. London*, **127**, 81.
DONNER, K. O. (1953) *J. Physiol. London*, **122**, 524.
GRANIT, R. (1941) *Acta Physiol. Scand.*, **2**, 334.
GRANIT, R. (1942a) *Acta Physiol. Scand.*, **3**, 137.
GRANIT, R. (1942b) *Acta Physiol. Scand.*, **4**, 118.
GRANIT, R. (1943a) *Acta Physiol. Scand.*, **5**, 108.
GRANIT, R. (1943b) *Acta Physiol. Scand.*, **5**, 219.
GRANIT, R. (1947) *Sensory Mechanisms of the Retina: with an Appendix on Electro-retino-graphy*, London.
HONIGMANN, H. (1921) *Arch. ges. Physiol.*, **189**, 1.
LATIMER, P. (1957) *Carnegie Inst. Wash. Year Book No. 56*, p. 259.
MUNZ, F. W. (1957) Ph.D. Thesis. *The Photosensitive Retinal Pigments of Marine and Euryhaline Teleost Fishes*, University of California, Los Angeles.
MUNZ, F. W. (1958) *J. Physiol. London*, **140**, 220.
RUSHTON, W. A. H. (1958) *Nat. Phys. Lab. Symposium* (No. 8), H.M. Stationery Office, London, p. 71.
SAITO, Z. (1938) *Tôhoku J. Exp. Med.*, **32**, 432.
SHIBATA, K. (1956) *Carnegie Inst. Wash. Year Book, No. 55*, p. 252.
WALD, G. (1937) *Nature*, **140**, 545.
WALD, G. (1953) *Federation Proc.*, **12**, 606.
WALD, G. (1955) *Nature*, **175**, 390.
WALD, G. & BROWN, P. K. (1958) *Science*, **127**, 222.
WALD, G., BROWN, P. K. & SMITH, P. H. (1953) *Science*, **118**, 505.
WALD, G., BROWN, P. K. & SMITH, P. H. (1955) *J. Gen. Physiol.*, **38**, 623.
WEALE, R. A. (1955) *J. Physiol. London*, **127**, 587.

DISCUSSION

PIÉRON

Nous remercions vivement le Dr. Dartnall de l'effort qu'il a fait — un peu ingrat — de nous montrer ce que l'on savait et ce que l'on ne savait pas encore en ce qui concerne la photo-chimie de la vision chromatique.

Il est certain qu'il y a là des problèmes extrêmement complexes.

Il nous apporte des données qui ouvrent des voies nouvelles avec ses méthodes propres.

Mais avant de discuter, je voudrais que le Prof. Rushton nous dise ce qu'il a obtenu de son côté, par sa méthode de réflexion de la fovéa chez l'homme.

RUSHTON

Monsieur le Président,

I'll say it in English because my French is so bad.

I should like very much the opportunity to speak a little bit about the cone pigments in the human. But, before we do this, would it not be better to give the word to those people who have some short comments to make on Dr. Dartnall's work before we forget the interesting things that he has said?

PIÉRON

Si vous voulez.

Nous allons d'abord aborder la discussion.

Je voudrais tout de suite souligner un point qui, je crois, est important.

Il me semble qu'à l'heure actuelle il est assez vain de vouloir trouver une correspondance exacte entre ce que l'on obtient par les électivités de réponse dans des cellules rétiniennes qui sont, comme celles étudiées par Granit, des cellules ganglionnaires ou, comme dans les expériences de Svaetichin, probablement des cellules horizontales, ou bipolaires. Car ce n'est pas d'une façon directe que des décompositions qui peuvent se produire dans les pigments photosensibles se traduisent du côté des réponses nerveuses. Il y a un intermédiaire extrêmement complexe.

Par conséquent, vouloir que les réponses de modulateurs de Granit ou que les réponses que Svaetichin observe correspondent à des processus pigmentaires précis, je crois que ceci est tout à fait vain.

Il faut dissocier les deux problèmes: le problème photo-chimique proprement dit, comme le disait le Dr. Dartnall, et les problèmes de l'électivité dans les réponses nerveuses qui, elles, sont conditionnées par des actions complexes.

Nous aurons l'occasion d'en reparler à propos des schémas.

Mais dès maintenant, je crois qu'il ne faut pas lier d'une façon étroite les données qui ont été fournies par l'expérimentation neurophysiologique rétinienne, et les données de l'exploration photochimique de la rétine. Voilà la remarque générale qui me paraît devoir être faite au préalable. Il y a donc intérêt à dissocier, il me semble, les deux points de vue. Je donne maintenant la parole à ceux qui ont des questions à poser ou des objections à présenter. J'espère qu'il y en aura.

BAUMGARDT

J'espère que l'on voudra bien m'excuser de prendre déjà la parole bien que je n'aie pas d'expérience propre en matière de photochimie. Pour ne pas m'obliger à interroger séparément les éminents spécialistes qui vous parleront ce matin, je poserai mes questions en bloc et dès maintenant.

Le Dr. Rushton a cité plusieurs expériences où les bâtonnets semblent être inhibés par les cônes lorsqu'on adapte la rétine à la lumière. Mais la fonction selon laquelle se produit cette inhibition est reliée au spectre de la rhodopsine.

Je rappelle également — c'est moi-même qui avait soulevé ce point avant-hier — que la mesure *in situ* de la densité de la rhodopsine dans la rétine humaine a fourni au Dr. Rushton des résultats qu'on ne peut interpréter autrement que par l'hypothèse que 95 à 100 pour cent de l'aire rétinienne testée réfléchissent la lumière comme si le pigment absorbant y était de la rhodopsine.

Il est difficile de ne pas en conclure que tous les récepteurs présents dans cette aire — cônes y compris — ont contenu de la rhodopsine pendant cette expérience. Ne devrait-on pas rapprocher cette conclusion de celles du Dr. Dartnall qui vient de nous exposer pourquoi les récepteurs de la vision diurne pourraient bien aussi contenir de la rhodopsine? Puis-je rappeler l'analyse très précise de Weale (1958) des travaux de divers auteurs, qui montre que la sensibilité individuelle d'un cône humain est pratiquement égale à celle d'un bâtonnet?

Or, d'après Rushton, les densités des pigments de cônes et de la rhodopsine mesurées à l'aide de sa méthode dans l'œil humain sont du même ordre de grandeur. Quand je dis 'même ordre de grandeur', cela signifie compris entre 0,1 et 0,3, c'est-à-dire variant dans un rapport inférieur ou égal à 1,6. D'autre part, jamais on n'a pu extraire un pigment de cônes, ainsi que le Dr. Dartnall vient de le rappeler.

J'avoue que le faisceau de ces arguments m'impression ne assez pour me faire poser la question suivante:

La rhodopsine ne produirait-elle pas par adaptation à la lumière des sous-produits qui, en s'accumulant dans les récepteurs au fur et à mesure que progresse cette adaptation, nous font mesurer des densités de pigments que nous interprétons comme pigments de cône?

Sans abandonner tant soit peu les belles recherches dont on nous a entretenus, ne devrait-on pas s'efforcer d'étudier surtout les liaisons éventuelles entre les pigments de cônes déjà trouvés et la rhodopsine?

PIÉRON

Je donne la parole au Dr. Rushton pour nous exposer son point de vue, puisqu'il a expérimenté avec sa méthode.

RUSHTON

Perhaps, before this, I might just answer Dr. Baumgardt.

The point that he has again raised and which I have now had time to study from my 1956 paper — which he kindly lent to me so that I could learn what it was about — is rather technical.

In that paper, I was dealing with the proportion of light reflected from the rod-occupied fraction of the retina. I had no evidence as to what light was reflected from the cones.

It was not clear then, and it is not clear to me now, whether any light is reflected back from the peripheral cones whose structure is such as to form rather an efficient light trap. And perhaps light going in there never comes back again.

In that part of the paper I was interested in making a lower estimate — an absolute minimum estimate — for the rhodopsin content of the rods. So I assumed that no light was being reflected from the cones and that gave the figure that Dr. Baumgardt mentions.

It is, of course, possible that light is reflected from the cones. In which case, there is more rhodopsin in the rods than my minimum figure. But let that be. It is rather technical to argue out in a meeting like this. We shall discuss this afterwards, if you are not satisfied.

Now, after Dr. Dartnall's communication ...

I am glad that I did not hear Dr. Dartnall's communication before starting on the experiments to measure the pigments in the human cones, because it would have been a very discouraging prospect. But I think the cones on the human fovea may be more favourable than any other cones in nature. They are so rod-like, they probably contain a good density of pigment and the geometry may be more favourable for reflection.

In any case, I want to put before you a few measurements that I think will convince you that we *can* measure the pigments in the cones. And I will speak of the protanopes.

But first, one word as to the method in principle. The principle is the method of the ophthalmoscope. The light is shone into the eye through a photometric wedge, and falls upon the fovea, and only upon the fovea. It is reflected from the back of the eye, is deflected in the ophthalmoscopic mirror and goes into a photo-electric cell. The light has been reflected from behind the retina and so it has been twice through the retina and thus has suffered absorption by the retinal pigments.

In principle, if we have a dark-adapted fovea and measure the light that comes back, it will be less than it might be because of absorption in the visual pigment. If we now bleach away the pigment, the light will come back more brightly. We may shift the photometric wedge to bring the photocell current to the value it had before; the change in density of the wedge must then be equal to the change in double-density of the pigment.

The technique of making measurements has been described in my communication to the Teddington Symposium (Rushton, 1958)* and it will suffice here to say that density measurements may be made in monochromatic light of various wavelengths while the fovea is being exposed to an independent bleaching light (or to darkness).

Fig. 1 shows the density of pigment on the fovea of a protanope, at first in the dark-adapted state, then the sudden fall due to a few seconds' exposure to a very bright light, and finally the return in the dark to the initial value after a period of about 8 minutes. The recovery curve is an exponential with time constant 130 seconds. This is what would be expected if we were measuring a visual pigment, but we can have a more sharp discrimination. If the light we use is not strong enough to bleach entirely, the amount bleached should be related to the intensity of the light in a way that is easy to calculate from photochemical theory.

The curve of Fig. 2 is the expected theoretical curve where abscissae give the log

* RUSHTON, W. A. H. (1958) *Nat. Phys. Lab. Symposium* (No. 8), H.M. Stationery Office, London, p. 71.

intensity of a 10-sec. bleaching flash, and ordinates show the fraction of the pigment left unbleached immediately at the end of that flash. The theoretical curve has one degree of freedom; it can slide horizontally across the figure, and, of course, I have taken a good position for it. From this position it is possible to calculate

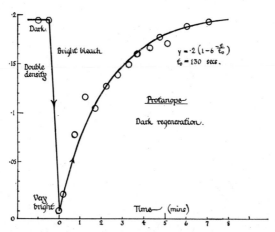

FIG. 1. Foveal pigment in *protanope*. Ordinates: density of pigment for double passage. The curve shows dark-adapted density, the rapid fall on bleaching with a very bright light, and the subsequent dark regeneration.

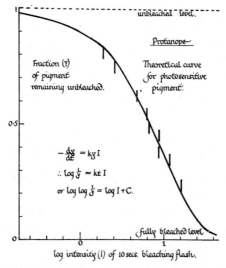

FIG. 2. Foveal pigment in *protanope*. Vertical lines, fraction of pigment left unbleached after 10 sec. flash of intensity I shown horizontally on log scale. Length of verticals, estimated error of single measurements. Theoretical curve may be slid horizontally to fit the observations.

the photosensitivity of the cone pigment and it comes out as about eight times the photosensitivity of rhodopsin in solution.

Though these results are good evidence that we are concerned with a photolabile pigment, the measurement is not sensitive to distinguish whether one pigment or a mixture of pigments is involved. The method which *is* sensitive is partial bleaching with lights of different wavelengths.

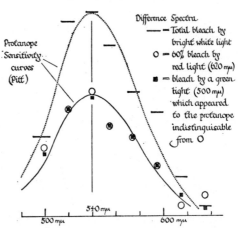

Difference Spectra
— — Total bleach by bright white light
O = 60% bleach by red light (620 mμ)
■ = bleach by a green light (500 mμ) which appeared to the protanope indistinguisable from O

Protanope Sensitivity curves (Pitt)

540 mμ
500 mμ   600 mμ

FIG. 3. Difference spectrum of fovea of *protanope*. O, bleaching by red light; ■, by green light which appeared the same to the protanope. Horizontal lines show wave bands of measuring light and the difference spectrum of full white bleach. The curves are Pitt's spectral sensitivity curves from the protanope.

Here (Fig. 3) is such an experiment where ordinates show the difference spectrum measured on the fovea of a protanope. The circles show the result of bleaching by a red light of 620 mμ; the squares show the result of bleaching with a blue-green light of 500 mμ. The protanope himself matched these two lights as being equally bright, which he could do well because for him they were also nearly of the same colour. The horizontal bars show the extent of total bleaching with bright white light and indicate by their length the wave bands employed in the measurement.

It is seen that a partial bleaching with red or with green light produces the same difference spectrum, not only the same in shape but the same in height, for these are the exact differences without scaling; this fact means that only one pigment is involved. For if there had been two, that which was more red sensitive would have been more bleached at wavelengths 620 mμ, and the other more bleached by wavelengths 500 mμ; but if only one pigment is involved, then the total bleach should have a difference spectrum the same as the partial bleach, but at a larger scale. This is seen also to be the case.

Now, when we have only a single pigment taking part in vision, we have the one condition where we can confidently predict about luminosity. It is what has been known so long in scotopic vision. If there is only rhodopsin subserving scotopic vision, then the rhodopsin absorption spectrum should be the scotopic luminosity spectrum. Similarly, if there is only one pigment on the fovea of the protanope, *its* absorption spectrum should correspond to the luminosity curve of the protanope. And the curve shown in Fig. 3 is, in fact, not just a curve drawn through the points, it is the luminosity curve of the protanope as determined by Pitt (1944).* So that this fits in quite satisfactorily. If this is the curve that Dr. Dartnall says might be a difference spectrum between rhodopsin and its yellow photo-product, it seems to me that that suggestion is absolutely impossible, because his idea requires the foveal sensitivity in the protanope to be maximal at 500 mμ where it is not, whereas my interpretation requires the maximum at 540 mμ where it is.

Now there is one thing more that you would like to know — what happens with the normal eye. We can show that the normal fovea contains a pigment which is absent on the protanope fovea by bleaching with a deep red light which has no effect upon the protanope. I have never found a protanope to show any change at all by bleaching his eye with this light using the maximum intensity that I have; but in the normal eye the change produced is shown in Fig. 4. This actually is my

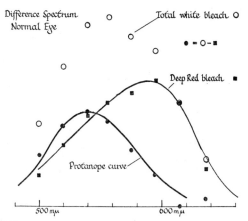

FIG. 4. *Normal* difference spectrum. ■, bleach with deep red light which is without effect upon protanope; ○, total bleach scaled to coincide with ■ at 615 mμ; ●, difference between ○ and ■ as shown. The protanope curve (Pitt) fits ●, but the other curve is drawn free.

own eye and it is seen that the curve labelled 'deep red bleach' is the difference spectrum of a pigment not present upon the fovea of the protanope. It is more red sensitive and has its maximum at about 590 mμ. The circles represent the difference spectrum when all the pigment is bleached away by a strong white light and they are here plotted so that they coincide with the deep red bleach at long wavelengths. The dots represent the difference between the total bleach and the deep red bleach and it is seen that this fits well the protanope curve. So we may conclude that the normal eye has two pigments, one of which is the protanope pigment and one pigment more sensitive to red.

It is not surprising that the protanope pigment is one of the two normal pigments in the red-green range because it is well known that the protanope accepts the normal colour matches and this is only readily explained if such pigments as the protanope possesses are normal pigments. Fig. 5 shows the same sort of thing.

I have repeated with a normal subject the experiment which is shown with the protanope in Fig. 3. There it was found that bleaching by red light or by blue-green

* PITT, F. H. G. (1944) *Proc. Roy. Soc. London* B, **132**, 101.

light produced the same density change provided that the red and green intensities were judged equal by the protanope. If, now, we bleach the normal subject with these two lights kept at the strengths which the protanope required, we should expect that the protanope pigment would be bleached the same by each light but that the red-sensitive pigment would be far more bleached by the red light. Consequently the difference of these two bleaches should represent a difference due to the red-

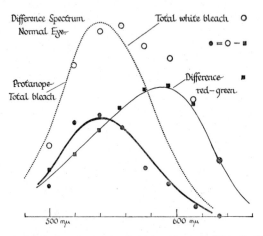

FIG. 5. *Normal* difference spectrum taken exactly as in Fig. 3. The difference between red and green bleach (with lights matched by protanope) which in Fig. 3 gave zero, here gives ■. The curve is the same as in Fig. 4, and total bleach, ○, and scaled difference, ●, are as in Fig. 4 with ● corresponding to the protanope pigment.

sensitive pigment alone. This difference is shown by the squares in Fig. 5 which lie closely upon the same curve as described the deep red bleach in Fig. 4. The difference between this and the total bleach is represented by dots which, as in Fig. 4, lie close to the curve for the protanope pigment. So it appears that the normal eye contains two pigments in the proportions shown in Figs. 4 and 5. The red-sensitive pigment may be called 'erythrolabe' (= red-taking), the green-sensitive pigment 'chlorolabe'. Fig. 5 also shows the total chlorolabe present in the protanope; it is seen to be about twice as much as chlorolabe in the normal.

Now we know from histology that the structure of the protanope retina is indistinguishable from normal; there is no degeneration of the cones but there is a total lack of erythrolabe and about twice as much chlorolabe as normal. This makes it very probable that the essential deficiency in a protanope is that he has only one class of cones sensitive in the red-green part of the spectrum. All his cones, in fact, have got filled with chlorolabe instead of perhaps half being filled with chlorolabe and half with — something else that we may talk about on another occasion.

WEALE

I make my comments with some trepidation very largely because Dr. Dartnall is my boss. I know that this is slightly unfair because you must have noticed what a very nice man he is. But I shake all the same. The idea that cones may contain visual purple is an intriguing one. One likes to slash about with Occam's razor. It simplifies the situation no end. But one point which I think has not been mentioned is this:

Admittedly no cone pigments have been found in solution, but no one has produced any evidence that cone outer limbs have been got into solution.

I have seen photographs of emulsions which quite clearly contained the rod outer limbs, but I have never seen a cone outer limb. Well, if the cone outer limbs aren't in solution, or in suspension, would you expect the cone pigments to be there?

The second point I'd like to raise, I raise with equal trepidation, but not because it deals with Dr. Dartnall, but because it deals with Dr. Rushton.

As I told you on Saturday, when I tried to indicate that there must be a neurological blockage between the cone monochromatic retina and the seat of perception respectively, I showed you Fig. 4* and would like to draw your attention to it again.

When you bleach the normal human fovea, you can obtain two humps. One of them is maximal at about 550 mμ and its spectral variation is similar to the first photosensitive reaction to be described for a pure cone retina, namely in that of the grey squirrel. The other maximum is at about 600 mμ.

But when bleaching is done not with white light as in Fig. 4, but with deep red light, the results shown in Fig. 5† are obtained. The half-black circles represent the change due to bleaching lasting 15 sec., the full circles that due to bleaching for 30 sec.

The question arises whether we are dealing with two pigments here; are the humps at 550 mμ really part of the red pigment, or have we been bleaching some of the 'squirrel' pigment as well?

Now the triangles represent the amounts obtained by Dr. Rushton. I have intentionally not used his curve. I have used his two individual sets of data.

You notice of course that he succeeded in bleaching a very much smaller amount (his scale being shown in the right-hand side). But I would remind you — and here I am quoting from memory and, as on other points, I'm open to correction — I think one of his sets was scaled. I don't know whether it was scaled up or down.

When we consider the sort of experimental errors which the data suffer from, the agreement isn't too bad. And, on the basis of this, one could still argue that this red bleach bleached only the pigment which, according to Dr. Rushton, is the red-sensitive one.

I repeated these red-bleaching experiments on subject B and used two filters. I used the 608, which is a pretty deep red, and a 206, which is a very deep red. And they were equated in brightness.

Unfortunately, I haven't got the slide, but I can tell you here and now that the type of bleach which I obtained was, within the experimental error, the same for the two types of filter. In other words, it made no difference, as regards this part of the spectrum at any rate, whether one used the deep red or the very deep red filter. Now, what did these results look like?

I would like to draw a composite diagram, if I may, because it will facilitate my interpretation.

We are going to have subject A on the left and subject B on the right. And we are going to have the white bleaches at the top and the red bleaches at the bottom.

Subject A, you may remember, had a difference spectrum shown at the top of Fig. 4.* And the red bleach produced results shown in Fig. 5:† the 30-sec. bleach had bleached out very nearly all the red-sensitive pigment. Subject B, on the other hand, had a quite different curve. His red bleach produced a maximum at about 550 mμ with a broad but lower hump at about 600 mμ.

* See page 128.   † See page 129.

M

In my opinion, these results indicate that the use of the deep red filter, as applied to the normal eye, fails to separate the two pigments. It bleaches to the advantage of the red-sensitive pigment but, at the same time, some of the green-sensitive 'squirrel' pigment is bleached as well.

The points of agreement between Dr. Rushton's and my data are numerous, but this is a crucial point, because he has told us that his deep red filter fails to bleach the pigment in the protanope.

The disagreement may not be as bad as you think, because it might be that the photosensitivy of the protanopic green-sensitive pigment may differ radically from that of the normal.

If my results are not due to an artefact then, I think, we are faced with two possibilities. Either the red-sensitive pigment difference spectrum really has the shape shown in Fig. 5† which, you may recall, agreed with Dr. Rushton's erythrolabe; or, this is merely a coincidence and the red-sensitive pigment has characteristics substantially different from those shown in Fig. 5.†

RUSHTON

I entirely agree with Dr. Weale upon the difficulty of being sure that a deep red light is only stimulating the red pigment and not anything else.

These results of Dr. Weale are the first that I have seen of his work and I don't know at all yet in detail anything about his equipment so I should like to have the opportunity to discuss these things with him. Such technical matters, however, are not suitable for a meeting like this.

All psychophysicists know that if we could say that a deep red light was stimulating a red pigment only and not stimulating the rest, our problems of linear transformations would at least become one degree easier. But it is certain that a deep red light, if bright enough, is going to stimulate both pigments.

I think it is possible that there is a difference between Dr. Weale's technique and mine. The thing that I enjoy about his approach is that it comes from the opposite end and may get over some of the difficulties that I can't get over. And, perhaps, I can get over some of the difficulties that he can't get over. He said he wants to concentrate on everything being done in as short a time as possible. I want to take a long time so that I can integrate out the noise in the system. Unfortunately both methods have their disadvantages.*

MRS. HURVICH

I should like to ask a question of Dr. Rushton that concerns the implications of the results of bleaching experiments for the presence or lack of colour discrimination in given types of individuals.

My question is whether or not there may be present in the retina more photopigments than the bleaching experiments actually indicate. The question arises because, when the protanope made the luminosity match between the short wave-

---

* KARPE, G. & TANSLEY, K. (1948) *J. Physiol. London*, **107**, 272; RUSHTON, W. A. H. (1958) *Nat. Phys. Lab. Symposium* (No. 8), H.M. Stationery Office, London; WEALE, R. A. (1953) *J. Physiol. London*, **121**, 548; (1950-1) *Rep. Inst. Ophthal.*, **3**, 18; (1953) *J. Physiol. London*, **122**, 322; (1955) *J. Physiol. London*, **127**, 587.
† See page 129.

length and the long wavelength spectral lights, I believe you said it was not a perfect match because the short wavelength looked slightly bluer.

In terms of the ordinary assumptions, that fact would imply the presence of more than one selective photopigment in order to provide a basis for that discrimination. And, therefore, I wonder whether or not the single photopigment actually measured for the protanope might not also be accompanied by some other photopigments that the bleaching technique did not reveal?

RUSHTON

That is easily answered.

It is absolutely certain that there was another pigment there and it was a deficiency in my presentation if I did not say that I was speaking only of the red-green range of the spectrum. Of course, there is also undoubtedly a blue-sensitive pigment — shall we call it cyanolabe? — that plays a part.

The reason why I can get rather a good approximation of the luminosity curve of the protanope to this single pigment is the well-known one. In the first place, blue contributes rather little to the luminosity curve, as has been known for a very long time. Secondly, my measurements never go into the blue. I can't get stable measurements with wavelengths shorter than about 500 mμ. I think because eye movements make the macular pigment dance about all the time.

That is why I like the possibility of Dr. Weale's quick measurements where there is not much time for the eye to move. He seems to be able to get better readings in this region.

In answer to Dr. Weale, one more point: Why do I not show luminosity curves? Why do I not show colour discrimination curves?

The reason is that, with the assumptions I have so far made, it is not possible to proceed either to luminosity curves or to colour discrimination curves. To do that it is necessary to make some additional assumptions.

There is enough to talk about without going that far. Nevertheless, I hope that we may have an opportunity of discussing what assumptions are likely when we have heard the contributions of Hurvich and Jameson to the theories of colour vision.

DARTNALL

I hardly know which of my two friends to reply to first, Dr. Weale or Dr. Rushton. They have both made points which are extremely difficult to answer.

Dr. Weale asks me 'What guarantee have you that you get cones out of the retina?' Well, of course, I haven't any guarantee at all. But I once ground up whole eyes with digitonin and I hardly think the cones could have fallen out under those conditions!

Dr. Rushton seems to have taken me up strongly on what I meant to be merely a light suggestion for consideration. The background of that suggestion was this. We now know quite a number of visual pigments and all of these, when plotted on a frequency scale, have pretty much the same shape. Now, in their elegant *in vivo* work, both Rushton and Weale aim to measure the absorption characteristics of visual pigments. Indeed, when working with rod retinae or with the cone-free part of the human retina, the results obtained do agree with the spectrum of rhodopsin. But the results for the all-cone retina of the squirrel (Weale) and the human fovea (Rushton) do not conform to this common pattern for the pigments we know in solution.

KRINSKY

Despite the lack of finding a cone pigment, as Dr. Dartnall has pointed out, I think that the fault does not really lie with the cone pigments, but with the biochemists who are trying to extract them.

One problem that we encountered in our laboratories in the daily preparation of iodopsin from chicken retinae is that the molecule of iodopsin is very unstable in comparison to rhodopsin. At times one gets a good preparation and other days one gets a bad preparation. The reason behind this we don't as yet know. Obviously it is a fault in our technique of preparing this molecule and I think that it's very possible that the same difficulty arises in trying to extract cone pigments from other retinae. The molecules could be much less stable than rhodopsin and, in the rather strenuous procedures that are used for isolating these compounds, they may be destroyed.

I would like to point out that although iodopsin has been found only in chicken retina, there is some unpublished work in Wald's laboratory, where Brown has found iodopsin with the same characteristics as the chicken iodopsin in the pigeon eye. This was only brought about due to the gift of a large number of pigeon eyes. It isn't present in very large concentration.

Well, one point — or two points rather — with respect to some of the comments that Dr. Dartnall made.

One of them dealt with the 430 pigment which, he believes, comes from the green rods of the frog retina.

I was just wondering if a sufficiently good difference spectrum has been obtained to determine where the negative limb of the difference spectrum comes out. Is it in the retinene$_1$ region?

The other question that I have deals with the presence of a stable intermediate in the bleaching of frog rod suspensions. And I was wondering what the effect of pH on this system was — inasmuch as one can vary the amount of yellow intermediates that are formed and their stability with pH? And if, indeed, one can accurately tell what the pH is within the isolated rods that one is dealing with? These may undergo, under certain circumstances, a large degree of glycolosis, producing a large amount of acid products, resulting in an extremely low pH.

DARTNALL

Regarding the 430 mμ pigment of the frog's retina, which I believe comes from the green-rods, Dr. Krinsky asks 'Is it a retinene$_1$ or a retinene$_2$ pigment?' I cannot answer that positively, but from the short-wave limb of the difference spectrum it would seem more likely to be a retinene$_1$ pigment.

As regard his other question about pH, I would remind him that the relevant experiments were done with suspensions, not solutions. As Arden's work of some 4 years ago showed, the bleaching of rhodopsin in visual cell suspensions is not influenced by the pH of the suspending medium. This insulation from outside influence, enjoyed by rhodopsin when in the visual cells, would seem to ensure that the results relate to the 'natural' pH inside the cell (if pH has any meaning in this connection).

WOLKEN

Stimulation by light of living organisms is mediated through photosensitive pigments within photoreceptors. The photoreceptors themselves are known as sensory cells, retinal cells, ocelli, ommatidia and rhabdomeres; in the vertebrate eyes they are the retinal rods and cones. This terminology was applied to indicate something of their phylogenetic as well as physical structure. Many of these photoreceptors can be isolated and some of their physical and chemical properties studied. Recent researches with newer techniques in electron microscopy have permitted us another order in the resolution, in approaching a molecular structure for a photoreceptor. This kind of morphological information, together with the data from other analytical methods, gives considerable hope for a molecular picture of a photoreceptor and its functioning. The structure and function of the photoreceptors have been discussed at a recent Conference on Photoreception of the New York Academy of Science (Wolken, 1958a), and a brief survey (particularly their structure) is here noted.

INVERTEBRATES

The invertebrates possess the greatest variety of photoreceptors and their structure and chemistry is least understood. Eyespots, sensory cells, compound ocelli, and compound eyes have arisen among annelids, molluscs and arthropods; in each instance with differences in organization. The invertebrate photoreceptors have been recently reviewed by the Milnes (1956), Wulff (1956) and de Vries (1956 and 1958).

Protozoa — The stigma or *eyespot* is a photoreceptor for light perception and has been described and studied in *Chlamydomonas, Volvox, Euglena* and other microorganisms. In the flagellate, *Euglena*, it is in the anterior part of the organism and appears in the light microscope as an orange-red area near the flagella. In the electron microscope, the eyespot area for *Euglena gracilis* is about 2μ in diameter and 3μ in length and consists of forty to fifty packed granules (rods) 100-300 mμ in diameter and embedded in a matrix (Wolken & Palade, 1953; Wolken, 1956a). Willmer (1955) suggests that structurally the most interesting feature in the embryological development of the rods and cones are the flagellum-like fibres that connect the outer and inner segments. Fauré-Fremiet and Rouillier (1957) have suggested from their studies of a chrysomonad *Chromulina* that the second internal flagellum associated with the stigma possesses a fine structure similar to that of the outer segments of the vertebrate retinal rods and cones. In *Euglena* the eyespot appears to be intimately linked to a flagellum at its base, and it is believed that the eyespot plus the flagellum act as a unit in phototactic response directing the organism towards light. From the action spectrum maximum absorption peak at 465 mμ, the rate of swimming, and the cross-sectional area of the eyespot, the threshold energy needed to produce the response was calculated to be $\sim 3 \times 10^{-11}$ ergs per eyespot per second.

Red variants of *Euglena* contain astaxanthin, an animal pigment, and some action spectra suggest that it may be the phototactic pigment. Other experiments indicate that β-carotene may also be present in the eyespot. It has been suggested that there may be at least two pigments in the eyespot. If, as suggested, all of the eyespot granules were covered with (a carotenoid) pigment as a monolayer or double layer, there would be $\sim 1 \times 10^6$ pigment molecules (Wolken, 1956, 1957). However, no one at present has isolated a photosensitive pigment from the eyespot of green *Euglena*.

Platyhelminths — In the flatworm, *Planaria*, the two eyes are sense organs consisting of pigment granules and sensory cells. The sensory cells' ends continue as nerves which enter the brain. The pigment shades the sensory cells from light in all directions but one, and so enables the animal to respond in a negative way to the direction of light. The sensory cells (retinal structures) are behind the dense pigment granules and as seen in the electron microscope appear as retinal rods. These retinal rods are about 5 μ in diameter with a more variable length of approximately 35 μ. The retinal rods' structure consists of dense plates or lamellae. There are eight to ten dense layers (or sixteen to twenty dense surfaces) per micron, the total thickness of these dense layers is ~400 Å, and each edge is about 100 Å in thickness. They resemble in structure the outer segments of the vertebrate retinal rods and cones. Little is known of the photosensitive pigment within these receptors. Pirenne & Marriot (1955) have studied the planarian aquatic flatworm, *Dendrocoelum lacteum* and found that its effectiveness or action spectrum showed two main absorption bands, one at 510 mμ designated as probably a rhodopsin and another in the ultra-violet at 370 mμ. They have calculated from their experiments that the absolute sensitivity or energy is $\sim 15 \times 10^{-9}$ ergs per eye per second.

Arthropods — The compound eye of the insect consists of ommatidia, each ommatidium made up of retinula cells; the differentiated part of the retinula cell is the rhabdomere. The rhabdomeres taken together form a rhabdome. Since the earliest investigations, the rhabdome has been considered the 'light trapping' area where the visual process is initiated. For example, the eye of the *Drosophila* is composed of approximately 700 ommatidia with each ommatidium consisting of seven retinula cells radially arranged forming a cylinder. Each ommatidium is 17 μ in diameter and varies from 70-125 μ in length. The electron-microscope studies indicate that the rhabdomeres are structurally packed rods or tubes, the thickness of the dense edges averaging 120 Å and the interspaces varying from 200-400 Å (Wolken *et al.*, 1957). Fernández-Morán (1956), Goldsmith (1957) and Miller (1957) have shown in insects and a crustacean (house fly, dragon fly, honey bee, spider and *Limulus*) that the rhabdomeres are in a definite arrangement within the ommatidium. The rhabdomeres are packed rod structures whose dimensions are of the same order of magnitude as that of the *Drosophila* rhabdomeres. It has been suggested that the arrangement of the rhabdomeres within the ommatidium and the *fine structure* within the rhabdomeres may be related to the analysis of polarized light (Fernández-Morán, 1956; Goldsmith & Philpott, 1957; Wolken *et al.*, 1957).

In three eye-colour mutants of *Drosophila melanogaster* it was found that the action spectrum is indicative of a pigment absorbing at 508 mμ, but this pigment has not as yet been isolated from the *Drosophila* rhabdomeres (Wolken, 1957; Wolken *et al.*, 1957b; Mellon & Contis, 1957). Wald & Hubbard (1957) have isolated a pigment from the rhabdomeres of the eyes of a crustacean, the lobster, and have designated this pigment as visual lobster rhodopsin since it has the pros-thetic group retinene$_1$. Recently a photosensitive pigment has been isolated from honey-bee and house-fly eyes. In the honey bee, Goldsmith (1958) found that he could extract a photosensitive pigment using neutral phosphate buffer. After partial purification by precipitation with ammonium sulphate and ethanol a difference spectrum showed a maximum absorption of 440 mμ. Similarly, with the house fly a photosensitive pigment was extracted in phosphate buffer and the extract was further purified by chromatographic techniques. This extract had an absorption maximum at 437 mμ, and the pigment appears to be a retinene$_1$-complex (Bowness & Wolken, 1958), or an ommochrome.

Molluscs — The cephalopod molluscs *Octopus* and *Sepia* have single lens eyes, resembling the vertebrate eye in its physical organization, however, the retina is not inverted as in the vertebrate eye and the photoreceptors are directly exposed to the incident light. The visual pigment is a rhodopsin.* Electron microscopy of the retina shows that the arrangement of the retinal cells is very much like the arthropod ommatidia with retinula cells and rhabdomeres. There are four rhabdomeres that make up each rhabdome. There is a striking similarity in its *fine structure* to that of the insect (Wolken, Capenos & Turano, 1957; Wolken, Mellon & Contis, 1957; Wolken, 1958b) and the *Limulus* (Miller, 1957). In both the *Octopus* and *Sepia* each retinal rod (rhabdomere) averages ~1 μ in diameter. The *fine structure* is that of densely packed rods or tubes (there are about twenty rods per micron) which are ~200 Å in thickness.

The area of the retina is ~1 cm², which would contain about 2000 rhabdomes comprising 8000 rhabdomeres (four rhabdomeres per rhabdome). This number of rhabdomeres is similar to the number in the insect, *Drosophila*, and from the surface area available, ~1 × 10⁹ pigment molecules could be packed as a monolayer on the surface.

VERTEBRATES

Retinal Rods and Cones — The pigment molecules are contained only in the outer segment of the retinal rods and cones of the eye. Previous microscopic studies by Schmidt (1934) had suggested that the retinal rod is chemically composed of alternate layers of lipid and protein. All the vertebrates' retinal rods that have been recently studied by electron microscopy (the retinal rods of frog, chicken, guinea-pig, rabbit, perch, whale, cattle and monkey) appear as double-membraned structures resembling piled-up plates, or lamellae, 100-200 Å in thickness with less dense interspaces 200-500 Å (de Vries, 1956; Wolken, 1957; Wolken & Schwertz, 1953; Sjöstrand, 1949, 1953; de Robertis, 1956). In some photoreceptors, techniques in low-angle X-ray diffraction have corroborated the electron microscopy showing a repeating unit of ~250 Å (Finean *et al.*, 1953). Less information is known about the cone structure but it too is a lamellar structure of dense and less dense layers ~200 Å.

SUMMARY

The photoreceptor geometry (length, diameter, thickness and number of dense layers) as determined from the electron micrographs is tabulated (Table I) and can be used in calculating the cross-sectional area of the pigment molecule or the pigment complex providing the pigment concentration is known (or experimentally determined) per photoreceptor. For all the plant and animal photoreceptors studied there are reported to be 1×10^6 to 1×10^9 pigment molecules per receptor unit. For example, for cattle and frog rhodopsin, the cross-sectional area has been calculated to be ~2500 Å² and the diameter of the molecule to be ~50 Å. This seems to be about the right order of magnitude for the rhodopsin molecule (Wald, 1956). The molecular weight for frog and cattle rhodopsin has been calculated to be 60,000 and 40,000 respectively (Wolken, 1957, 1956b).

We can distinguish now from our microscopic studies three kinds of structurally built photoreceptors: granules either isolated or more generally packed as a mosaic, a lamellar packing of discs or plates that are double membraned, and tightly packed rods or tubes. Although there are many differences in the macrostructure of the photoreceptors, there is a great similarity in the ultramicrostructure. The variety of the photoreceptor apparatus and their schematic structural relationship is represented in Fig. 1. The exact orientation of the pigment molecules or the other

* BROWN, P. K. & BROWN, P. S. (1958) *Nature*, **182**, 1288.

molecules within these structures has not yet been accurately determined. Just where the pigment, lipid, lipoprotein and protein are located within the photoreceptor is assumed from the chemical reactions of the fixing agents and various stains with the biological material. There is some experimental evidence to indicate that the pigment molecules most probably reside in the (osmium fixed) dense layer of the photoreceptor (Thomas, 1955; Goedheer, 1955). If so, there are just enough pigment molecules in each of the (dense) interfaces to cover all of the available surfaces (Wolken & Palade, 1953; Wolken & Schwertz, 1953; Wolken, 1956). The dense layer in the retinal rods is a double layer containing lipids and lipoprotein. The pigment molecules are most probably complexed with a protein or lipoprotein macromolecule and are oriented within these dense layers. This arrangement is shown in the schematic model for the retinal rod in Fig. 2 in the text.

TABLE I

*Animal Photoreceptors**

(Average measurements from electron micrographs)

Animal	Photoreceptor	Diameter (μ)	Length (μ)	Total thickness[†] of plate or rod (Å)	Number stria/μ	Kind of packing
INVERTEBRATES Protozoa *Euglena*	eyespot	2.0	3	—	—	rods or tubes
Platyhelminth *Planaria*	sensory cell	5.0	35	140	20	plates or discs
Arthropod *Drosophila*	rhabdomere	1.2	~60	120	23	rods or tubes
Mollusc *Octopus* *Sepia*	retinal rod — rhabdomere ,,	1.0 ,,	~65 ,,	200 ,,	20 ,,	rods or tubes ,,
VERTEBRATES Perch	retinal rod — outer segment	1.5	40	150	60	plates or discs
Frog	,,	6.0	55	150	45	,,
Chicken	,,	3.5	35	250	40	,,
Whale	,,	1.4	—	200	45	,,
Cow	,,	1.0	10	220	40	,,
Monkey	,,	1.3	22	250	50	,,
Man	,,	1.0	28	250	50	,,

* Compiled from experimental data (1) WOLKEN, J. J. (1958) *Ann. N.Y. Acad. Sci.* **74**, 164.
† Dense edges ~50-100 Å.

The ordered structure as observed in the electron microscope and studies of its photoconductive properties is suggestive that the photoreceptors have similarities to a semi-conductor.

REFERENCES

BOWNESS, J. M. & WOLKEN, J. J. (1958) *134th Meeting of the American Chemical Society, Abstracts of Papers*, 29c.
BOWNESS, J. M. & WOLKEN, J. J. (1959) *J. Gen. Physiol.*, **42**, 779.
DE ROBERTIS, E. (1956) *J. Biophysic. and Biochem. Cytol.*, **2**, 319.
DE VRIES, HL. (1956) *Progr. Biophys. and Biophys. Chem.*, **6**, 208.
DE VRIES, HL. (1958) *Ann. N.Y. Acad. Sci.*, **74**, 196.
FAURÉ-FREMIET, E. & ROUILLIER, C. (1957) *C. R. Acad. Sci., Paris*, **244**, 2655.
FERNÁNDEZ-MORÁN, H. (1956) *Nature*, **177**, 742.
FINEAN, J. B., SJÖSTRAND, F. S. & STEINMAN, E. (1953) *Exp. Cell. Res.*, **5**, 557.
GOEDHEER, J. C. Thesis; State University, Utrecht, Holland.
GOEDHEER, J. C. (1955) *Biochim. et Biophys. Acta*, **2**, 254.
GOLDSMITH, T. H. (1958) *Proc. Nat. Acad. Sci. (U.S.)*, **44**, 123.
GOLDSMITH, T. H. & PHILPOTT, D. E. (1957) *J. Biophysic. & Biochem. Cytol.*, **3**, 429.
GOLDSMITH, T. H. (1958) *Ann. N.Y. Acad. Sci.*, **74**, 223.
MILLER, W. H. (1957) *J. Biophysic. and Biochem. Cytol.*, **3**, 421.
MILNE, L. J. & MILNE, M. J. (1956) *Radiation Biology III*, New York, p. 621.
PIRENNE, M. & MARRIOT, F. H. C. (1955) *Nature*, **175**, 642.
SCHMIDT, W. J. (1934) *Z. Zellforsch u. mikroskop. Anat.*, **22**, 189.
SJÖSTRAND, F. S. (1949) *J. Cellular. Comp. Physiol.*, **33**, 383.
SJÖSTRAND, F. S. (1953) *J. Cellular. Comp. Physiol.*, **42**, 15.
THOMAS, J. B. (1955) *Progr. in Biophys. and Biophys. Chem.*, **5**, 109.
WALD, G. (1956) *Enzymes Units of Biological Structure and Function*, New York, p. 355.
WALD, G. & HUBBARD, R. (1957) *Nature*, **180**, 278.
WILLMER, E. N. (1955) *Ann. Rev. Physiol.*, **17**, 339.
WOLKEN, J. J. (1956a) *J. Protozool.*, 3, 211.
WOLKEN, J. J. (1956b) *J. Cellular Comp. Physiol.*, **48**, 340.
WOLKEN, J. J. (1957) *Trans. N.Y. Acad. Sci.*, **19**, 315.
WOLKEN, J. J. (1958a) *Ann. N.Y. Acad. Sci.* **74**, 164.
WOLKEN, J. J. (1958b) *J. Biophysic. and Biochem. Cytol.* **4**, 835.
WOLKEN, J. J., CAPENOS, J. & TURANO, A. M. (1957a) *J. Biophysic. and Biochem. Cytol.*, **3**, 441.
WOLKEN, J. J., MELLON, A. D. & CONTIS, G. (1957b) *J. Exp. Zool.*, **134**, 383.
WOLKEN, J. J. & PALADE, G. E. (1953) *Ann. N.Y. Acad. Sci.*, **56**, 873.
WOLKEN, J. J. & SCHWERTZ, F. A. (1953) *J. Gen. Physiol.*, **37**, 111.
WULFF, V. J. (1956) *Physiol. Rev.*, **36**, 145.

AUERBACH

As a contribution to this discussion I would like to present some further aspects of our psychophysical studies in human beings.*† Dark adaptation was measured during its photopic phase in trichromats, protanopes and a tritanope. The resulting photopic sensitivity curves show certain reproducible maxima which allow conclusions concerning the sensitivity of individual photopic mechanisms and their interactions.

As to the method employed, each experiment began with a 5-minute preadaptation to a bright red light (Wratten 26) of the retinal area tested (7° off fovea). After its discontinuation dark-adaptation curves were determined for various wavelengths

* AUERBACH, E. & WALD, G. (1955) *Am. J. Ophthalmol.*, **39**, Part II, 24.
† AUERBACH, E. & WALD, G. (1954) *Science*, **120**, 401.

by ascertaining the thresholds to short monochromatic stimuli during the photopic phase. Monochromatic light was obtained from a 100 Watt zirconium arc lamp focused on the entrance slit of a grating monochromator. Two neutral wedges in front of the exit slit regulated the brightness of the outcoming monochromatic test light before it reached the eye of the subject. Individual readings of each dark-adaptation curve were repeated three to four times per minute.

By taking measurements of dark adaptation throughout the visible spectrum, mostly in steps of 10 mμ, families of photopic dark-adaptation curves were obtained. From them sensitivity curves were read off.

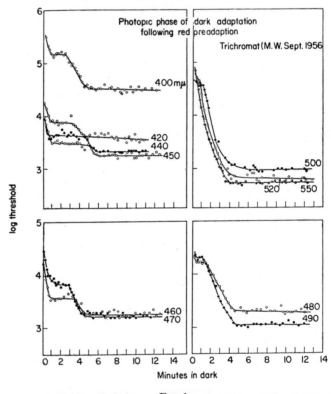

Fig. 1

Fig. 1 and Fig. 2 show such curves from experiments in trichromats, the former for measurements from 400 to 550 mμ, the latter from 620 to 700 mμ. In the spectral ranges from 400 to 500 mμ and 620 to 700 mμ dark-adaptation curves are obtained which possess two photopic plateaux. However, under the conditions of these experiments a characteristic difference in the appearance of the first plateau in each series is notable. Those of the test series from 400 to 500 mμ show very little or almost no influence of the preadapting red light; they attain their thresholds within 15 to 45 seconds in the dark. The photopic mechanism responsible for this plateau is, therefore, 'spared' by the adapting light. It appears in isolation for a period of 1 to 5 minutes, this period depending on the wavelength tested. It is longest (5

minutes) for stimuli of 450 mμ where implicitly the delay in the mechanism responsible for the second plateau is greatest. This delay is shortest for stimuli of 400 mμ
and of 500 mμ where at the same time the increment between the two plateaux
is largest. Simultaneously with the increase of this isolation period the threshold
falls until it attains a minimum to stimuli of 450 mμ, the same wavelength at which

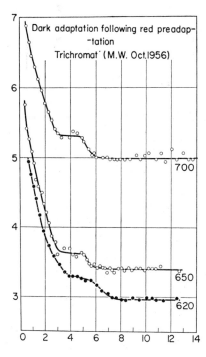

FIG. 2

the isolation period is maximal. Thus the mechanism appears to be most sensitive
to stimuli of 450 mμ. This will be shown more clearly in Fig. 3.

Each of the two plateaux represents, therefore, the response of a different photopic
mechanism. The mechanism which is isolated by using a red preadaptation and
which is represented by the 'spared' first plateau of dark-adaptation curves is the
response of a short-wave mechanism. The second plateau, not being 'spared' by
the red preadaptation, i.e. needing a rather long recovery period, is the response of
a medium-wave mechanism. Its sensitivity function for this reason must partly
overlap with that of a long-wave mechanism. It recovers slowly in the dark until
its threshold falls below that of the short-wave mechanism and thus becomes
measurable.

However, no two plateaux are measurable for stimuli above 500 mμ and below
620 mμ (Fig. 1). From this fact it may be concluded that in this spectral region the
overlap of the individual sensitivities of both medium- and long-wave mechanisms
is so wide that they cannot be separated by the method used.

There is a marked difference in appearance of the first plateau in dark-adaptation curves between 620 and 700 mμ as compared to the series of tests in the short-wave range. Here the recovery period lasts about 3 minutes following removal of the preadapting light until the threshold of the first plateau is reached (Fig. 2). On the assumption of a spectral overlap of the sensitivity functions of photopic medium- and long-wave mechanisms the slow recovery of the first plateau in this spectral range indicates that one is dealing here with a medium-wave mechanism and that

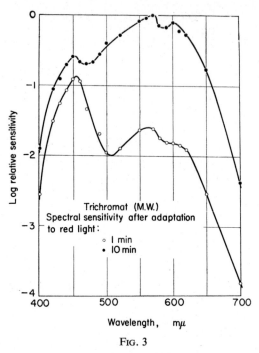

FIG. 3

its sensitivity function overlaps to a great extent that of a long-wave mechanism. It is thus very much influenced by the red preadaptation but naturally not as much as the mechanism responsible for the second plateau; the latter must, therefore, be ascribed to a mechanism active in the long-wave range.

It follows that the preadapting red light influences simultaneously at least two closely overlapping mechanisms in this spectral range, the influence being greater on the mechanism represented by the second plateau than it is on that represented by the first plateau. This explains why two photopic plateaux are obtained. The appearance of the two plateaux is different in the short-wave range. Here the mechanism represented by the first plateau is isolated because it is not influenced by the preadaptation. However, the overlap of the mechanisms in the long-wave range is not as wide as in the range above 500 mμ and below 620 mμ where no separation as indicated by the two plateaux could be achieved by the method used.

To demonstrate the different mechanisms clearly, it is necessary to plot two photopic sensitivity curves, one after 1 minute, the other after 10 minutes in the dark. The choice of the 1-minute curve is evident; it should cover the complete spectral range of the isolated short-wave mechanism. The 10-minute sensitivity curve represents the final photopic threshold, and consequently both a medium-wave and a long-wave mechanism (Fig. 3).

More can be observed from this pair of sensitivity curves. The short-wave mechanism is represented by an isolated peak in the 1-minute curve, showing its maximum of sensitivity at 455 mμ. (This result is an amplification of a similar

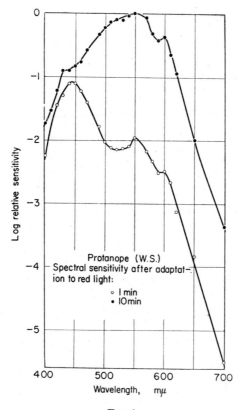

Protanope (W.S.)
Spectral sensitivity after adaptation to red light:

∘ l min
• l0min

Wavelength, mμ

Fig. 4

curve published several years ago (Auerbach & Wald, 1955).) In addition this curve shows very definitely the influence of the adapting red light. Although both the maximum of a medium-wave mechanism at 570 mμ and a shoulder at around 600 mμ are clearly present, they are much less sensitive than the 'spared' peak at 455 mμ. This is not the case in the 10-minute curve. Here the peaks of a medium-wave mechanism at 570 mμ and of a long-wave mechanism at 600 mμ are clearly demonstrable.

However, two experimental facts cast doubts as to whether the spectral position of the photopic mechanisms has been truly represented by the maxima in the sensitivity curve of trichromats. Trichromatic subjects see a short-wave stimulus as violet at the threshold of the first plateau. Secondly, the mechanism at 455 mμ is not extinguished after 10 minutes in the dark where one measures at the threshold of the second plateau. This appears to imply that the overlap of the different sensitivity functions in such subjects is so wide that the red-responsive mechanism cannot be extinguished completely by the method used. By this token some influence of this mechanism, i.e. some extension of this mechanism to the short-wave range appears possible, thus preventing a complete isolation of the short-wave mechanism in trichromats and exerting simultaneously an influence on the medium-wave mechanism.

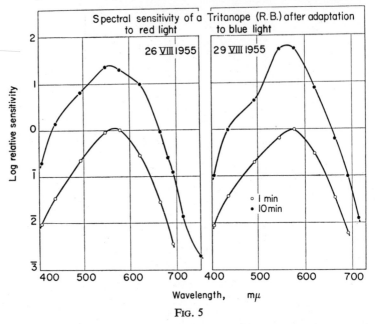

Fig. 5

It was, therefore, desirable to repeat these experiments with protanopes, the only category of colour-defectives who are 'colour-blind'. The sensitivity curves achieved under the same conditions as with trichromats show in protanopes a shift of both the short-wave and the medium-wave maxima to 445 mμ and to 550 mμ (Fig. 4). Hence, because of the red-responsive mechanism being absent in protanopes,* it appears that the true spectral location of maximum sensitivity of the short-wave mechanism is at 445 mμ, and of the medium-wave mechanism at 550 mμ.

In this context an experiment performed with a tritanope may be briefly mentioned (Fig. 5). The sensitivity curve after preadaptation to red light does not show any indication of a short-wave mechanism, thus showing that this function is not present. The long-wave maximum does not appear in this curve because not enough spectral points have been measured.†

PIÉRON

Les données qu'on obtient par les méthodes psychophysiques, sont évidemment plus simples et elles donnent des indications sur ce qu'on désirerait trouver au point

* RUSHTON, W. A. H. (1955) *J. Physiol. London,* **129,** 41P.

† This work sponsored by the National Council to Combat Blindness Inc., New York, has been done in Dr. Wald's laboratory at Harvard University.

de vue des bases photochimiques sans que la coïncidence soit obtenue d'une façon tout à fait satisfaisante.

Il y a là des possibilités, simplement, de problèmes qui se posent, pour obtenir une certaine correspondance entre ces deux ensembles de données.

Mais la question est évidemment très complexe, d'autant que — je le rappelle — il n'est pas certain que nous puissions, avec les courbes de visibilité spectrale, obtenir des résultats qui renseignent complètement sur les bases de la vision chromatique.

Et même, il me semble qu'il y a simultanéité d'une excitation lumineuse réellement indépendante des systèmes chromatiques, même dans la vision photopique.

S'il y a seulement une certaine participation à la courbe de luminosité spectrale fournie par la mise en jeu des systèmes de réception chromatique, la situation est trop complexe, pour qu'on se fonde sur une courbe de visibilité spectrale seulement.

Il y a là une possibilité, pour des mécanismes différents, fondés sur des 'patterns' nerveux différents, d'intervenir.

Il me semble que la vision chromatique ne peut s'expliquer complètement que par l'intervention des mécanismes nerveux intermédiaires entre la réception photo-chimique et la réception corticale, mécanismes nerveux qui se rencontrent déjà au niveau de la rétine.

Dès lors, quand on s'adresse simplement aux courbes de lucivité, de visibilité spectrale, qui peuvent correspondre à un système relativement simple de trans-mission nerveuse, vous ne pouvez pas trouver une image satisfaisante des aspects qui interviennent dans la vision chromatique proprement dite, lorsque les inter-médiaires rétiniens nerveux sont intervenus.

C'est là le point tout à fait remarquable de la différence de valence dans les réceptions entre l'efficacité lumineuse et l'efficacité chromatique. Il est tout de même remarquable qu'une lumière bleue qui contribue si peu à la visibilité générale puisse, au point de vue chromatique, l'emporter sur une longueur d'onde complé-mentaire, qui possède, au contraire, une efficience lumineuse extrêmement con-sidérable.

Il y a là, sous l'influence de la lumière bleue, l'éveil d'un mécanisme qui est particulièrement efficient au point de vue chromatique, mais qui n'a, au point de vue lumineux, qu'une efficacité à peu près négligeable.

De telle sorte que, encore une fois, il y a là une sorte de divorce entre les méca-nismes de la vision chromatique et le mécanisme, qui doit être beaucoup plus simple, de la vision lumineuse.

Cela peut entraîner, évidemment, des difficultés dans l'interprétation quand on veut passer des mécanismes récepteurs photochimiques, aux aspects divers que nous obtenons dela vision chromatique elle-même.

Mais cela, c'est essentiellement le problème que nous devons discuter maintenant — des schémas généraux qui peuvent rendre compte de la vision chromatique.

Il est bien certain que c'est l'objection que l'on fera ou que l'on peut faire au système trichromatique classique d'avoir envisagé cette relation très simple de l'additivité des stimulations de longueurs d'onde différentes en ce qui concerne les faits de luminosité générale dans le système de vision photopique.

Je crois que c'est cela qui ne peut pas être maintenu et qui oblige à revoir, par conséquent, l'ensemble du schéma explicatif, en ne s'en tenant plus à ce modèle, séduisant parce qu'il était extrêmement simple, mais qui se heurte à de très grosses difficultés et oblige, justement, à faire appel, il me semble, à des schémas un peu différents.

Mais ce sera évidemment le travail de cet après-midi et de demain, que d'examiner, d'après ce que nous savons, en fait, des mécanismes d'excitation aussi bien photochimiques que nerveux, comment nous pouvons, avec cela, tâcher d'expliquer les modalités de la vision chromatique.

PSYCHOPHYSICAL PROBLEMS

I

THE TRICHROMATIC SCHEME

W. S. Stiles

Introduction — Trichromatic ideas derive from psychophysical studies and apply primarily to human colour vision. Direct physical measurements of bleachable pigments — other than rhodopsin — in the living human eye (Rushton, 1958) place parts of the trichromatic scheme on a more objective footing. However, an approach through the psychophysical measurements is still essential. Strictly there is no wholly trichromatic scheme: the consequent use by normal individuals of eight or nine main colour names indicates a division somewhere in the stimulus-response arc into at least a corresponding number of 'channels'. Trichromatic theory does not stipulate that there are just three visual pigments (cone pigments), just three receptor types each containing only one pigment, just three nerve pathways each transmitting signals from one type of receptor, and just three colour sensations associated with activity in the respective pathways, although parts of this statement may be true. The crux of the trichromatic scheme is that at some stage in the visual process, all light stimuli, whatever their spectral energy compositions, are converted into an activity specifiable by three variables, and whatever the subsequent elaborations of the response system, stimuli leading to the same values of these variables produce the same visual effects. The further condition must be added that a specification by two variables is not possible. In human colour vision the number of variables (dimension number) is arrived at by experiments on the colour matching of mixtures of stimuli. For other animals 'colour matching' or the determination of the equivalence of different mixtures of stimuli can in principle be carried out by behaviour experiments. These are difficult, but for insects, notably the bee, a definite conclusion on the dimension number of their colour vision has been reached in this way (see von Frisch, this Symposium). For experimental animals, electrophysiological methods may be used to study the equivalence of different stimulus mixtures. For example, Bongard & Smirnov (1957) applying a micro-electrode method, found that for single optic nerve fibres of the frog, spectral stimuli were equivalent to various mixtures of two fixed primary stimuli. Here, conclusions about the dimension number are not so direct as from behaviour experiments. If the same quantitative equivalences held for all the fibres whose response depended in greater or less degree on the stimulation of the particular retinal region — a result not easy to establish — the dimension number of the region could not exceed two. It might be reduced to one if — improbably — some of the information conveyed by the signals along the nerve fibres was suppressed at higher levels.

For human colour vision the precision of colour matching is, under some conditions, high and it is appropriate to consider whether the equivalence of stimuli obeys the laws of a simple linear system. Obedience to these laws makes possible more specific conclusions than those that follow from the fixing of the dimension number.

Laws of Linear-Trichromatic Colour Matching and their Implications for the Visual Process

The basic experiment of colour matching — with side-by-side or slow alternating presentation of the stimuli — yields metameric pairs, i.e. stimuli of different spectral composition but identical appearance (brightness and colour). Colour vision in a particular region of the retina is linear-trichromatic if (i) metameric matches are *invariant under symmetric adaptation* in which the two matching fields are subjected to physically identical or to metameric adapting stimuli, (ii) matching is *additive*, (iii) matching is *three-dimensional*. By an obvious change in (iii), the conditions for linear-dichromasy, linear-tetrachromasy, etc., are obtained. Linear-trichromatic vision would be ensured if visual response resulted, in so far as the stimulation in the given retinal region was concerned, solely from light absorption under 'dilute solution' conditions (the absorption factor $1-e^{-\alpha}$ equal approximately to α) by just three photosensitive pigments, with no limitation on the way they were distributed in the retinal end-organs, on the way their light absorption initiated nerve activity in these end-organs or on the complexity of the neural system beyond, provided the latter was sufficiently refined to transmit a three-variable response. While two pigments would not suffice, more than three could be present if they occurred everywhere as three independent pigment mixtures of invariable composition (at least within the intensity range in which linear-trichromasy held), the absorption of light by one pigment in the mixture being completely equivalent (visually) to absorption in another pigment. A mixture satisfying this last condition may be described as an *indifferently responding mixture*. Similarly, the 'dilute solution' condition could be relaxed for any pigment if the pigment was not appreciably bleached in the permitted intensity range and if it was immaterial at which particular point in the light path through the end-organ a light quantum was absorbed. No alternative to the pigment explanation of linear-trichromatic vision appears tenable.

Extent to which the Normal Eye is Linear-Trichromatic

Colour vision for test stimuli imaged on the foveal retina is linear-trichromatic or very nearly so if the test stimuli cover an area neither too small nor too large (bipartite field between about 0.7° and 2° diameter) and if the level of adaptation of the test area is not too high (not above about 3000 trolands). But some deviations from additivity have been reported (Blottiau, 1947; Trezona, 1954), as well as a tendency, in some observational conditions and with highly saturated blue metamers, for matching to become virtually two-dimensional over a limited colour range (blue-green degeneracy: Fry (1958), Stiles & Burch (1955)). For very small bipartite fields (<0.7°) under steady and prolonged fixation, matching is two-dimensional or dichromatic (König, Willmer & Wright, 1946). The extent to which this phenomenon of foveal dichromasy depends on the steady fixation used in its investigation is not yet clear. In colour matching with the customary bipartite foveal matching fields (1° to 2° diam.) some effects of fixation—particularly in saturated blue fields — may have contributed to apparent deviations from additivity. The extreme condition of steady fixation is reached when by optical devices, which eliminate the effect of involuntary eye motions, the retinal image is maintained in a fixed position on the retina. With such stabilized retinal images investigated by Ditchburn & Fender (1955), Riggs *et al.* (1953), Ditchburn (1958), the appreciation of colour rapidly deteriorates. McCree (1957, 1958) has found that for some subjects, fixating in the normal way without optical aids, the colour difference of juxtaposed spectral stimuli, of different wavelength but matched in brightness, may be completely nullified in a few seconds unless the wavelengths are very widely separated in the spectrum (e.g. one in the red, the other in the green or blue). Recently, Farnsworth (1958) has shown that three major investigations of colour discrimination differ in the main in the relative discriminations in the directions greenish-yellow to violet and bluish-green to red, respectively, and that their differences correspond approximately to the times of observation used in the three works. It has become increasingly evident that for sensitive tests on additivity in colour matching a close control of temporal effects is necessary. For larger field sizes (>2°), physically uniform test stimuli of highly saturated colours no longer appear uniform and, strictly, ordinary colour matching is impossible (colour break-up at the fovea). With sufficiently large fields (10°), however, fairly satisfactory three-dimensional matching is possible by ignoring the foveal colour break-up, but there is a failure of additivity unless observations are limited to high intensities. For stimuli imaged wholly on the extrafoveal retina, side-by-side matching is extremely difficult but the main experimenters (Wright, 1946; Gilbert, 1950; Moreland, 1955), have found three-dimensional matching possible although it must certainly become non-linear at low intensities. Their results, and also the extrafoveal colour-discrimination measurements of Weale (1955), indicate an increasing contraction in the range of distinguishable colours in moving away from the fovea. Moreland concluded that colour vision becomes nearly monochromatic (dimension number 1) at about $50°$ in the extrafoveal retina, his test stimuli being of approximately $1.3°$ diam. On the other hand, recent work by the slow alternation method of colour matching, carried out with a $5°$ test field at $10°$ from the fovea by Friedrick, Bongard & Smirnov (1957), suggests that extrafoveal colour matching is four-dimensional and that to obtain complete and stable (i.e. unaffected by symmetric adaptation) matches for all stimuli, mixtures of four primaries are necessary.

The causes of the foregoing divergencies from linear-trichromasy comprise in order of certainty:

(*a*) the participation in colour matching, even at moderately high intensities, of a fourth independent visual pigment (rhodopsin) contained in the end-organs of the extrafoveal retina,

(*b*) variations, in the foveal and parafoveal regions, of the density of the macular pigment which acts as a yellow filter covering all the end-organs,

(*c*) variations with position in the numbers of the cone end-organs having particular pigment contents or in the organization into component response mechanisms of these end-organs,

(*d*) 'adjustments' in the neural apparatus which under certain observational conditions may degrade the colour discrimination potentially available from the pigment and end-organ equipment.

There remains the breakdown of foveal colour matches after high symmetric adaptation. This has been shown by Wright (1936) not to arise (or at least not to arise wholly) from the bleaching of a filter pigment (e.g. macular pigment) that covers all end-organs: for matches not involving short-wave stimuli it appears to be attributable (Brindley, 1953) to just one of the photosensitive visual pigments (the 'red' pigment with maximum absorption at long wavelengths) which is either present in high density, so that the form of its spectral absorption curve changes on bleaching, or which consists of a mixture of two pigments one of which bleaches much more easily than the other. The former hypothesis demands a pigment density considerably higher than that indicated by the objective measurements (Rushton, 1958).

A comparison of the adaptation level at which breakdown of colour match begins, with the probable amount of bleaching according to the objective data of Rushton, is of interest. Immediately after adaptation to about 3000 trolands of yellow (578 mμ) light, the match of spectral yellow (580 mμ) with a mixture of green (550 mμ) and red (680 mμ) is perceptibly upset. The objective data on the 'red' pigment indicate about 10 per cent bleaching after adaptation to 3000 trolands of yellow (580 mμ), and about 60 per cent bleaching following adaptation to 30,000 trolands. The latter adaptation demands an increase by a factor of nearly two in the red component of the mixture matching spectral yellow (Brindley, 1953). Thus match break-down and bleaching of the 'red' pigment occur in corresponding intensity ranges. But, to obtain an explanation of the break-down of colour matches in terms of bleaching of pigment some hypothesis on the mode of action is required: neither the hypothesis of a change in shape of the spectral absorption curve of the 'red' pigment produced by the reduction of density by bleaching, nor the assumption that the 'red' pigment is really an indifferently responding mixture of two pigments with very different bleaching rates, is easy to reconcile with the objective data.

Extension of the Trichromatic Scheme by Psychophysical Measurements going beyond Straightforward Colour Matching

The quantitative data of colour matching for normal subjects provide spectral curves which are linear combinations of pigment photosensitivity functions, but they do not uniquely determine the latter. Various psychophysical studies lead to fundamental spectral sensitivities that might be identified with pigment photosensitivities given in each case certain assumptions. The main methods used are:

(a) production of artificial monochromasy (dichromasy) by the complete exhaustion of two (one) of the pigments by intense coloured light leaving only one (two) pigment(s) visually effective,
(b) colour matching of two stimuli, presented in the same or opposite eyes, under asymmetric adaptation, and the application to the results of the von Kries coefficient law or an elaboration of it,
(c) increment threshold measurements analysed on the assumption of independent component mechanisms with characteristic spectral sensitivities,
(d) comparison of colour matching data of normals and colour defectives assuming that colour defectives lack one normal pigment or have two of the normal pigments present only as an invariable, indifferently responding, mixture (see Section 2).

These methods agree fairly well on the spectral location and approximate form of two of the fundamental spectral sensitivities that might be identified with pigment absorption curves: these spectral sensitivities resemble (when suitably corrected for absorption losses in the eye media, etc.) the rhodopsin absorption curve displaced so that its maximum is at about 540 mμ ('green' fundamental) or about 445 mμ ('blue' fundamental). The divergent results for the 'red' fundamental fall into two categories depending on whether the curve has a second maximum in the short-wave region of the spectrum (around 445 mμ) as well as a main maximum at long wavelengths (in the range 550 to 600 mμ). The two types correspond broadly to what can be deduced from method (*d*) by the two main hypotheses on the cause of deuteranopia (lack of one normal pigment — one maximum — or invariable, indifferently responding mixture of two normal pigments — two maxima), although in neither case has the fundamental the shape to be expected for a rhodopsin-type pigment. The 'green' fundamental almost certainly corresponds to Rushton's objectively determined pigment 54 (chlorolabe): his pigment 59 (erythrolabe) agrees best with the 'red' fundamental on the pigment mixture hypothesis of deuteranopia, and in fact the objective measurements show that the deuteranope lacks neither of the pigments observed in the normal. No pigment corresponding to the 'blue' fundamental has yet been established objectively. It appears probable that the psychophysical fundamentals derived by some methods may, in reality, be properties of component visual mechanisms activated by light absorptions in more than one pigment, and that there may be more than three such mechanisms. This applies particularly to the results obtained by increment threshold analysis (method (*c*) above) which provides some evidence for as many as seven different (although not unrelated) basic spectral sensitivities (Stiles, 1958).

If colour vision in a particular retinal area is linear trichromatic, then the retinal activity induced by a stimulus of spectral energy distribution $E_\lambda d\lambda$ can be expressed by the three tristimulus values $r = \int E_\lambda r_\lambda d\lambda$, $g = \int E_\lambda g_\lambda d\lambda$, $b = \int E_\lambda b_\lambda d\lambda$, where r_λ, g_λ, b_λ are any three independent linear combinations of the empirical colour-matching functions determined for that area. The assumptions made in the extended psychophysical methods are of various kinds but they all lead in one way or another to quantitative relations, expressed in terms of the tristimulus values, which experiment should confirm provided (*a*) the assumptions are valid, and (*b*) in calculating the tristimulus values one particular set of linear combinations is used for r_λ, g_λ, b_λ. This unique set is then accepted for the fundamental spectral sensitivities. For example, in work on colour matching under conditions of asymmetric adaptation (method (*b*) above), if the stimuli $E_\lambda' d\lambda'$ and $E_\lambda d\lambda$ applied to the dissimilarly adapted areas have tristimulus values r', g', b' and r, g, b respectively, then the matching conditions are expressible in the general functional form,

$$f_1 (r', g', b'; K') = f_1 (r, g, b; K)$$
$$f_2 (r', g', b'; K') = f_2 (r, g, b; K)$$
$$f_3 (r', g', b'; K') = f_3 (r, g, b; K)$$

where K′ and K are symbols representing the values in the two areas of the several variables required to define their adaptations. This implies no more than that asymmetric colour matching is three-dimensional. On the simplest assumption about the functions f_1, f_2, f_3 (the assumption corresponding to the von Kries law of coefficients) the matching conditions reduce to

$$k'_r r' = k_r r, \quad k'_g g' = k_g g, \quad k'_b b' = kb$$

where k'_r, k_r, k'_g, etc., are adaptation constants independent of r' r, g'_g etc. If asymmetric colour matching experiments confirm these matching conditions with one set of linear combinations for r_λ, g_λ, b_λ, they will certainly not do so with another. On the von Kries hypothesis, asymmetric colour matching must obey the additive law: if r'_1, g'_1, b'_1 in one area matches r_1, g_1, b_1 in the other and similarly r'_2, g'_2, b'_2 matches r_2, g_2, b_2, then the mixture $r'_1 + r'_2$, $g'_1 + g'_2$, $b'_1 + b'_2$ matches the mixture $r_1 + r_2$, $g_1 + g_2$, $b_1 + b_2$. The work of Walters (1942), Wright (1946) and Hunt (1953) on asymmetric colour matching by the binocular method has shown that the additivity law is at best a first approximation and may be seriously in error in certain cases. Accepting that the matching conditions must involve functions non-linear in the tristimulus values, these functions might still each depend on only one tristimulus value; f_1 (r′; K′) = f_1 (r; K), f_2 (g′; K′) = f_2 (g; K), f_3 (b′; K′) = f_3 (b; K). But the measurements of Hunt, showing that *all* colours become more saturated as the level of adaptation (to white light) is raised, make this hypothesis improbable without perhaps excluding it completely. Hunt (1958) in his analysis of asymmetric adaptation, suggests (in effect) that the asymmetric matching conditions have the form:

$$k'_r r' + k'_g g' + k'_b b' = k_r r + k_g g + k_b b$$
$$f_2 (r'/g' \; ; \; K') = f_2 (r/g \; ; \; K)$$
$$f_3 (g'/b' \; ; \; K') = f_3 (g/b \; ; \; K)$$

where f_2 and f_3 are non-linear in the ratios of the tristimulus values, and k'_r, k_r, etc., are adaptation parameters. The precise form of f_2 and f_3 remains to be determined. To sum up, there is good evidence that in colour matching under asymmetric adaptation an equalization is being made between activities in the test areas which do not depend linearly on the absorptions by the photosensitive pigments in these areas and that the conditions for match cannot be represented by three equations each involving the absorption by one pigment only.

The kind of development of the trichromatic scheme demanded by experiments on asymmetric adaptation is paralleled by the several theoretical systems, based to some extent on physiological models, that have been proposed (Piéron (1939), Shklover (1958), MacAdam (1958), Hurvich & Jameson (1958), and several earlier workers) to explain, or at least to represent economically, data on the matching of one quality of colour stimuli, such as hue or saturation, in the presence of differences of other qualities, such as brightness. In general these assume a non-linear (logarithmic or power law) conversion of each of the basic tristimulus values into 'first-order' responses and the coupling of these responses, often by simple differencing, into higher order responses in terms of which simple criteria for constant hue, saturation, etc., are postulated. At this stage the trichromatic conception has already played its part, and emphasis shifts to the opponent colour and other more psychological concepts to be dealt with by other reporters.

REFERENCES

Extended accounts of trichromatic principles are given in the standard treatises:
A. WRIGHT, W. D. (1946) *Researches on Normal and Defective Colour Vision*, London.
B. LE GRAND, Y. (1957) *Light, Colour and Vision*, London.
C. BRINDLEY, G. S. (1957) *Progr. Biophys. and Biophys. Chem.*, **8**, 49.

BONGARD, M. M. & SMIRNOV, M. S. (1957) 'Spectral sensitivity curves for receptors connected to a single optic nerve fibre in the frog', *Biophysics*, **3**, 328.
BONGARD, M. M., SMIRNOV, M. S. & FRIEDRICK, L. (1958) 'The four-dimensional colour space of the extra-foveal retinal area of the human eye', *Nat. Phys. Lab. Symposium* (No. 8), H.M. Stationery Office, London.
BLOTTIAU, F. (1947) *Rev. opt.*, **26**, 193.
BRINDLEY, G. S. (1953) 'The effects on colour vision of adaptation to very bright lights', *J. Physiol. London*, **122**, 332.
DITCHBURN, R. W. & FENDER, D. H. (1955) 'The stabilized retinal image', *Opt. Acta*, **2**, 128. (This paper describes the optical methods for stabilized images.)
DITCHBURN, R. W. (1958) *Nat. Phys. Lab. Symposium* (No. 8), H.M. Stationery Office, London. (For a brief note on colour effects.)
FARNSWORTH, D. (1958) *Nat. Phys. Lab. Symposium* (No. 8), H.M. Stationery Office, London.
FRY, G. A. (1958) 'Chromatic adaptation with special reference to the blue-green region of the colour-mixture diagram', *Nat. Phys. Lab. Symposium* (No. 8), H.M. Stationery Office, London.
GILBERT, M. (1950) *Proc. Phys. Soc. London B.*, **50**, 714.
HUNT, R. W. G. (1953) 'The perception of colour in 1° fields for different states of adaptation', *J. Opt. Soc. Amer.*, **43**, 479.
HUNT, R. W. G. (1958) 'Adaptation and the trichromatic theory', *Nat. Phys. Lab. Symposium* (No. 8), H.M. Stationery Office, London.
HURVICH, L. M. & JAMESON, D. (1958) 'Further development of quantified opponent-colour theory', *Nat. Phys. Lab. Symposium* (No. 8), H.M. Stationery Office, London.
KÖNIG, A., WILLMER, N. & WRIGHT, W. D. See *A* above, p. 338, or *C*, p. 336.
MACADAM, D. L. (1958) 'Beat-frequency hypothesis of colour perception', *Nat. Phys. Lab. Symposium* (No. 8), H.M. Stationery Office, London.
McCREE, K. J. (1958) 'Effects of steady fixation on colour-matching', *Lecture delivered to Phys. Soc. Colour Group*, May 1957, and *Ph.D. Thesis, London*.
MORELAND, J. D. (1955) 'The perception of colour by extrafoveal and peripheral vision', *Ph.D. Thesis, London*.
PIÉRON, H. (1939) 'La dissociation de l'adaptation lumineuse et de l'adaptation chromatique', *L'année Psychologique*, **40**, 1.
RIGGS, L. A., RATLIFF, F., CORNSWEET, J. C. & CORNSWEET, T. N. (1953) 'The disappearance of steadily fixated visual test objects', *J. Opt. Soc. Amer.*, **43**, 495. (Describing optical methods for stabilized images.)

RUSHTON, W. A. H. (1958) 'Human cone pigments', *Nat. Phys. Lab. Symposium* (No. 8), H.M. Stationery Office, London.

SHKLOVER, D. A. (1958) 'The problem of the equicontrast colorimetric system', *Nat. Phys. Lab. Symposium* (No. 8), H.M. Stationery Office, London.

STILES, W. S. (1958) 'Colour vision: the approach through increment-threshold sensitivity', *Proc. Nat. Acad. Sci. U.S., Washington* (in the press).

STILES, W. S. & BURCH, J. M. (1955) 'Interim rep. to the C.I.E. on the N.P.L.'s investigation of colour matching', *Opt. Acta*, **2**, 168.

TREZONA, P. (1954) 'Additivity of colour equations', *Proc. Phys. Soc. London* B., **66**, 548; ibid., **67**, 513.

WALTERS, H. V. (1942) 'Some experiments on the trichromatic theory of vision', *Proc. Roy. Soc. London* B., **131**, 27.

WEALE, R. A. (1955) 'Colour vision in the peripheral retina', *Brit. Med. Bull.*, **9**, 55.

WRIGHT, W. D. (1936) 'The breakdown of a colour match with high intensities of stimulation', *J. Physiol. London*, **87**, 23.

DISCUSSION

PIÉRON

Je pense que, avant de donner la parole à M. Hurvich, il est possible de poser des questions à M. Stiles, afin d'examiner ce nouvel aspect de notre symposium.

DARTNALL

If I have understood Dr. Stiles correctly he said that his green-mediating mechanism agrees with the shape of the rhodopsin curve. Now Dr. Rushton's chlorolabe does not agree with this pattern. And yet, Dr. Stiles said, I think, that these were equivalent processes.

STILES

Dr. Dartnall raises the question whether the spectral absorption curve or spectral photosensitivity curve (action spectrum) of Rushton's pigment 540 mμ — chlorolabe — does correspond to a rhodopsin curve merely displaced along the frequency axis. The reference to this in my report was indirect. I indicated that different psychophysical methods led to a 'green' fundamental which, when suitably corrected for light losses in the eye media, etc., was of rhodopsin type. I then said that this 'green' fundamental corresponded almost certainly to Rushton's chlorolabe. To try to reply more directly to Dr. Dartnall I would add the following. The mean spectral luminosity curve of the protanope (Pitt's results) which may be identified, at least over most of the spectrum, with the uncorrected 'green' fundamental, approximates after correction to the shape of the rhodopsin absorption curve, and Rushton* has found for a protanope that within the uncertainties of his measurements stimuli that match in luminosity produce the same amount of bleaching of chlorolabe. It would appear, therefore, that the action spectrum of chlorolabe is also of rhodopsin type. Inferences, from the observed difference spectrum about the shape of the spectral absorption curve of chlorolabe are subject to uncertainty because of the possible effects, on the short-wave side of the maximum, of the products of bleaching. The difficulties of the *in situ* measurements are in any case very great and it may be premature to use them to distinguish between a rhodopsin and a non-rhodopsin shape for chlorolabe. If chlorolabe should prove not to be of rhodopsin type I think there would be a conflict with psychophysical measurements.

RUSHTON

There are just two things I want to say.

First of all that I would be very sorry if anybody thought that the sort of curves that I can get from the human fovea compare at all in accuracy with the curves that Dr. Dartnall gets.

* RUSHTON, W. A. H. (1958) *Nat. Phys. Lab. Symposium* (No. 8), H.M. Stationery Office, London.

Mine are quite crude and, if those curves fit the luminosity curve as well as you saw this morning — as on the average they seem to do — that is something to be going on with. But upon finer details I just cannot argue. It is impossible to get accuracy of that sort.

The second thing is related to what Dr. Stiles said about Brindley's artificial monochromacy.

By looking into a very bright red light he got an artificial protanopia where he saw the spectrum as a protanope does.

I have repeated that, though not at all with Brindley's accuracy. But qualitatively I have got his result with one modification:

You could argue that the monochromacy appears because something in the retina has been removed, for example, the red-sensitive pigment, or alternatively in the brain the red-sensitive centres might have been fatigued.

In my experiment, I used the method of Craik and pressed upon the eyeball until vision failed. That is to say, I could see nothing from that eye. I fixated steadily with the other eye, and my assistant focused the bright red light down the axis of my blind eye.

We gave 40 seconds of bleaching with the strongest red light that I have and I could never see that light at all with the ischaemic eye. I closed the other eye for a moment from time to time and not once could I see the red light, so there was no stimulation of the psychological centres. There was no fatigue of the brain. Nothing got to the brain.

The light was removed and then the pressure was released. First of all, there was a splendid blue-green after-image — a big circular patch in the middle of the eye — confirming Craik's proof some 15 years ago, that the after image is formed in the retina; what starts the after-image is something going on in the retina. And looking at the spectrum I experienced Brindley's artificial protanopia. No red seen. A cut-off at the red end of the spectrum, and a long yellow range from about 520 mµ, stretching out to 620 mµ. So this is a peripheral affair and has nothing to do with centres in the brain.

PIÉRON

Je crois qu'il faut vraiment faire attention: on ne peut pas juxtaposer purement et simplement, comme on a trop tendance à le faire, la périphérie et le cerveau.

La périphérie de l'appareil visuel est un centre. Vous n'avez pas avec l'œil, un système récepteur qui soit éloigné des centres. C'est une expansion du cerveau qui est venue rejoindre les éléments récepteurs dans l'œil.

Vous avez donc dans l'œil un centre nerveux qui joue un rôle essentiel dans la réception chromatique.

Vous ne pouvez pas expliquer les phénomènes chromatiques en vous adressant simplement aux phénomènes photochimiques, quelles que soient les possibilités abstraites d'y arriver. Il faut que vous envisagiez ce fait qu'il y a, dans la rétine même, dans le centre nerveux de la rétine, des phénomènes d'excitation et d'inhibition. Cela est absolument essentiel. Et quand vous voulez vous rendre compte des changements dus à une adaptation chromatique, vous avez, d'un côté, évidemment, une baisse de sensibilité générale, mais qui n'a qu'une électivité partielle pour les radiations qui ont provoqué l'adaptation.

Et vous avez des phénomènes d'extinction de la possibilité d'éveil chromatique avec, comme corrélatif, une exagération formidable de la sensibilité chromatique à d'autres radiations, et qui se manifeste même spontanément, sans stimulation extérieure, dans les images consécutives.

Mais cela, vous ne pouvez l'expliquer que par l'intervention des systèmes nerveux de l'œil. C'est là qu'il y a des phénomènes durables. C'est là qu'il y a des phénomènes inhibiteurs, et excitateurs, et ce sont eux seuls qui peuvent nous rendre compte des détails de la vision chromatique.

J'insiste toujours sur cette idée: la vision lumineuse est une chose qui, évidemment, peut dépendre à peu près directement des phénomènes d'excitation réellement périphériques, mais quand vous parlez de la vision chromatique, vous avez des phénomènes d'équilibre — d'équilibre entre des systèmes antagonistes. Il y a une lutte et des antagonismes. Vous n'avez pas seulement des phénomènes additifs; ceux-ci existent du côté lumineux. Mais ici vous avez des phénomènes inverses.

Dans la théorie trichromatique, on est obligé de faire appel à la notion que l'égalité d'une action excitatrice de l'une des composantes fondamentales exerce des actions inhibitrices sur les deux autres, et que quand il y a action égale des trois, les inhibitions compensent complètement les possibilités excitatrices.

Il y a un élément positif, d'un côté, et deux éléments négatifs, de l'autre, qui sont égaux à l'élément positif.

Vous annulez une excitation. La lumière blanche ne peut pas être considérée comme étant le résultat de l'excitation de trois composantes chromatiques. La lumière blanche résulte de l'annulation des effets chromatiques des lumières qui ont une action élective. Il y a un processus d'abolition. C'est un fait certain que là, nous avons, non pas de l'addition pour faire du blanc, comme résultante de trois couleurs. C'est une erreur absolue. C'est la suppression de la couleur qui nous permet la lumière blanche, comme quand la vision scotopique est en jeu.

La vision photopique peut donc — et nous en avons des exemples — nous fournir de la lumière blanche, sans aucune excitation chromatique, chez les achromates à cônes dont nous avons maintenant un certain nombre d'exemples, et qui sont, par conséquent, d'une très grande importance.

Maintenant, la notion du jaune est une notion essentielle. Dans la conception trichromatique, c'est le rouge et le vert qui se combinent en une couleur jaune. Mais il y a l'autre conception qui consiste à dire: le rouge et le vert sont complémentaires, c'est-à-dire s'annulent réciproquement, et c'est quand ils sont arrivés à s'annuler que le jaune apparaît, parce que le jaune est une couleur distincte. Le jaune ne serait donc pas dû à une combinaison de deux couleurs, mais à une annulation d'un système, qui serait le système rouge-vert. C'est à quoi nous arrivons maintenant, si nous envisageons les schémas dérivés de Hering.

Mais avant, si vous le voulez bien, nous pourrons peut-être bien prendre quelques minutes de repos, à moins que quelqu'un veuille encore prendre la parole tout de suite.

Nous aborderons, dans un instant, la deuxième partie avec le schéma du type Hering.

II

THE OPPONENT-PAIRS SCHEME

L. M. Hurvich

Mr. President, Ladies and Gentlemen,

This afternoon's session, which covers the psychophysical problems of colour vision, was announced in the original programme for this symposium as presenting the alternative trichromatic and tetrachromatic colour-vision schemes. The case for the trichromatic schema has just been presented by Dr. Stiles, and with many aspects of what Dr. Stiles has said, my colleague and I could not agree more. Presumably you are now to hear a presentation and defence of the tetrachromatic schema. What we have actually agreed to do is to discuss the opponent-colours theory.

This view, as you know, was originally formulated by Hering and, as we have been emphasizing in our own writings (Hurvich & Jameson, 1957), the opponent-colours theory is also a three-variable one. Now, it is true that the respective views of Helmholtz and Hering have usually been contrasted as supporting three- versus four-colour theories. Nevertheless, the fundamental difference between the two types of theory is not one of three versus four independent variables. Certainly Hering (1875) made it quite clear that the assumed physiological basis of his own theory was a three-dimensional one, and it may come as a surprise to some to learn that even Helmholtz (1896) himself regarded Hering's theory as a three-variable schema. Since the number of independent variables, in the mathematical sense, was not originally an issue, it is regrettable that it later did develop into a controversial question. Much time has been spent unnecessarily arguing it. This much said, however, is not to say that there are no essential differences between the Young-Helmholtz and Hering viewpoints and concepts. Although the real theoretical issue has never been the number of independent variables assumed, the two views do differ fundamentally in the way in which they conceive the three-variable visual system to be structured and to function. The real theoretical issue is the manner in which the different theories conceive the relations of the physiological variables to visual experience on the one hand, and to the action of the stimulus on the other. In these respects the theories differ sharply.

Although it would be difficult to find any present-day trichromatic formulation, aside from those presented in text-books, that follows strictly the classical Helmholtzian theory, it is of value to begin our discussion by examining the essential ingredients of this theory.

In its classical and most parsimonious form, the Young-Helmholtz theory is simple. In addition to the rods, which subserve twilight vision, the eye contains three kinds of cone photo-receptors. Each type of cone contains a differently selective photochemical substance. Each cone is in turn associated with its own specific nerve fibre and each cone-photochemical-nerve fibre system is correlated with one of three specific fundamental colour sensations, namely, red, green and blue (or violet). All visual sensations are considered as compounded of varying amounts of these three excitatory systems. Black is the condition of zero excitation and white arises from the equal excitation of all three. Yellow presumably arises from equal red and green excitations.

In the Hering theory, on the other hand, the three variables of the visual system are three pairs of physiological processes that are directly associated with three pairs of unique sensory qualities. The two members of each of the three pairs are opponent. That is, the paired physiological processes are assumed to be opposite and antagonistic in nature and the paired sensory qualities are also mutually exclusive. These paired and opponent visual qualities are, as you all know, red-green, yellow-blue and white-black.

I might point out here parenthetically that it was the unjustified concern with only the two chromatic pairs, namely red-green and yellow-blue, that was responsible for Hering's theory coming to be known as a tetrachromatic view, in contrast to the Helmholtzian one which, because of its emphasis on the three primary hues, red, green and blue, was consequently tagged as trichromatic (Kries, 1905). Only by omitting the white-black pair of physiological processes and its associated visual qualities do we lose sight of the fact that the Hering schema is a system of three paired variables.

Let us return to the discussion of the three opponent pairs of processes.

It is premised in the Hering schema that each of the three assumed neural-response systems is capable of two modes of response that are physiologically opponent in nature. The assumption that the blue and yellow physiological events are opponent or antagonistic accounts for the fact that the sensory response can be either blue or yellow but not both at the same time. Similarly, since red and green physiological events are mutually antagonistic, either red or green sensations can occur, but no sensation that can be described properly as a greenish-red or a reddish-green one.

On the other hand, we may experience red-blues, or green-blues, and likewise we may experience blue-greens and yellow-greens, and so on. In short, the binary combinations that are simultaneously experienced are the combinations of non-opponent individual members of the different pairs.

In this schema, furthermore, the white-black system is also envisaged as an opponent one, with whiteness and blackness as mutually exclusive physiological and sensory properties. Mid-grey is not regarded as an additive combination of white and black. Rather, it is conceived as an intrinsic basal-activity sensation that is associated with the equilibrated condition of the whole visual system. In the absence of any external visual stimulus, we assume the state of the visual system to be a condition of active equilibrium and it is this equilibrium condition which is associated with the neutral grey sensation achieved after a long stay in complete darkness. Non-balanced excitations in the paired visual responses can then be related to various degrees of departure from the basal mid-grey condition.

In the opponent white-black system, such unbalanced excitations are related to departures from mid-grey towards either the whiteness or blackness direction. The whiteness sensation arises from direct light stimulation. The blackness sensation arises, of course, neither by direct light stimulation nor by the simple absence of light, but rather by way of either simultaneous or successive contrast during or following light stimulation of some part of the retina. Let us remember that the Helmholtzian view calls for experiencing the deepest blacks only after a long stay in the dark.

One of the most striking demonstrations of the reality of blackness as an induced sensation is seen in experiments on haploscopic matching with non-symmetrical adaptations, where the test colour is viewed in a surround of some specified chromaticity and luminance and where the comparison field provided by the tri-colorimeter is viewed in a dark surround. No manipulation of the colorimeter primaries will permit a colour match to be made to the test-field which is surrounded by an illuminated area. The induced black provided by the surround of the test colour and its absence in the case of the comparison field negates all efforts at complete matching. Only by providing an illuminated surround to induce blackness also in the three-variable comparison field can complete matches be made.

I might mention, in connection with Professor Piéron's opening remarks, that in such situations with an illuminated white surround one can readily see browns with radiations in the region of 580 mμ. One needs only the illuminated white surround. But the same 580 mμ radiation in a non-surrounded area can be reduced in intensity as far as extinction without ever producing any brown experience.

So much for the very sketchiest of outlines of these two fundamentally different theoretical positions. How adequately does each of these two different views handle the phenomena of colour vision? It seems to us that this important question must first be answered if we are to advance our understanding of the nature of colour vision.

o

The Young-Helmholtz view, in principle a three-cone, three-nerve, three-sensation theory, derives directly from the basic fact of colour mixture, namely, that all visible hues can be matched by the mixture in proper proportions of only three physical light stimuli and, consequently, the theory is readily quantified by means of linear transformations of colour-mixture data. Any such transformation, naturally enough, handles the data of colour mixture adequately. But the investigator is usually concerned with some other particular measurable functions of colour vision, for example, with the data of wavelength discrimination or saturation discrimination, or with the changes brought about by chromatic adaptation or colour-blindness, and so on. Thus, almost every serious adherent of this theory, including Dr. Stiles, proposes his own particular set of transformations when he attempts to express the trichromatic theory in a form that will also consistently handle the problem of major concern to him.

When the broad explanatory or predictive power of the theory in any given quantitative form is tested, however, it quickly becomes evident that it cannot handle more than a limited number of facts satisfactorily. The data of colour mixture, whence the transformed curves are derived are, of course, handled best. What tends to be overlooked is that most of the available psychophysical functions in colour vision are rarely handled quantitatively by any single theoretical formulation. When such comprehensive tests are made, these formulations tend to fail badly.

The literature is replete with attempts to reconcile some form of the so-called three-colour theory with selected aspects of dichromatic or anomalous colour vision and yet no satisfactory inclusive account has been forthcoming. More important still is that some facts of colour experience seem unassimilable into the framework of the simple Young-Helmholtz theory with its three independent fundamental process-sensation systems. How, we may ask, is this theory of three independent processes to be made to account for the apparent linkages that seem to occur between specific pairs of colours as either the stimulus conditions or the conditions of the human observer are varied? How explain that the red and green hues in the spectrum predominate at low stimulus levels and the yellow and blue components increase concomitantly as the spectrum is increased in luminance — the well-known Bezold-Brücke phenomenon. To our knowledge, no theory of the Helmholtzian type even begins to provide an answer.

Why, as stimulus size is greatly decreased, does discrimination between yellow and blue hues become progressively worse than that between red and green — so-called foveal tritanopia? To our knowledge, no theory of the Helmholtzian type, which treats so-called small-field tritanopia as a blue-component deficiency, provides any clue for the simultaneous yellow losses that occur under these circumstances.

Why do the hues drop out in pairs in instances of congenital colour defect or when the visual system is impaired by disease? The words *protanopia* and *deuteranopia* still in common use to differentiate two types of red-green blindness but which mean, respectively, loss of the first system and loss of the second system, should stand as constant reminders of the failure of the traditional view in this area.

Moreover, since the sensation of white is granted no separate physiological process in the parsimonious Young-Helmholtz theory, but occurs as a fusion product of three equally large fundamental hue sensations, how do we account for the large degree of independence of white and chromatic qualities when the adaptation of the visual system is varied? Why, after having exposed the eye to white light, thereby decreasing its whiteness sensitivity, do we perceive that the saturation of all colours has been increased? If exposure to white light alters only the sensitivity of the white-black process of the opponent-colours theory, this relative strengthening of colour quality is to be expected. If, however, the white light serves only to desensitize equally the three chromatic processes of the Helmholtz theory, why are the colour responses not diminished in the same way as the white? Hering & Brückner (1904), Troland (1916), and Professor Piéron (1939) have all been concerned with some aspect of this adaptation problem.

None of the series of phenomena that I have just touched upon poses any theoretical difficulties for the alternative hypothesis of Hering with its postulated three pairs of opponent physiological processes that are associated respectively with the three pairs of opponent sensory responses, red-green, yellow-blue and white-black.

As a matter of fact, when suggestions are made as to how the classical Young-Helmholtz schema might be modified in order to account for some of these intractable facts, the *ad hoc* explanatory devices suggested tend to bring the theory closer and closer to the opponent-pairs concept. To cite only a few examples: Wright (1947), in seeking an explanation for his adaptation data, suggested the possibility of some form of linkage between the red and green systems; Professor Piéron (1943) has found it necessary to propose a fourth cone to mediate the achromatic responses; Walls's (1952) development of what he calls the excess hypothesis assumes separate luminosity and hue processes, and physiological antagonisms are implied by the difference principle suggested by Thomson (1952) and the difference equations used by MacAdam (1957) and Shklover (1957). Whether or not the mechanisms implied by the use of such difference formulae are actually recognized to imply opponent physiological processes is immaterial. The result is, in any event, to introduce into the three-component theory one of the basic concepts of the opponent-colours theory.

Traditionally, the chief drawback of the Hering theory was that it was not expressed in quantitative terms and, hence, its explanatory powers were limited to the qualitative realm of discourse and not subject to precise test with respect to quantitative psychophysical functions.

It is this situation that we sought to correct when we first attempted a quantitative experimental determination of the opponent sensory responses. Obviously we have no time to present the quantitative development of the opponents notion in any detailed fashion here. Many of you are already familiar with this development from our writings (Hurvich & Jameson, 1955a, b, 1956; Jameson & Hurvich, 1955, 1956a, b). Nevertheless, we should like to present some slides that will illustrate:

(1) our formulation of the theoretical model,

(2) our experimental determinations of the opponent response functions basic to the theory, and

(3) some comparisons between a few psychophysical functions derived on the basis of the theory and comparable functions measured experimentally in various laboratories.

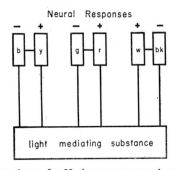

Fig. 1. Basic schema for Hering opponent-colours mechanism.

Fig. 1 shows the basic schema for the opponent-colours mechanism in diagrammatic form. The three paired opponent response systems are labelled b–y, g–r and w–bk. The convention of positive and negative signs is used to indicate the opponent nature of the paired processes and responses. It may be pointed out here that there has been almost universal misunderstanding of Hering's notion of the locus of the opponent processes. He did not localize the opponent processes in the retinal photochemicals, or what he called the 'Empfangstoffe', labelled here 'light mediating substance'. Rather, he assumed that the opponent processes are neurochemical in nature and that they are located in what he called the 'Sehsubstanz', which for Hering included retinal, optic nerve and central neural elements.

Our own schematic model is shown in Fig. 2. We have postulated, as you can see, three independent photosensitive materials, which we call α, β and γ

Neural Responses

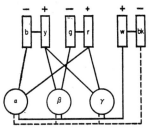

Photochemical Absorptions

Neural Responses

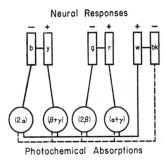

Photochemical Absorptions

$$y-b = k_1(\beta+\gamma-2\alpha)$$
$$r-g = k_2(\alpha+\gamma-2\beta)$$
$$w-bk = k_3(\alpha+\gamma+\beta)-k_4(\alpha+\beta+\gamma)$$

FIG. 2. Schematic diagram showing relations between photosensitive materials α, β and γ and the neural opponent response processes y-b, r-g, and w-bk.

and which form the mediating link between incident light stimuli and the three opponent visual response processes.

The three independent photosensitive materials may be contained in discrete retinal units with complex interconnections to the neural response systems, as shown in the upper portion of the figure, or two or more of these materials may be combined in receptor units having simpler connections to the neural response systems, as set out in the lower portion. There is no way of differentiating these models in terms of visual behaviour; but however the three photochemicals may be segregated or combined in the retina and whatever the number of different photoreceptor units, there remain only three photosensitive materials, α, β and γ and the theory remains a three-variable opponent-colours schema.

I hasten to point out to the physiologists present that the straight lines drawn in this schematic diagram are by no means intended to represent simple neurological pathways. Since we are dealing with stimulus events on the one hand, and sensory events on the other, the intervening neural mechanisms are conceived only in terms of net effects.

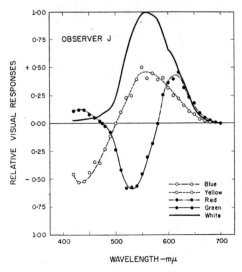

FIG. 3. Chromatic and achromatic response functions for equal energy spectrum for observer J.

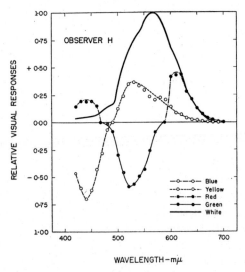

FIG. 4. Chromatic and achromatic response functions for equal energy spectrum for observer H.

What are the spectral distributions of the three basic response variables of the Hering theory? A set of functions that we have measured experimentally is shown in each of the next two slides for each of two observers.

The results for one observer are shown in Fig. 3.

Fig. 4 shows the results for the second observer. The white functions are taken as identical with the measured luminosity function and are represented by the solid curve. The induced, rather than the directly stimulated, black component of the achromatic white-black response pair is not shown on the figure. It would have the same distribution as the white but would be of opposite sign, since the strength of the black contrast response is directly related to the magnitude of either the surrounding or the preceding whiteness or brightness.

The paired chromatic functions were measured by a hue-cancellation technique, which time does not permit us to describe here, and they are identified by the code. However, it might be easier to trace them for you. Here is the yellow function, and the blue function and here — the long wavelength component of red, the green and the short wavelength red component. These functions are assumed to be directly correlated with the net response activity of the visual nervous tissue (retina, optic nerve and visual centres), and should not be taken as photochemical absorption spectra about which these data tell us nothing.

The psychophysical opponent response functions shown in these figures provide a direct description of the appearance of the spectrum for these observers for a neutral condition of bright adaptation and at the moderate level of luminance for which the functions were obtained. Thus, all wavelengths evoke some whiteness as well as hue; the whiteness and brightness of an equal energy spectrum is relatively small at the two spectral extremes and is relatively high at the intermediate wavelengths. The short wavelengths appear as red-blue hues (violets); there is a narrow band of pure or unique blue where the red-green function is equal to zero; then come the blue-greens followed by a narrow band of unique green at the wavelength where the yellow-blue function is equal to zero; this is followed by the yellow-greens, and then pure yellow occurs at the second intersection of the red-green function with the zero ordinate value. Finally, the yellow-red hues appear in the long wavelength region. At this point, for instance, where the yellow-blue function is in equilibrium, we have green excitation and white excitation or green and white responses only. Throughout this wavelength region, however, we have green, yellow and white. Similarly, yellow and white are excited at the point where red and green are again counterbalanced and beyond this point in the long wavelength region we have yellow, red and white.

Since colour-mixture experiments simply involve matching the three perceived qualities evoked by one stimulus, by mixing three other stimuli to yield the same perceived qualities it is possible to determine the colour-mixture relations that are inherent in these response curves for any three arbitrarily selected stimulus primaries. That is, for a colour match, the red-green value, the yellow-blue value and the white value of the total visual response to any wavelength of unit energy must be matched by the totals of the three corresponding values for the three mixture primaries when the latter stimuli are combined in the proper proportions. Thus, to determine the proportions of any three mixture stimuli that are required to match any given spectral wavelength one needs only solve three simultaneous equations based on the three paired response functions. Colour-mixture relations calculated

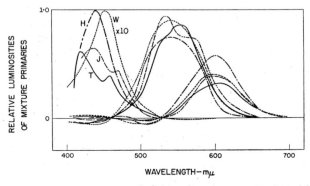

FIG. 5. Calculated colour-mixture functions for observers H (Hurvich) and J (Jameson), and experimental colour-mixture functions for T (Thomson) and W (Wright) (Ishak, 1952, and Wright & Pitt, 1935).

in this manner, for wavelengths from 420 mμ to 700 mμ, from smoothed visual response data for our two observers, are compared in Fig. 5 with two sets of experimentally determined colour-mixture functions for the same three mixture primaries.

The experimental functions are the published data of Wright & Pitt (1935) and Thomson (1952). Here we have Professor Wright's colour-mixture curves (W) and here are the transformations of our own chromatic response functions (J and H). These data are those of Thomson (T). I think the similarities are clear.

Just as it is possible to derive colour-mixture data from the opponent response functions, it is also possible to derive generalized opponent response functions from colour-mixture data (Judd, 1951). The theoretical derivations that follow will be based on such generalized functions arrived at from the average CIE colour-mixture data.

A series of constant hue contours, as measured experimentally by Purdy (1937) are shown in the upper portion of Fig. 6. This is really an experimental

measure of the Bezold-Brücke effect and each curve in this graph shows the change in wavelength required to maintain a fixed hue as luminance is varied. In other words, the particular contour that starts at about 540 mμ, for instance, indicates that to maintain a constant hue Purdy found it necessary to adjust the wavelength to a lower value at the higher luminance and to a still lower wavelength at the maximum luminance. Similar wavelength changes are expressed by each of the other constant hue contours represented.

Whereas all of Purdy's attempts to reconcile his experimental data with the usual trichromatic view were unsuccessful, the lower portion of the figure shows a comparable series of functions as theoretically derived on the basis of our opponent-colours formulation. The essential theoretical requirement

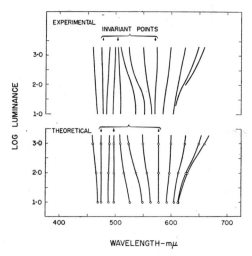

FIG. 6. Constant hue contours as measured by Purdy (1937) and as predicted by theory.

to account for this phenomenon is that the yellow and blue processes be linked, that the red and green processes be linked, and that the two paired systems vary independently and differently as functions of stimulus luminance (see Fig. 2 in Mrs. Hurvich's report, page 262).

Changes in the form of wavelength-discrimination functions that are measured at different intensities have the same theoretical requirements. In Fig. 7 there are shown wavelength-discrimination functions as determined by Dr. Weale at two luminance levels and comparable functions that we derived from the opponent-colours theory. The theoretical derivations are based on changes with respect to wavelength in the quantitative expressions for both hue and saturation at different luminances.

We have many other comparisons of experimental psychophysical data

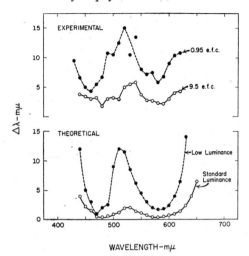

Fɪɢ. 7. Wavelength-discrimination functions for two luminance levels as measured
by Weale (1951) and as predicted by theory.

with theoretical derivations both for individuals with normal colour vision
and for various kinds and degrees of colour defect. Many such comparisons
are available in our published papers and, rather than continuing the exposition along these lines, it seems preferable to conclude with a few remarks
concerning the compatibility of the opponent-colours schema with some of
the information that is now available in the neurophysiological literature.

The conceptual model for the opponent-colours theory, as originally
presented by Hering, drew its sharpest criticism on the grounds that it was
bad physiology. Some of this criticism was based on an erroneous interpretation of Hering's views that I have already mentioned — an interpretation
that incorrectly assigned the opponent processes to the photochemical
activities in the retinal cells. Actually, Hering's (1888) own concept of
mutually opponent neural processes, each capable of being activated by
external stimulation, was far ahead of the knowledge of neurophysiology at
the time it was proposed. This concept now turns out, however, to be
perfectly consistent with the picture of neural function that is only just
recently beginning to be built up from electrophysiological studies of the
visual neural apparatus.

As we all know, nerves do not simply respond or fail to respond when a
stimulus is presented to the appropriate end-organ. Rather, they may respond
according to any of a number of quite specific patterns. For example, a nerve
fibre may (1) discharge at the onset of stimulation and subsequently gradually
become quiet; (2) discharge at both onset and cessation of stimulation with a
quiet period in between; (3) cease any spontaneous activity when first

stimulated and remain electrically quiet during continued stimulation but respond with a burst of electrical impulses when the stimulus ceases to act. I refer here, of course, to Hartline's (1938) original work.

The on- and off-phases of discharge are mutually inhibitory processes. They are associated with slow electrical potentials of opposite sign and they cancel each other when the experimental conditions are so manipulated as to cause both on- and off-discharges to impinge simultaneously on the same ganglion cell. In Granit's (1955) opinion, the evidence from electrophysiology provides a 'belated vindication of Hering's view' that the visual system is characterized by mutually opponent neural processes.

The concept of mutual interaction among the various elements of the physiological field — a concept that we have not had time to discuss this afternoon — is also basic to the opponent-colours theory and is critical to an understanding of both area effects and simultaneous contrast and induction phenomena. Here again we find the researches in electrophysiology indicating that individual nerve elements never act independently and visual function must be thought of in terms of the integrated action of all the units of the neural visual system (Hartline, 1941).

Hartline *et al.* (1956), as we all know, have found that even in the very simple Limulus eye, the discharge of impulses in any one optic nerve fibre depends not only upon the stimulus to the specific receptor unit from which that fibre arises, but also on the stimulation over the entire population of mutually interacting elements. Both excitatory and inhibitory interaction of the sort to be expected in accordance with the opponent-colours theory have actually been demonstrated in the neural responses of the vertebrate visual system by Hartline (1941), Kuffler (1953) and Granit (1955).

The way in which the postulated three independent systems of paired opponent processes (yellow-blue, red-green, white-black) are differentiated neurally, is still a matter for conjecture. The critical importance of this general problem, Professor Piéron has already stressed in one of the earlier sessions concerned with insect vision. Hering himself thought that it was a matter of process specificity, but was willing to use the concept of material or structural specificity, which he guessed would be more readily comprehended by most interested readers of his views at the time he presented them. Despite the more orthodox view that all nerve impulses are qualitatively similar, our own theoretical preference at this time is the conjecture that a particular colour quality is more probably determined by a particular state of the nervous tissue than by activity of a particular structural element in the nervous network. Thus, we would be inclined to look for a difference between yellow-blue and red-green processes rather than to isolation of yellow-blue or red-green fibres or nerve cells.

We hope that more information of the sort that, for example, Svaetichin

and his associates have reported for the fish on the reverse polarity effects associated with stimulation by different parts of the spectrum — some of Svaetichin's data were shown by Dr. Rushton in an earlier session — will be forthcoming for other species more closely related to the human animal and that we will thus gain more specific knowledge concerning the actual physiological processes involved in human colour vision.

REFERENCES

GRANIT, R. (1955) *Receptors and Sensory Perception*, New Haven.
HARTLINE, H. K. (1938) *Am. J. Physiol.*, **121**, 400.
HARTLINE, H. K. (1941-42) *Harvey Lectures*, **37**, 39.
HARTLINE, H. K., WAGNER, H. G. & RATLIFF, F. (1956) *J. Gen. Physiol.*, **39**, 651.
HELMHOLTZ, H. v. (1896) *Handbuch der Physiologischen Optik* (2nd ed.), Hamburg and Leipzig.
HERING, E. (1875) *Österr. Akad. Wiss. Math.-natur., Kl. Sitz ber., Abt. III*, **70**, 169.
HERING, E. (1888) *Zur Theorie der Vorgänge in der lebendigen Substanz*, Prague.
HERING, E. & BRÜCKNER, A. (1904) *Pflügers Arch. ges. Physiol.*, **94**, 533.
HURVICH, L. M. & JAMESON, D. (1955a) *Trans. N.Y. Acad. Sci.*, **18**, 33.
HURVICH, L. M. & JAMESON, D. (1955b) *J. Opt. Soc. Amer.*, **45**, 602.
HURVICH, L. M. & JAMESON, D. (1956) *J. Opt. Soc. Amer.*, **46**, 416.
HURVICH, L. M. & JAMESON, D. (1957) *Psychol. Rev.*, **64**, 384.
ISHAK, I. G. H. (1952) *J. Opt. Soc. Amer.*, **42**, 844.
JAMESON, D. & HURVICH, L. M. (1955) *J. Opt. Soc. Amer.*, **45**, 546.
JAMESON, D. & HURVICH, L. M. (1956a) *J. Opt. Soc. Amer.*, **46**, 405.
JAMESON, D. & HURVICH, L. M. (1956b) *J. Opt. Soc. Amer.*, **46**, 1075.
JUDD, D. B. (1951) *Handbook of Experimental Psychology* (Edited by Stevens, S. S.), New York.
KRIES, J. v. (1905) *Nagel's Handbuch der Physiologie der Menschen*, Brunswick.
KUFFLER, S. W. (1953) *J. Neurophysiol.*, **16**, 37.
MACADAM, D. L. (1958) *Nat. Phys. Lab. Symposium* (No. 8), H.M. Stationery Office, London.
PIÉRON, H. (1939) *Année psychol.*, **40**, 1.
PIÉRON, H. (1943) *Sciences (Rev. assoc. Franç. avancement sci.)*, **70**, 265.
PURDY, D. M. (1937) *Am. J. Psychol.*, **49**, 313.
SHKLOVER, D. A. (1958) *Nat. Phys. Lab. Symposium* (No. 8), H. M. Stationery Office, London.
SVAETICHIN, G. (1956) *Acta Physiol. Scand.*, **39**, Supp. 134, 1.
THOMSON, L. C. (1952) *Ophthal. Lit.*, **6**, 3.
TROLAND, L. T. (1916) *Trans. Illum. Eng. Soc.*, **11**, 957.
WALLS, G. L. & MATTHEWS, R. S. (1952) *New Means of Studying Color Blindness and Normal Foveal Color Vision*, Berkeley.
WEALE, R. A. (1951) *J. Physiol. London*, **113**, 115.
WRIGHT, W. D. (1947) *Researches on Normal and Defective Colour Vision*, St. Louis.
WRIGHT, W. D. & PITT, F. G. H. (1935) *Proc. Phys. Soc. London*, **47**, 205.

DISCUSSION

PIÉRON

Je vous remercie de votre exposé. Vous avez présenté le système de Hering tel qu'il l'avait conçu.

Mais j'avoue que je ne suis pas du tout d'accord avec vous sur le troisième terme du couple que vous avez conservé, pour des raisons, sans doute, de symétrie.

En réalité, je maintiens qu'il n'y a pas de sensation élémentaire dans la ligne blanc-noir et qu'il s'agit là uniquement de perceptions.

Vous avez fait appel à des notions de contrastes. Mais, en réalité, si vous isolez le stimulus, de manière à avoir une sensation élémentaire, et non pas un pattern perceptif, le noir n'existe pas.

Lorsque, dans un photomètre de Pulfrich, vous examinez des échelons de leucie, depuis le noir jusqu'au blanc, du moment que vous ne connaissez pas la lumière qui est reçue par la surface que vous examinez, vous voyez des surfaces lumineuses, achromatiques, si c'est une lumière blanche que vous avez utilisée.

Jamais vous ne pouvez voir la couleur 'noir'. Alors, on dit: 'Mais quand on a fatigué l'œil avec une plage très lumineuse on regarde et on voit du noir.' Vous voyez du noir sur une surface éclairée, parce que vous avez une région qui vous donne une impression lumineuse affaiblie par rapport à la région environnante — comme s'il y avait effectivement une zone noire, c'est-à-dire un albedo très inférieur à celui de la région environnante.

Mais si vous vous mettez dans l'obscurité, ce n'est pas du noir que vous voyez, c'est de la lumière. L'effet consécutif est un effet lumineux.

Le contraste est dû à une moindre excitabilité d'une région de la rétine, et alors cette région de moindre excitabilité vous donne le même effet que si vous aviez une surface qui réfléchit moins de lumière. Mais vous avez toujours à faire à des perceptions de leucies, c'est-à-dire à des perceptions d'albedo. Vous connaissez les objets par la réflectivité des surfaces.

Ceci exige, non pas une sensation seulement, mais un ensemble de sensations dont se dégage l'interprétation perceptive. Il faut une interprétation pour voir du gris ou pour voir du noir. Il n'y a pas une sensation élémentaire qui y corresponde.

Mais vous n'avez pas besoin, dans vos conceptions, de ce couple. Le couple blanc-noir ne sert à rien. Il sert si vous examinez des surfaces d'objets. Alors, là, en effet, vous avez des perceptions qui n'existent pas comme sensations élémentaires, des perceptions interprétatives, des perceptions de brun, de rose, qui n'existent pas avec de la lumière toute seule.

Quand vous avez à faire à des sensations élémentaires, il n'y a rien de tel. Devant des surfaces éclairées, vous avez des 'chromoleucies' qui sont — encore une fois — des interprétations perceptives.

Mais vous n'avez aucunement besoin du couple blanc-noir dans une théorie, vous avez besoin d'un système qui donne de la lumière, et de systèmes en couples opposés donnant alors le mécanisme chromatique, jaune-bleu et rouge-vert.

Là, alors, fait intéressant, cela peut s'accorder avec des données neuro-physiologiques sur les phénomènes d'opposition et de contraste.

213

HURVICH

There is one respect in which the present disagreement on the white-black process is fortunate. I have overheard people wondering — we have been doing it ourselves — if all controversy about colour vision is on the verge of coming to an end. One gets the impression that everyone is beginning to think in terms of difference formulae, whether or not the physiological concept of opponent neural processes is explicitly acknowledged. However, the fact that Professor Piéron is so strongly opposed to the concept of a white-black process indicates that there is still a future ahead for us. And now we shall be able to concentrate on arguing out this specific point. I think that, here again, the difference may not be as great as it seems. It is a question of what one emphasizes. Professor Piéron seems to be emphasizing a difference here which I think Hering was well aware of and concerned with in his writings.

Our own position on the white-black mechanism is this. We are concerned with the fundamental mechanisms that are operating in producing any visual sensations. This is true whether the situation is a highly artificial and rigorously controlled laboratory one, or whether it is the everyday situation such as the one I am now in when I look down on the table and see a black notebook and other coloured objects. Whether in the laboratory or in the present situation I would not see blacks if there were no opponent white excitations in the surrounding areas of the visual field. In the highly controlled laboratory situation we frequently try to minimize the complexity of interacting areas in the visual field unless these interactions are themselves being investigated. On the other hand, complex interactions comprise the very essence of the everyday viewing situation. It is to the complexities of the interactions in the visual field that we look for differences in perceived qualities. Our outlook is thus quite different from what Professor Piéron seems to be emphasizing, namely, that the difference in the two situations is to be attributed to a difference in interpretation — an interpretation that 'a little man in the brain' somehow or other seems to give to the situation. This 'interpretation' orientation smacks to me of the old 'unconscious inference' Helmholtzian approach. We, on the other hand, are primarily interested in the lawful properties of the mechanism on which the visual information must be based.

If we do consider the interactions in the everyday situation, I think the difference between brightness and lightness as matters of interpretation, which is what I believe Professor Piéron is arguing for, disappears. Moreover, the opponent white-black mechanism depends for its expression on both spatial and temporal opponent interactions, and when we remember this fact, I think Professor Piéron's objection to it also disappears.

I don't know whether I am making the point clear to Professor Piéron or the rest of you, but I hope we'll have a chance to discuss it more fully later.

PIRENNE

Au sujet du blanc et du noir, différents observateurs ont noté un phénomène qui à première vue ne semble pas tout à fait en accord avec les remarques de M. Piéron. Pour ma part cependant, je n'ai pas une conception suffisamment nette de la théorie de Hering pour voir comment ce phénomène pourrait s'y intégrer.

Il a été observé notamment par Asher* et, indépendamment, par moi-même,† et il doit avoir été observé par d'autres. Dans l'obscurité complète on fixe un point lumineux rouge tout en observant une plage lumineuse périphérique dont l'intensité est, disons 100 fois le seuil absolu. Cette plage après quelques secondes — cinq a dix dans mon cas — devient complètement invisible, c'est-à-dire que, à part le point rouge, on ne voit plus rien du tout quoique la luminance physique de la plage soit toujours la même.

Mais lorsque la plage est brusquement éteinte — ce qu'au début de mes expériences je voulais utiliser pour vérifier que la plage était vraiment devenue invisible — alors l'observateur voit surgir à l'endroit où elle se trouvait, une plage noire, plus noire, plus foncée que l'obscurité totale qui remplit le champ visuel en dehors du point de fixation. L'effet est frappant chez la plupart de ceux qui ont essayé l'expérience.

Ici je voudrais mentionner que Creed‡ il y a longtemps déjà a fait appel aux phénomènes de l'*off-effect* pour expliquer la sensation de noir, et il semble possible que, lorsqu'on a un objet brun, par exemple, il puisse y avoir des réponses *off* en même temps que les réponses des récepteurs pour le rouge, si bien qu'on se trouverait dans un système théorique ou il y aurait un mélange d' 'excitations noires', si l'on peut dire, avec les 'excitations rouges', ce qui donnerait du brun.

Il n'y aurait pas antagonisme, mais plutot addition. Le noir serait dû à des excitations supplémentaires qui s'ajouteraient aux autres excitations spécifiquement chromatiques. De toute façon les observations rapportées plus haut sont nettes, et l'on est forcé d'admettre que l'on voit parfois du 'noir' qui est plus noir que l'obscurité totale.

PIÉRON

Dans ces phénomènes consécutifs, il est difficile, évidemment, de savoir exactement ce qui se passe.

Il est possible que vous ayez des oscillations. Il y a des phénomènes oscillatoires. Vous le voyez avec les phénomènes colorés. Vous avez dans la fuite des couleurs ces phénomènes d'oscillations qui marquent des effets consécutifs.

Que se passe-t-il exactement quand, dans l'obscurité, vous avez examiné votre plage lumineuse? A ce moment-là, on suppose, n'est-ce pas, cette plage lumineuse.

Est-ce qu'il n'y a pas possibilité, dans ce cas, de quelque chose qui reste? Si vous avez eu quelques mouvements d'yeux surtout — un fond qui reste lumineux, avec une région qui est moins lumineuse dans une certaine partie, et qui vous donne l'effet de noir?

L'effet de noir est alors un effet de 'pattern', quand il y a des éléments lumineux et une partie moins lumineuse, comme devant des inégalités d'albedo et tout se passe comme si nous nous trouvions en présence d'une surface refléchissante qui nous donne également de la lumière.

Vous parlez du brun. Est-ce que réellement, quand vous mettez des cartes de Munsen colorées dans un photomètre de Pulfrich, vous pouvez voir du brun? Voilà toute la question.

Je crois que l'on ne voit pas de brun dans ces conditions-là. Vous ne voyez que les couleurs que peut donner la lumière. Le brun est une interprétation de

* Asher, H. M. F. (1956) *J. Physiol. London*, **134**, 18P.

† Pirenne, M. H., Marriott, F. H. C. & O'Doherty, E. F. (1957) *Med. Research Council (Brit.) Spec. Rept.*, Ser. No. 294, p. 56.

‡ Creed, R. S. (1931) *J. Physiol. London*, **73**, 247.

chromoleucies qui naissent, lorsque vous avez des renseignements sur la lumière que reçoit une surface, et la lumière qu'elle vous renvoie.

Mais si on ne connaît pas l'éclairement reçu par la surface brune, on ne voit pas de surface brune, on ne voit qu'une région colorée avec une tonalité spectrale, plus ou moins lumineuse.

PIRENNE

Je suis bien d'accord avec M. le Président. Je ne vois jamais de brun dans l'obscurité totale. Mais si l'on regarde un morceau de chocolat placé devant un écran blanc dans une chambre éclairée, alors, l'œil se déplaçant, l'illumination rétinienne devient beaucoup plus faible lorsque l'image du chocolat tombe sur une partie de la rétine qui précédemment recevait la lumière blanche de l'écran. Ceci pourrait produire un effet *off*.

Je crois que c'est ce que M. Piéron appelle l'effet de 'pattern'.

PIÉRON

Oui. C'est bien là un effet de 'pattern'.

WRIGHT

I am glad that Dr. Hurvich has at least made clear that the Hering theory is a three-variable theory. That, at least, removes one possible field of argument and contention, which Dr. Judd also made clear some years ago when he put the Hering theory into quantitative form.

I would like to ask Dr. Hurvich two questions.

Can his formulation of the theory explain the convergence of the confusion loci of colour-defective observers in the chromaticity chart? Also can he explain the location of the fundamental stimuli in the chromaticity chart as derived from colour-adaptation experiments?

Nothing has been said this afternoon about any evolutionary ideas, but it seems to me that we can assume that in an earlier form of vision we just had light-sensitive receptors. Then, on a kind of Ladd-Franklin theory, our colour vision evolved and was a subdivision into a two-receptor process, which we might assume to be a yellow-blue process, and that subsequently the yellow receptors subdivided into red and green processes.

We can, on a basis of that sort, reach a fairly orthodox type of three-receptor process and theory and yet have some understanding and some conception of why there should be a linkage between red and green, and between yellow and blue processes.

I would not myself have much doubt about some sort of linkages occurring at certain stages between the retina and the visual cortex, and if I may nail my particular flag to the mast, I do not personally believe in a separate whiteness receptor.

May I give just one small piece of evidence for this belief: I think if we had a whiteness receptor, I should expect the whiteness sensation to swamp the colour sensation so much that we could not expect the extraordinarily high wavelength discrimination which we have, for example, in the yellow part of the spectrum.

Having said all that, I am personally very glad that Dr. Hurvich is considering the Hering theory and advocating it so strongly. Only in this way can we see how far it satisfies all the requirements of a satisfactory theory.

Our ignorance about the processes of colour perception is still so vast that we have got to examine all possibilities and, in the end — I hope not too soon — we may find out the truth of things.

HURVICH

I made some notes as you spoke and see here that I have written that you hoped we would resolve these things 'and not too soon'. Did you say 'and not too soon'? I was just wondering if my rapidly made note was correct.

With respect to your two questions, I think they bring out the differences in our points of view most clearly. Your questions relate:

(1) to the possibility of our predicting for colour defectives the convergence points on the conventionally standardized CIE trichromatic charts, and
(2) to the locations of our three fundamental stimuli on such a chart. This is a comparable question because I assume that you would expect the convergence point to be a fundamental stimulus point.

If I discuss the second question first it might indicate why, given the orientation we have, we tend not to look for 'fundamental stimuli', and why this seems to us to be a wrong question to ask.

Let us look again at Fig. 3 (p. 206) and let us assume for a moment that the functions plotted there represent the way in which the visual system of a given observer responds at various wavelengths. If the wavelength 450 mμ is used for unit energy, the ordinate value represents the excitation of the blue-response system as of this extent, the negative sign being purely arbitrary to indicate a process here that is opposite to the yellow response which is plotted as positive. You see the red response and the white response. Thus the radiation at 450 mμ evokes excitations of three processes to the indicated magnitudes. Another stimulus, 550 mμ, evokes a white response of the indicated magnitude, a yellow response of the indicated magnitude, and a green response of the indicated magnitude. There is obviously no reason for considering any real stimulus more fundamental than any other. It is true that the wavelength 580 mμ, which leaves the red and green systems exactly in balance but excites this magnitude of yellow, gives a unique yellow hue, but still with some white, so that a desaturated unique yellow is seen. This is a unique hue response and a unique spectral locus, but there is nothing more fundamental about the wavelength 580 mμ than any other wavelength from this point of view.

We might take the more conventional approach and transform these data into a set of colour-mixture functions. Depending on one's arbitary choice of mixture primaries one obtains a set of colour-mixture curves, and a different set for each new choice of primary stimuli. I have indicated earlier how this simple transformation can be carried out, and how colour-mixture curves that represent amounts of mixture stimuli can be determined from our sensory response functions shown in Fig. 3. However, only by suddenly ignoring the differences between a stimulus and a sensation could we conclude that some one set of these colour-mixture functions has now become equivalent to a set of three fundamental sensory responses. Whatever the transformation, colour-mixture curves represent amounts of colour-mixture stimuli, and we see no reason to treat them as sensory responses and to conclude that we have suddenly hit upon three 'fundamental' stimuli.

P

Still another approach is to look at the colour-mixture curves for dichromats. In this case, only two colour-mixture primaries are needed and the third colour-mixture curve disappears. Again, only by ignoring the difference between a sensation and a stimulus could we conclude that this third 'missing' curve represents the distribution of red and green sensory responses that are lost by the protanope (or the red and green sensations lost by the deuteranope). We do not draw any such conclusion.

One can, of course, conceive and compute an imaginary stimulus that might be absorbed exclusively by one of three photosensitive materials. But again, so long as we remember that there is a considerable nervous apparatus that intervenes between photochemical absorption and sensory response, and that the absorption of a photochemical is hardly the sensation of 'red', or 'green', or 'blue', we have no reason to look upon such an imaginary stimulus as fundamental, with respect to colour sensations.

I think this answer covers the import of both of Dr. Wright's questions. With respect to the specific question about the convergence loci of confusion lines for colour defectives, the answer is 'yes', we can predict these loci. If we use the theoretical chromatic and achromatic response functions for dichromats that we have published in the *Journal of the Optical Society of America*, it is a simple matter of calculation to predict equivalent stimuli for such individuals. When we plot the equivalent stimuli on the chromaticity chart, the lines connecting them are, of course, the confusion lines for the given type of dichromat. We do not, however, believe that the intersection of a set of these confusion loci represents the stimulus that would excite a fundamental sensation in normal vision, missing in dichromatic vision.

Dr. Wright also asked if the facts of hue discrimination do not conflict with our theoretical formulation. In particular, he was concerned about the possibility of having good hue discrimination in the yellow region of the spectrum where, according to the response functions that we are using in our theoretical formulation, there is considerable white response and very little hue.

That the theory is not inconsistent with the facts of sensitivity is, of course, established by the success with which we can predict the measured discrimination functions using the opponent-process theoretical formulation. Without reviewing our procedure in detail, we need only note that there is a very rapid rate of change in hue in the pure yellow region of the spectrum with which Dr. Wright is concerned. It is a transition point at which red is just dropping out and green is just beginning to come in. Moreover, as Dr. Weale has stated, wavelength-discrimination experiments not only involve discrimination of changes in hue but also of changes in saturation from one wavelength to the next. As all saturation experiments, including those of Dr. Wright, have shown, it is in this same yellow region that spectral saturation is also changing most rapidly. Although spectral saturation is low in the yellow region, as both the theoretical formulation and the actual data of Dr. Wright's saturation functions show it is not the absolute level, but the rate of change with respect to wavelength that is important for wavelength discrimination.

If I recall Dr. Stiles' inquiry correctly he asked whether our experiments were not just a roundabout way of doing a regular colour-matching experiment, since we use our so-called response functions to derive colour-matching data. The first point to be made in this connection is that we were not doing regular colour matches at all. Our experiment was designed to determine the relative energies of paired spectral stimuli for a previously specified end-point, namely, absence of opponent hues. This end-point was not a colour match between two sides of a bipartite field.

If one remembers that the results both of our form of experiment and of the colour-matching experiment (as well as of all other psychophysical experiments in colour) are attributable to the activity of the same underlying nervous tissues and mechanisms — whatever their natures — then it is of course not surprising that the various forms of experiments are interrelated. One can, as we have shown, derive colour-mixture curves as well as other psychophysical functions from what we think of as the more basic response functions. If all that concerns one is colour mixture then I suppose our cancellation experiments are a roundabout way of getting colour-mixture curves.

Frankly, if we wanted colour-mixture curves, we would do a regular colour-mixture experiment. We did the hue cancellation experiments because they give us more information than a colour-matching experiment. They give us quantitative estimates of perceived colour qualities, which we cannot get from mixture data alone. Moreover, since all psychophysical experiments ultimately depend on these perceived qualities, either identity of perceptions in match experiments or differences in discrimination experiments, we can use the basic response data to derive these other functions.

Dr. Stiles also inquired whether the subtractions in our theory were arithmetic or logarithmic and at what level the opponent activities are subtracted.

First, our conceptualization is one of opponent interactive activities and 'subtraction' can be spoken of only in terms of the formalized mathematical model as a way of expressing net activities. In this model we have found an arithmetic treatment to be very successful in handling a multiplicity of quantitative psychophysical data. The psychophysical data themselves give us no way of knowing at what level the specific processes are acting in specific ways. If Dr. Stiles says there are others who think they can decide about that, I can only say 'good'. We have no objection whatsoever.

STILES

I find myself substantially in agreement with Professor Hurvich's remarks in reply to my questions. On his last point on the essential limitation of psychophysical measurements, I am glad to think that this is now well understood. It would follow, I think, that, in organizing their results into formal theoretical schemes introducing such concepts as absorption by photosensitive pigments or conversion of the direct effects of light absorption into higher level activity, psychophysicists should take particular care that their assumptions are not at variance with the information obtained by other investigators using objective methods.

PIÉRON

Je vous remercie. Cette intéressante discussion pourra reprendre demain, à propos du rapport de synthèse du Professeur Le Grand sur les différents schémas psychophysiques.

III

EXPOSÉS ET RAPPORT DE SYNTHÈSE
SUR LES SCHÉMAS PSYCHOPHYSIQUES

PIÉRON

Nous devons, dans cette séance, examiner les conceptions de mécanismes qui sortent des deux schémas les plus classiques.

Comme ici nous avons MM. Scheglmann et Hansel, qui ont des conceptions particulières, justement au point de vue de ces mécanismes, nous allons tout d'abord leur donner la parole avant que M. Yves Le Grand envisage tout l'ensemble de ces schémas de manière exhaustive.

Le Dr. Scheglmann a la parole.

SCHEGLMANN

Meine sehr geehrten Damen und Herren!

Ich danke Herrn Professor Piéron, dass er mir die Gelegenheit gibt, hier in deutscher Sprache zur Diskussion zu sprechen.

Gestern wurde der Gegensatz zwischen den beiden grossen Theoremen des Farbsehens: der Drei-Komponententheorie von Young-Helmholtz und der Vier-Komponenten- bezw. Gegenfarbentheorie von Hering offenbar. Beide Theoreme gehen von *speziellen* Phänomenen aus, Young-Helmholtz von der Mischungsökonomie und Hering von der Gegenfarbenökonomie. Eine endgültige Entscheidung zu Gunsten des einen oder des anderen Theorems ist bis heute nicht möglich und dürfte wohl auch nicht zu erwarten sein. Das liegt m. E. an dem speziellen Ausgangspunkt der beiden Theoreme, von denen jedes nur einen Teil der Farbsehphänomene zu erklären vermag.

Um aus dem Dilemma heraus zu kommen, müsste man m. E. einen *allgemeineren Ausgangspunkt* suchen, welcher die beiden speziellen enthält. Dieser allgemeine Ausgangspunkt ist meiner Meinung nach *das Spektrum mit seinen fünf Hauptspektralfarben Rot, Gelb, Grün, Blau und Violett*. Schon ein flüchtiger Vergleich zeigt, dass in diesen fünf Grundfarben sowohl diejenigen der Drei-Komponententheorie als auch die der Gegenfarbentheorie enthalten sind, denn Rot-Grün-Violett (Young-Helmholtz) + Rot-Gelb-Grün-Blau (Hering) = Rot-Gelb-Grün-Blau-Violett.

Angesichts der grundlegenden Bedeutung des Spektrums in allen naturwissenschaftlichen Disziplinen muss man sich eigentlich wundern, dass es bisher keine Farbsehtheorie gibt, welche vom Spektrum ausgeht. Diese Lücke versuchte ich zu schliessen, indem ich *eine Fünf-Komponenten- bezw.- Spektraltheorie des Farbsehens* entwickelte. Deren Grundzüge möchte ich kurz darstellen:

Die erwähnten fünf Hauptspektralfarben kann man an jedem spektrum auf den ersten Blick feststellen. Nun spricht man zwar, insbes. seit Newton, tranditionellerweise von sieben Spektralfarben. Diese stammen jedoch nicht aus der unmittelbaren Anschauung, sondern aus dem Vergleich mit der sieben stufigen Tonleiter. Die unmittelbare Anschauung zeigt nur fünf Hauptspektralfarben. Goethe weist in seiner Farbenlehre bereits auf sie hin, wenngleich er, wohl wegen seiner Kontroverse mit dem Standpunkt Newtons, diesen Weg nicht weiterverfolgt hat. Hering erwähnt bei der Konkretisierung seiner Gegenfarbentheorie, dass das Rot-Grünsystem im Violett ein weiteres Dissimilationsmaximum habe. Brückner, ein Schüler Herings, der die Valenzkurven Herings darstellte, kommt somit zu fünf Maximas: (*a*) Rot (+), Grün (−), Violett (+); (*b*) Gelb (+), Blau (−).

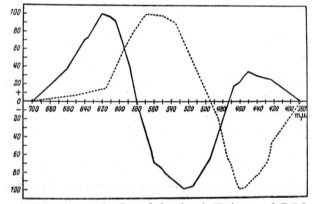

Abb. 1. Valenzkurven der Gegenfarbentheorie Herings, nach Brückner.

Tschermak (1929), ebenfalls ein Schüler Herings, vertrat die Auffassung, dass man nur mit den fünf Hauptspektralfarben alle übrigen in voller Sättigung und Nuance durch Mischung reproduzieren kann; weder drei noch vier reichen nach ihm dazu aus, da man damit die volle Sättigung nicht überall erreicht. Phänomenal sind also die fünf Hauptspektralfarben ein gut gesicherter Ausgangspunkt für farbsehtheoretische Erwägungen; vor allem sind sie ein unmittelbar Naturgegebenes und kein Produkt abstrahierender Reflexion, wie die Grundfarben von Young-Helmholtz und Hering.

Man war von jeher bestrebt, für die postulierten Grundempfindungen nervöse Strukturen (Farbapparate) in der Retina zu finden. Bekanntlich nahm bereits Young drei Nervenfasern an. Leider konnte man trotz eifrigen Suchens bisher in der Retina weder drei noch vier Nervenstrukturen finden und musste somit auf einen der wichtigsten Beweisfaktoren verzichten. In diesem Dilemma gab man sich schliesslich mit drei Zapfensehstoffen zufrieden. Neuerdings stellt sich aber heraus, dass auch hier die Rechnung nicht aufgeht. Sicher sind Sehstoffe vorhanden; sie haben jedoch wahrscheinlich nur eine Hilfsfunktion, indem sie die Lichtreize auf das Nervensubstrat

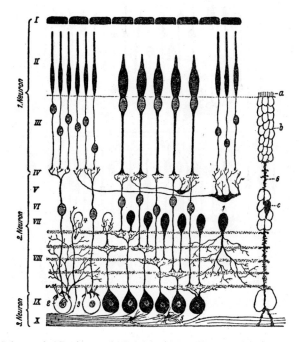

ABB. 2. Schema der Retina nach Cajal, von Greeff: VIII innere pl. Schichten, IV äussere pl. Schicht.

übertragen. Da aber die Empfindungen in Letzterem entstehen, müssen in ihm unterscheidbare Strukturen vorhanden sei, und zwar in der Retina.

Geht man von fünf Grundfarben aus, so ist es leicht, in der Retina eine entsprechende Anzahl nervöser Strukturen zu finden. Ich meine damit *die fünf inneren plexiformen (bezw. retikulären) Schichten.* Sie kommen in den Retinae der gesamten Wirbeltierreihe vor und sind anatomisch einwandfrei ausgewiesen und zwar zuerst von Ramon y Cajal (1894), später von Greeff, Schaffer, Callius und neuerdings von Polyak (1948).

Ich bin also der Meinung, dass die inneren plexiformen Schichten, die Farbapparate für die fünf Hauptspektralfarben Rot, Gelb, Grün, Blau und Violett sind. Einen Hinweis auf die Zuordnung dieser fünf Grundempfindungen zu den fünf Schichten geben die *Flimmerfarben der Benhamschen Scheibe*. Bekanntlich erscheint bei ihr der 1. Reizstreifen rötlich und die folgenden erscheinen in spektraler Reihe. Ich vermute, dass Rot deshalb zuerst anspricht, weil der entsprechende Farbapparat den Zapfen am

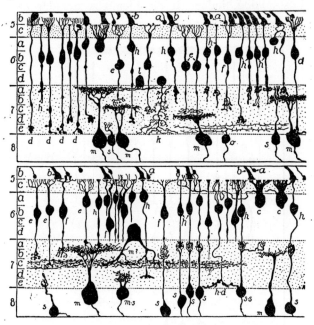

ABB. 3. Retina nach Polyak (1948) 7 a-e innere pl. Schichten.

nächsten liegt und somit hier die Erregungen zuerst ankommen. Es würde demgemäss die 1. Schicht für Rot relevant sein. Im Ganzen ergäbe sich dann folgende Zuordnung:

Zapfen
äussere pl. Schicht
1. inn. pl.   „ : Rot
2. „   „   „ : Gelb
3. „   „   „ : Grün
4. „   „   „ : Blau
5. „   „   „ : Violett

Wie bereits erwähnt ist eine Erweiterung auf fünf Komponenten bereits von Hering und seiner Schule angebahnt worden und zwar in der Weise, dass sich zwei Teilsysteme ergeben: (*a*) Rot, Grün, Violett; (*b*) Gelb, Blau. Auf eine derartige Unterscheidung weisen auch bestimmte Phänomene hin. So erscheinen beim Brücke-Bezold-Phänomen nur mehr die Farben Rot, Grün und Violett; hingegen beim Bezold-Abney-Phänomen nur mehr Gelb und Blau. Janicki & Lau (1926) kamen auf Grund ihrer Untersuchungen des Brücke-Bezold-Phänomens zu der Auffassung, dass Rot, Grün und Violett eine niedrigere Schwelle haben als Gelb und Blau. Sie weisen in diesem Zusammenhang darauf hin, dass der Ansatz Herings auf fünf Grundfarben zu erweitern sei. — Auch von der Retinaanatomie aus ergibt sich ein Hinweis auf eine Zweiteilung des fünfschichtigen Farbsystems. Nach Cajal (1894) ist nämlich die 2. und 4. Schicht besonders häufig gemeinsam innerviert (s. Abb. 4).

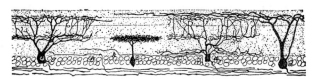

ABB. 4. Gemeinsame Innervation der 2. und 4. inneren pl. Schicht, aus Cajal.

Diese Daten erlauben es, innerhalb des fünf gliederigen Farbsystems 2 *Farbteilsysteme* anzunehmen:

1. Rot — Grün — Violett
2. Gelb — Blau

Jedes dieser beiden Teilsysteme ist in sich kompensativ dh. es ergibt zusammen Unbunt. Das 1. Teilsystem enthält die Grundfarben der Drei-Komponententheorie, das 2. Teilsystem enthält das, was Hering hinzubrachte, also das Gegenfarbenpaar Gelb — Blau.

Von der Hypothese der Farbteilsysteme aus lassen sich die *Farbfehlsichtigkeiten* gut erklären. Demnach würde dei Funktionsuntüchtigkeit des 1. Farbteilsystems *Deuteranopie* entstehen und bei Funktionsuntüchtigkeit des 2. Farbteilsystems *Tritanopie*. Bei *Protanopie* vermute ich dieselbe Ursache wie bei Deuteranopie, jedoch zusätzlich einen Defekt in der äusseren pl. Schicht oder bei den Sehstoffen. Es dürfte auch ein Zusammenhang der Teilsysteme mit der *Gelb-Blau-Blindheit der Fovea* und der Rot-Grünblindheit der Retinaperipherie bestehen, denn die Anzahl der Schichten ist in der Fovea reduziert, ebenso nimmt nach Cajal (1894) die Anzahl der Schichten in der Retinaperipherie ab.

Ehe ich mich den physiologischen Daten zuwende, möchte ich noch auf eine Besonderheit der Retinastruktur hinweisen, die auf die Bedeutung der inneren pl. Schichten für das Farbsehen hindeutet. In dem Schema von Greeff nach Cajal, Abb. 2 ist das zu sehen. Es werden *hier nur die Zapfen zu jeweils einer der fünf Schichten abgeleitet*; hingegen werden die *Stäbchen direkt* zu den Körpern der Ganglienzellen abgeleitet *ohne die inneren pl. Schichten zu berühren.* Da nun nach der *Duplizitätstheorie* nur die Zapfen farbempfindlich sind und diese wie erwähnt durchwegs zu den inneren pl. Schichten abgeleitet werden, ergibt sich rein vom Anatomischen her ein Hinweis auf die Bedeutung der inneren pl. Schichten für das Farbsehen. Andererseits lässt dieser Sachverhalt den Schluss zu, dass *die äussere pl. Schicht*, in welche Stäbchen und Zapfen einmünden, für das Sehen des Unbunt von Bedeutung ist. Hier vermute ich also einen 2 *teiligen Unbuntapparat.*

Nun komme ich zu den *physiologischen Daten.* Hier ergeben sich aus dem *Elektroretinogramm* bei Farbreizen (Farb-ERG) Hinweise auf die spektrale Reihenfolge. Kohlrausch stellte bereits 1918 mit der Methode der Aktionsstromgleichung fest, dass Rot die höchste ERG-Kurve ergibt und die Kurven der übrigen Spektralfarben in spektraler Reihenfolge niedriger werden. Abb. 5 zeigt Kurven von Kohlrausch:

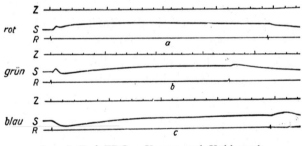

ABB. 5. Farb-ERG — Kurven nach Kohlrausch.

Neuerdings hat Müller-Limmroth (1951) mit äquienergetischen Spektrallichtern dies elbe Reihenfolge der Kurvenhöhen erzielt.

Die unterschiedlichen Kurvenhöhen legen den Gedanken nahe, dass in der Retina strukturabhängige Dauerpotentiale vorhanden sind, welche die Zapfenerregungen auf die verschiedenen Niveaus heben. Entsprechend den Kurvenhöhen müsste dann Rot das höchste Dauerpotential haben. Ich bezeichne diese hypothetischen Dauerpotentiale als *Retinapotentiale*, bezw. soweit sie die fünf farbigen Grundempfindungen betreffen als *Farbpotentiale.* Sie dürften durch den Lebensprozess der Amakrinen entstehen. *Die Farbpotentiale wären demnach die spezifischen Sinnesenergien des Farbsehens.* Ihre Höhe wäre in relativen Zahlen:

		relative Potentialhöhe
1. Schicht	Rot	5
2. „	Gelb	4
3. „	Grün	3
4. „	Blau	2
5. „	Violett	1

Diese Farbpotentiale dürften die Zapfen ständig different *abstimmen*, so dass also der Erregungskomplex in die richtigen Farbschichten abgeleitet werden kann. Auch die Weiterleitung der Erregungen zum primären Sehzentrum und zur Sehrinde dürfte durch diese Abstimmungen gebahnt sein.

Der *Empfindungsprozess* würde demnach folgendermassen verlaufen: Die Sehstoffe — ihre Anzahl und Art kann offen bleiben — übertragen die Reize auf die Zapfen. Durch die Abstimmungen werden dann die Erregungen in die entsprechenden inneren pl. Schichten abgeleitet. In diesen entsteht bei Voraussetzung des Zusammenhangs mit den höheren Zentren und der Intaktheit derselben die Farbempfindung.

Wenngleich mein Stoff noch keineswegs erschöpft ist, so muss ich nun doch abbrechen, da die Redezeit zu Ende geht. Ich hoffe, dass es mir trotz der fragmentarischen Kürze dieser Ausführungen gelungen ist, sie auf die Fruchtbarkeit des Fünf Komponentenansatzes hinzuweisen: Das Spektrum ist die naturgegebene Farbordnung. Eine Farsehtheorie, welche vom Spektrum ausgeht, dürfte daher der Natur der Dinge am nächsten kommen.

Anmerkung: Der Verfasser war bis zum März dieses Jahres Dozent am Psychologischen Institut der Universität Leipzig. Er musste von dort fliehen und arbeitet jetzt am Psychologischen Institut der Universität Tübingen. Die bisherigen Veröffentlichungen zur Theorie erschienen in Leipzig (siehe Literaturverz). Eine grössere, zusammenfassende Veröffentlichung ist geplant.

LITERATURVERZEICHNIS

TSCHERMAK, A. (1929) Licht & Farbensinn, *Handbuch der norm. & path. Physiologie*, Bd. XII/1, S. 418 ff.

JANICKI, L. & LAU, E. (1926) Über die Abhängigkeit der Farbe von der Intensität, *Z. Sinnesphysiol.*, **57**.

CAJAL, RAMON Y (1894) *Die Retina der Wirbeltiere*, Wiesbaden.

KOHLRAUSCH, A. (1918) Die Netzhausströme in Abhängigkeit von der Wellenlänge des Lichtes und dem Adaptationszustand, *Arch. Anat. und Physiol. Psychol.*, Abt.

MÜLLER-LIMMROTH, H. W. (1951) Das ERG des Frosches unter Einwirkung von Strychnin, Urethan und Santonin nach Belichtung mit energiegleichem Licht verschiedener Wellenlänge, *Pflügers Arch. ges. Physiol.*, **254**, 155 ff.

Vom Verfasser: SCHEGLMANN, L. (1954) *Z. Psychol.*, **157**, *Heft* 3-4, J. A. Barth-Verlag, Leipzig; (1955-56) Eine 5-Komponententheorie des Farbsehens I, *wiss. Z. d. Univ.*

Leipzig, 5. *Jhg.*, *Heft* 1, gesellsch. & sprachwiss. Reihe; (1956-57) Eine 5-Komponentheorie des Farbsehens II, *wiss. Z. d. Univ. Leipzig*, 6. *Jhg.*, *Heft* 5.
Verzeichnis der Abbildungen (*Herkunft derselben*)
Valenzkurven — TRENDELENBURG, W. (1943) *Der Gesichtssinn*, Bln.
Retina n. Cajal — TRENDELENBURG, W. (1943) *Der Gesichtssinn*, Bln.
Retina n. Polyak — POLYAK, S. L. (1948) *The Retina*, Chicago.
2. & 4. Schicht — CAJAL, R. Y. (1894) *Die Retina der Wirbeltiere*, Weisbaden.
Farb-ERG — KOHLRAUSCH, A. (1929) Elektrische Erscheinungen am Auge. *Handbuch der norm. & path. Physiologie*, Bd. XII.

PIÉRON

Nous allons tout de suite passer à l'exposé de M. Hansel.

HANSEL

I would like to draw attention to two well-known phenomena which, taken together, may throw some light on the nature of the retinal photoreceptors. First, it is possible to obtain neutral matches by means of two complementary lights, one being of any wavelength up to about 494 mμ, and the other of a suitable wavelength greater than about 570 mμ. Second, as was pointed out by Grünberg in 1905, the wavelength of lights which combine in this way are connected by a simple equation of the form:

$$(496 - \lambda_1)(\lambda_2 - 563.7) = 260.3$$

In terms of the trichromatic theory three sensitivities are equally excited by two complementary lights. Let the sensitivities be represented by r, g, b. Consider two of the sensitivities r and b in Fig. 1. If L_1 (of intensity L_2) be

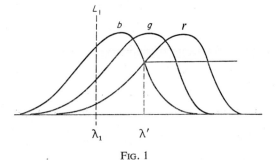

FIG. 1

fixed at λ_1, L_2 may occupy the range of wavelengths greater than the wavelength at which r and b intersect (λ'), and at each wavelength the intensity L_1 may be adjusted to make the total excitation of r equal to that of b. If now the total excitation of g varies at these values of L_2 so that it is less than that of r (or b) at one extreme position of L_2 and greater than that of r (or b) at the other extreme, there will be a position at which it will be equal to that of r and thus also b.

It will also be seen that wavelengths which can form a complementary pair must fall outside the intersection points of any two sensitivities — that is, unless double intersection points are involved which would create even greater difficulties than those to be discussed. Thus, we should expect the outermost intersection points of the three curves to be at wavelengths greater than 494 mμ and less than 570 mμ.

The phenomenon pointed out by Grünberg would make it likely that the three curves are similar in form, for it is difficult to see how three sensitivities of quite different types could arise so as to produce the smooth hyperbolic relationship which has been observed. It is also thought to be unlikely that the sensitivities would have maximi in the ranges of wavelengths in which complementary pairs occur. For if, say, the b sensitivity had a maximum at 450 mμ we would expect this to manifest itself in the relationship connecting the wavelengths of the complementary lights, whereas it is only the *intensity* of light required at 450 mμ which approaches a minimum value and the hyperbolic relationship connecting wavelengths is in no way affected.

This phenomenon can also be approached in terms of Hering's theory, and in so far as Hering's theory can be represented in terms of three fundamental sensitivities, the above arguments also apply. It will be seen in Fig. 2a that

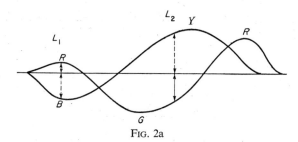

Fig. 2a

for a neutral match to occur, the negative and positive components of both the *BY* and *GR* curves have to yield products equal but opposite in sign, with suitable values of L_1 and L_2. As the Hering formulation can be consistent with the trichromatic theory and also describes more adequately a number of colour phenomena it will be elaborated in the ensuing argument.

It may first be noted that the *GR* curve of Hering's theory when specified so that its neutral points agree with those observed in a variety of phenomena (such as the position of yellow in the spectrum, the neutral points for the tetartanope, and the neutral points of the Bezold-Brücke phenomenon) approximates in form to the differential of the *BY* curve. The *BY* curve itself is not dissimilar to the differential of the scotopic luminosity characteristic.

If the *BY* and *GR* curves were generated by three sensitivities of approximately similar form but displaced to a small extent relatively to each other in the spectrum, this feature would arise and we should expect the maximi of the three sensitivities, before correction for macula absorption, to be around 500 mμ.

Hering's theory may be represented in terms of known physiological processes if the *BY* curve is generated by two sensitivities acting in opposition, (Fig. 2b), only positive components being present as is necessary when trans-

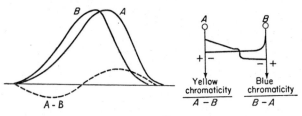

FIG. 2b

mission is by nerve impulses. Thus given two sensitivities *A*, and *B* (Fig. 2b *B*—*A* represents Hering's *BY* curve. The positive component of *A*—*B* (represented by $\overline{A-B}$ now constitutes the yellow chromaticity and $\overline{B-A}$ constitutes the blue chromaticity. Two receptors would be firing in opposition to each other, the resultant being either $\overline{A-B}$ or $\overline{B-A}$. This type of mechanism is not unlikely as it constitutes one of the fundamental processes of the nervous system, and is precisely the type of neural mechanism involved in the reciprocal innervation of muscle. As the neutral point of such a dichromatic system would be around 500 mμ it could be set up if one sensitivity (*A*) employed rhodopsin and the other (*B*) rhodopsin modified so that its absorption characteristic was shifted slightly towards the blue end of the spectrum.

The *GR* characteristic of Hering's theory could be formed if a third sensitivity *C* arose, with its absorption shifted to a different extent towards the blue end of the spectrum from *B*. The three sensitivities *A*, *B* and *C* could then create three dichromatic systems, represented by *A*—*B*, *A*—*C*, and *C*—*B*. The *GR* curve of Hering's theory is now represented by (*C*—*B*)—(*A*—*C*).

It is often assumed that the intersection point of two of the fundamentals should correspond to the yellow point of the spectrum. If the crossover point is at 569 mμ or less, it is close to the neutral point for tritanopes, but is low when compared with the yellow point in the spectrum (about 575 mμ). On the other hand, if a neutral point is present at 575 mμ a second neutral point would be expected at 470 mμ. The neutral point at 569 mμ will not yield a second neutral point in the spectrum and, in fact, the two crossover points at 494 mμ and 569 mμ are at such positions that second neutral points will fall at the extremes of the spectrum, as if the *b* and *g* and the *g* and *r* curves meet at these points.

Thus in so far as intersection points at 494 mμ and 569 mμ are indicated by the positions at which complementary pairs of lights are found, the systems *directly* derived from the sensitivities, i.e. having intersection points at these wavelengths, would be those of the deuteranope (or protanope) and tritanope.

Thus in Fig. 3, *A—B* represents the *BY* curve and the deuteranopic

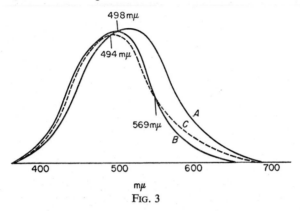

Fig. 3

system* and *C—B* the tritanopic system.† *(C—B)—K(A—C)* now represents the *GR* curve (and the tetartanopic system).‡ *A—C* by itself represents the protanopic system§ (not used directly in normal vision).

As the absorption characteristic of *C* approaches *B* the *GR* curve vanishes and the deuteranopic system is left in operation; as *B* approaches *C* the *GR* curve vanishes and the protanopic system is left in operation. Intermediate degrees of shift bring about the different states of anomalous trichromatism. The tritanopic characteristic arises with absence of *A*, or as *A* approaches *B* and the tetartanopic condition with failure of transmission of the *B* and *Y* chromaticities.

It will be noted that whilst tristimulus specifications will hold when one curve is subtracted from the other, the actual sensitivities need not conform to tristimulus specifications as a common element is lost by subtraction. So far as the luminosity characteristic itself is concerned, it is thought that this will be compounded by addition of some of the chromaticities formed by subtraction. Thus $K(\overline{B-C})+(\overline{A-B})$ gives a close fit to the luminosity characteristic.

---

* In the form 0.07*X*, +0.945*Y*, −1.015*Z*, giving a neutral point at 498 mμ.
† In the form 0.46*X*, −0.359*Y*, −0.101*Z*, giving a neutral point at 569 mμ.
‡ In the form 0.525*X*, −0.483*Y*, −0.042*Z*, giving neutral points at 471 mμ and 575 mμ.
§ In the form −0.46*X*, +1.359*Y* −0.899*Z*, giving a neutral point at 494 mμ.

It is thus possible for light absorbers of the rhodopsin form with maximi around 500 mμ or less (before screening) to set up chromaticities which have sensitivities corresponding to those expected from a variety of data and such chromaticities would cancel out in a manner similar to that postulated by Hering.

Whilst rhodopsin-type pigments have been isolated from the human retina, other hypothetical pigments are dependent on the assumptions underlying the technique by which they are determined. In some cases it is possible that it is a chromaticity characteristic which is being determined rather than that of one of the light absorbers. The correspondence between the shape of the photopic and scotopic luminosity characteristics above 650 mμ suggests that rhodopsin is involved in photopic vision, but it is difficult to account for the photopic characteristic between 560 mμ and 650 mμ in terms of rhodopsin unless receptors act in opposition in the manner indicated.

From Fig. 3 it will be seen that if A is the rhodopsin characteristic and B has a relatively small absorption beyond 650 mμ, the sensitivity at the red end of the deuteranopic characteristic, $\overline{A - B}$, will be that of rhodopsin. With dark adaptation a lower threshold of A will result in it finally taking over in scotopic vision. The presence of only B and C in the fovea will result in tritanopia and absence of scotopic vision.

During the course of light adaptation, A will initially be in action during scotopic vision. At higher levels of illumination as B and C come into operation they will attenuate to an increasing extent the output of A. Thus the luminosity characteristic will change, shifting gradually towards the red end of the spectrum. When the photopic state is reached, B and C, besides creating the chromaticities, will give increasing degrees of negative feedback, thus compensating for increases in the level of illumination.

VUE D'ENSEMBLE SUR LES SCHÉMAS PSYCHOPHYSIQUES

Y. LE GRAND

On vous a tellement parlé de théories de la couleur que je n'ai plus rien à dire du tout.

Néanmoins, il est peut-être utile d'essayer d'introduire un peu de cartésianisme, puisque nous sommes dans un lieu où la pensée a toujours été en honneur: dans le Collège de France — essayer d'introduire un peu de logique et, peut-être, un peu d'ordre dans cette idée tumultueuse des théories de la vision des couleurs.

Je voudrais d'abord, historiquement, faire remarquer que ce ne sont pas Young, d'une part, et Hering, de l'autre, qui sont responsables ni des trois ni des quatre couleurs, et que bien des siècles avant eux c'était une idée tout à fait commune.

Les quatre couleurs principales en deux paires sont une conception d'artistes sensibles à la beauté et à la qualité propre de la sensation colorée, et Léonard de Vinci dit sensiblement ce que Hering devait dire plusieurs siècles après.

De même que les trois fondamentales de Young étaient, dès le XVIIème siècle, un lieu commun, et que, par exemple, Mariotte présentait — je ne pense pas à notre collègue qui est ici, mais au physicien célèbre pour la loi de la compression des gaz — présentait, donc, le trichromatisme comme une constatation tout à fait triviale.

Vous savez qu'en 1722 le graveur Leblon, inventeur de la technique de la gravure en couleurs par planches successives, après avoir commencé ingénument par les sept planches qu'il croyait correspondre aux sept couleurs newtoniennes du spectre, a progressivement et empiriquement obtenu d'aussi bons résultats avec trois planches.

Mais ce que Young a fait le premier, c'est que cette division de la lumière en trois, il a deviné qu'elle n'était pas une propriété physique de la lumière, comme on le croyait jusque là, mais une simplification physiologique introduite par la rétine.

Young y a été conduit uniquement parce qu'il était convaincu de la réalité des ondulations lumineuses de Huyghens — d'ailleurs, un peu plus tard, il devait apporter un argument décisif à la théorie des ondulations, par sa célèbre expérience d'interférences des 2 trous — et que si dans la théorie de l'émission de Newton il est facile d'imaginer trois types différents de particules lumineuses, cela devient quasi inconcevable en hypothèse ondulatoire.

C'est exactement ce que dit Young dans son célèbre mémoire de 1802.

'Comme il est presque impossible, écrit-il, d'imaginer que chaque point sensible de la rétine contienne un nombre infini de particules, chacune capable de vibrer à l'unisson avec chaque ondulation possible, il devient nécessaire de supposer leur nombre limité, par exemple, à trois.'

Remarquez que Young n'avait introduit le nombre de trois que parce que c'était l'idée courante, mais que n'importe quel autre nombre aurait été aussi possible. Donc, Young n'a pas inventé le nombre trois; il l'a pris dans les conceptions de ses prédécesseurs.

Mais son idée géniale a été de placer dans la rétine — et non plus dans la nature de la lumière elle-même — cette simplification physiologique. Il est donc normal que le symbole du trichromatisme soit attribué à Young.

Plus généralement, on peut supposer m types différents de récepteurs dont chacun soit susceptible de répondre de n façons différentes.

En outre, on peut, dans certaines théories, supposer un récepteur distinct (que j'appellerai $p = 1$, s'il existe; $p = 0$, s'il n'existe pas) pour expliquer la vision photopique.

Chez un sujet normal, la condition mathématique du monde des couleurs à trois dimensions que le Dr. Stiles a fort bien expliqué hier, impose une condition mathématique très simple:

$$mn + p \geqslant 3.$$

A partir de là, toutes les hypothèses sont évidemment possibles, et je vais rapidement les prendre dans l'ordre.

La plus simple de toutes est $m = 1$, c'est-à-dire un seul type de récepteur, un seul type de cônes, si vous voulez, susceptible de répondre de trois façons différentes ($n = 3$).

C'est, par exemple, la théorie de Polyak, qui suppose que chaque cône de la rétine est imbibé d'un mélange de trois substances photoréceptrices qui, chacune, agit électivement sur l'une des bipolaires reliés à ce cône — ce qui serait d'accord avec les mensurations de Vilter, qui considère qu'il y a trois fois plus de bipolaires que de cônes.

C'est également la base de la théorie de Ingelstamm, à laquelle on a déjà fait allusion, qui suppose que la structure feuilletée des cônes, que démontre l'étude au microscope électronique, agit comme des filtres interférentiels, permettant, par des conditions de résonance, d'avoir un certain nombre, trois, par exemple, de réponses différentes à l'intérieur de chaque cône.

Néanmoins, sa théorie de résonance ne semble pas très probable pour une raison très simple: c'est qu'elle serait extrêmement sensible à la direction des rayons.

Vous savez que le filtre interférentiel change beaucoup de longueur d'onde quand on le regarde obliquement. Dans ces conditions, si cela peut expliquer les faibles variations de tonalité dans l'effet Stiles-Crawford, cela n'expliquerait pas que des lumières arrivant très obliquement sur les cônes, telles qu'il en arrive par diffusion dans la rétine elle-même, comme, par exemple, par diffusion sur la tache aveugle — donnent une impression colorée qui est pratiquement identique à celle que l'on obtient par l'excitation directe.

Dans ce même type de théorie, je voudrais aussi rappeler une théorie récente de Shaw qui fait intervenir la dispersion rotatoire des pigments à l'intérieur de chaque cône.

Il y a une autre possibilité: c'est $m = 1$, et $n = \infty$, c'est-à-dire une théorie à variation continue, comme Wundt et Edridge Green l'avaient proposée.

Evidemment, elle soulève une grosse difficulté; c'est que les nombres plus grands que 3 doivent être ramenés à la trivariance visuelle. Il faut supposer des conditions d'interaction qui, physiologiquement, sont difficiles à imaginer.

Un autre type classique est évidemment la théorie de type Hering, à savoir deux couples antagonistes, avec un troisième récepteur pour le blanc $m = 2$, $n = 2$, $p = 1$, afin de ne pas chagriner le Professeur Piéron, je ne parlerai pas d'un troisième couple antagoniste; je n'insisterai pas sur cette théorie qui a été fort bien exposée par le Dr. Hurvich et passerai à la théorie trichromatique de Young, sous sa forme la plus rudimentaire, c'est-à-dire trois récepteurs, chacun recevant d'une seule façon, sans récepteur spécialisé pour le blanc, soit: $m = 3$, $n = 1$, $p = 0$. Ces récepteurs sont généralement supposés sur la base de trois pigments différents, chacun imbibant un type donné de cône.

Bien entendu, d'autres hypothèses sont possibles. Par exemple, chez les poulets, comme on nous l'a rappelé, il y a des globules colorés placés devant les cônes. Il est possible qu'avec une seule substance photochimique, du type iodopsine, on puisse avoir néanmoins dans ce cas trois types de réponse.

Il existe également la possibilité de plusieurs réponses avec une seule substance photosensible dans laquelle des produits de décomposition peuvent être inclus, comme Lythgoe l'avait proposé il y a déjà une trentaine d'années, hypothèse que le Dr. Dartnall nous a rappelée dans sa communication.

Je vous cite également pour mémoire une théorie qui fut proposée, il y a une dizaine d'années, par Segal, et dans laquelle un seul pigment photosensible existait, à savoir le pourpre rétinien, mais dans des états physiques et des conditions d'écran différents.

En outre, Segal supposait que les récepteurs étaient étagés en profondeur, mais c'est un point peut-être un peu accessoire dans notre nomenclature mathématique.

Une autre hypothèse est $m = 3$, $n = 1$, $p = 1$, c'est-à-dire la théorie de

Young, à laquelle on adjoint un récepteur spécial pour la luminosité, comme MacDougal l'avait proposé; plus récemment, le Professeur Piéron en a fait une théorie très séduisante, sous le nom de la tétrade de cônes.

Je voudrais vous rappeler sommairement les raisons pour ce récepteur de luminosité indépendant. Les principaux arguments pour son existence sont les suivants:

D'abord le phénomène de Aubert, suivant lequel un point coloré sur un fond gris de même luminance paraît incolore, ce qui s'explique très bien, évidemment, si les récepteurs de luminance sont relativement nombreux par rapport aux récepteurs de couleur —bien qu'à vrai dire les données physiques sur l'étalement de la structure de l'image pourraient expliquer le même phénomène.

Ensuite, et surtout, l'indépendance des effets d'adaptation colorée et d'adaptation chromatique, sur lesquels le Professeur Piéron a beaucoup insisté avec raison.

Et troisièmement, la difficulté d'expliquer l'additivité des luminances, c'est-à-dire la loi d'Abney dans le cas où il n'y a pas de récepteur spécial pour la luminosité.

A vrai dire, ce dernier argument perd beaucoup de sa valeur depuis que des recherches modernes laissent entrevoir la possibilité d'additivité arithmétique au niveau élémentaire de la réception, avant la transformation logarithmique.

Le récepteur du type Piéron peut être obtenu évidemment par un mélange des trois pigments des cônes, tandis que si c'est un pigment indépendant, il devient nécessaire de supposer une liaison supplémentaire pour conserver la trivariance.

Mais je voulais faire remarques que, dans ce cas, il y a une hypothèse très simple à laquelle, il me semble, on n'a pas pensé: ce serait la suppression du cône bleu. Un type de cônes serait sensible au rouge, le second type au vert, le troisième serait le récepteur de luminosité, et le bleu serait simplement un effet différentiel de l'excitation du blanc et de l'ensemble rouge-vert.

Je ne veux pas du tout dire que la réalité soit ainsi faite. Néanmoins, c'est un schéma qui, s'il était soutenu par quelqu'un, aurait peut-être beaucoup d'arguments pour lui. Par exemple, on expliquerait facilement, qu'on ne trouve pas de récepteur bleu et d'autre part, que, dans la fovéa où il y a surtout les deux types de récepteurs (rouge et vert) et peu de récepteurs de luminance, il se manifeste un dichromatisme fovéal.

D'autre part, cela rendrait compte également de la faible sensibilité différentielle et la mauvaise acuité relative à la fondamentale bleue; et enfin, en admettant que les bâtonnets puissent intervenir, on réconcilierait, en un sens, Willmer avec Young et tout le monde serait content.

Il existe encore, évidemment, d'autres possibilités: ainsi $m = 3$, $n = 2$, et $p = 0$. C'est une théorie hexachromatique, dérivée de Hering et qui a été proposée par un certain nombre de psychologues; et enfin, toutes les théories dans lesquelles *m* est plus grand que trois, par exemple la théorie polychromatique soutenue par Hartridge. Vous avez, je crois, de cette façon, épuisé mathématiquement à peu près toutes les possibilités, à moins, évidemment, qu'on ne complique encore le problème.

Evidemment, à partir du moment où on suppose l'existence de trois pigments photosensibles, il est bien évident que la façon dont ils sont répartis dans des récepteurs est sans importance pour la colorimétrie.

C'est un fait que le Dr. Stiles l'autre jour a mentionné: puisque toute la colorimétrie repose uniquement sur la notion de stimuli équivalents, c'est-à-dire de deux lumières qui donnent exactement la même impression au sujet, mais où l'œil ne fonctionne que comme appareil de zéro, à partir du moment où les trois pigments sont affectés de la même façon par les deux stimuli, les lumières apparaîtront identiques quel que soit le mélange des pigments et quels que soient les mécanismes neurophysiologiques qui viendront ensuite.

Il est donc évident qu'à partir des lois de mélange des couleurs et de la colorimétrie, on ne peut rien démontrér d'autre que l'existence des trois pigments, et de pas plus de trois pigments.

Il est même possible que ces trois pigments soient répartis tout à fait au hasard, qu'il y ait une distribution continue dans les cônes, c'est-à-dire d'avoir apparemment un nombre infini de récepteurs à propriétés réceptrices différentes, comme Guild l'avait proposé il y a assez longtemps, sans que néanmoins les lois de la colorimétrie cessent de s'appliquer.

Jusqu'ici nous sommes restés sur un plan purement mathématique, pourrais-je dire, mais il faut revenir un peu à la réalité. Qu'est-ce que l'expérience nous enseigne sur ces diverses possibilités?

D'une part pour les pigments, les belles recherches du Dr. Rushton ont prouvé — autant qu'en ce monde on puisse prouver quelque chose — l'existence de deux pigments au moins dans la fovéa de l'homme normal.

D'autre part, d'intéressantes expériences de Brindley, semblent démontrer qu'il ne peut pas en exister plus de trois. Je vous rappelle que Brindley a étudié la rupture d'égalisation des équations colorées après une adaptation colorée très intense, effet qui est probablement dû à un effet d'écran des pigments eux-mêmes, ou de leurs produits de décomposition.

Il est très remarquable que toutes les lumières adaptatives, quelles que soient leurs longueurs d'onde, produisent à luminance donnée le même changement dans le rapport du rouge 680 au vert 550 nécessaire pour une égalisation avec le jaune 580 mµ.

Ce remarquable phénomène, comme Brindley l'a montré, est une preuve assez directe du fait qu'il ne peut pas exister plus de trois pigments, à moins de supposer des mécanismes physiologiques de compensation qui sont, d'un point de vue biologique, assez peu vraisemblables.

On peut dire que, à propos du nombre de pigments photosensibles, il y en a au moins deux et probablement pas plus de trois, donc vraisemblablement trois.

Cela ne veut pas dire qu'il n'existe que trois types de récepteurs, puisque, comme je vous l'ai dit tout à l'heure, on peut concevoir des mélanges quelconques de ces pigments à l'intérieur d'un type donné de cône, sans que toutes les lois linéaires du trichromatisme cessent de s'appliquer.

C'est ce qui se passe quand on quitte le domaine de la colorimétrie pour arriver aux études relatives aux seuils différentiels, par exemple, qui sont un second degré qui échappe, en quelque sorte, à la colorimétrie.

On franchit une nouvelle étape dans laquelle, cette fois, ce ne sont plus les pigments seuls qui vont intervenir, mais la façon dont ils se groupent pour réaliser des récepteurs donnés.

Comme type d'expériences de ce genre, je vous rappellerai les très belles recherches du Dr. Stiles, puisqu'il a omis d'en parler — c'est un fait remarquable de ce colloque, que chaque rapporteur oublie curieusement de parler de ses propres recherches, et laisse aux autres le soin d'en dire un mot.

Vous savez que, par sa méthode du seuil différentiel bicolore, le Dr. Stiles, après de longues et difficiles expériences, a pu arriver à isoler un certain nombre de récepteurs différents, et il arrive à la conclusion qu'il y aurait probablement dans la rétine au moins cinq types différents de récepteurs.

Par des expériences sur les conditions d'adaptation colorée, le Dr. Mac-Adam pense aussi qu'il doit y avoir cinq ou six espèces de récepteurs rétiniens — ce qui n'est pas du tout contradictoire, comme je vous le faisais remarquer, avec le fait qu'il y ait uniquement trois pigments, puisque ces récepteurs peuvent être conçus comme contenant des mélanges en proportion quelconque, et qu'en particulier il est facile de voir que, de cette façon, il doit exister sept types principaux obtenus par mélanges en proportions quelconques des trois pigments.

On peut donc dire que si la colorimétrie ne donne de réponse qu'au niveau pigments, le second niveau — à savoir: la façon dont ces pigments se répartissent dans les récepteurs — peut être, jusqu'à un certain point, étudiée par des méthodes de seuil différentiel ou d'adaptation.

On peut également les étudier par des méthodes fondées sur les anomalies de la vision des couleurs dont on vous parlera tour à l'heure.

Mais il reste un troisième niveau dont on n'a pas, jusqu'ici, parlé du tout — jusqu'ici: dans cet exposé — c'est celui de la façon dont les couleurs nous apparaissent, c'est-à-dire la psychologie de la vision colorée.

C'est là où Hering triomphe, bien entendu.

La façon dont les couleurs sont vues, et diverses notions, par exemple la vision du jaune qui jusqu'ici semblent échapper totalement au schéma de Young, ou moins nécessiter pour s'expliquer des interactions surajoutées —

surajoutées peut-être un peu artificiellement, comme dans des schémas de tétrade par exemple — au contraire, vont d'elles-mêmes au niveau supérieur, quand on suppose que les récepteurs se sont groupés d'une certaine façon, qu'il y a eu ces *pools* qui sont à la mode, non seulement en économie européenne, mais aussi dans les théories de la vision des couleurs, à un échelon postérieur de la réception.

C'est ici, comme je vous le disais, que Hering sonne de la trompette, et que Young se cache honteusement.

Cela ne prouve pas du tout que Young ait eu tort, mais simplement, que son rôle est terminé. Et dès 1881, Donders l'avait bien vu. Il avait vu qu'il fallait ramener Young au stade photorécepteur — nous dirions maintenant même, au stade pigments — tandis qu'à un stade ultérieur, c'est Hering qui a représenté la réalité.

Donders fut le premier, en 1881, à patronner ces théories de 'zones' dont la plus élaborée fut explicitée par Müller en 1930.

Dans un article de 1949, le Dr. Judd a très clairement montré comment la théorie de Müller s'articule avec les frères ennemis, Young et Hering, et peut les réconcilier dans une synthèse satisfaisante.

Seulement, à ce moment-là — en 1949 — le lieu du passage de Young à Hering était supposé dans le nerf optique ou à un niveau ultérieur, même dans le cerveau, alors que maintenant il paraît bien probable — et même Svaetichin a commencé d'en donner une preuve — que ce passage se fait dès la rétine elle-même, peut-être même dès le niveau des bipolaires.

Ce n'est pas très surprenant, puisque, comme le Professeur Piéron l'a fait remarquer, le rétine est déjà un cerveau périphérique d'une prodigieuse complexité synaptique.

Il me semble donc que c'est dans une théorie de zone du type Müller que l'espoir d'établir un schéma cohérent de la vision des couleurs peut être cherché.

Cette théorie des zones se rattache un peu à ce que le Dr. Scheglmann nous disait tout à l'heure: il est très possible qu'effectivement, au niveau des plexiformes, vous ayez, finalement, après le niveau où Hering était valable, une dernière transformation qui ferait apparaître au niveau des cellules ganglionnaires une certaine division en cinq lignes, reflétant à ce moment-là les cinq couleurs que les gens de bonne foi (je ne veux pas dire Newton, qui voulait absolument en trouver sept, par analogie avec la gamme des sons) mais que les gens qui n'ont pas d'idées préconçues voient dans le spectre.

Jusqu'ici on n'a pas beaucoup utilisé les anomalies colorées. Comme introduction à ce que le Dr. Dubois-Poulsen va nous dire dans une minute, je voudrais vous rappeler les diverses prédictions que les théoriciens ont essayé de faire sur les anomalies.

Depuis que Tuberville, en 1684, attira l'attention sur l'existence d'anomalies dans la vision colorée, anomalies que Dalton devait décrire sur lui-même en 1798, d'une façon qui fut classique et qui a rendu son nom célèbre d'une façon fâcheuse, la plupart des explications se sont fondées sur la théorie que Palmer avait, en 1777, proposée, à savoir que les anomalies devaient provenir d'une déficience de la structure de l'homme normal.

Alors, cette déficience peut être, naturellement, interprétée par chacun en faveur de sa propre théorie.

Dans la théorie de Young, on en déduit immédiatement l'existence de trois types — je laisse pour le moment les anomalies du trichromatisme, je parle seulement des formes de dichromatisme — trois types de dichromatismes qui semblent bien effectivement exister, quoique les tritanopes soient plus rares que les autres.

Mais il s'en déduit une conséquence qui est contredite par l'expérience, à savoir que seuls les tritanopes monoculaires voient bien en rouge et vert, comme la théorie de Young le prédit, alors que les autres voient du jaune et du bleu, ce qui au premier abord est évidemment ennuyeux pour la théorie de Young.

Remarquez que c'est ennuyeux, mais qu'on peut s'en tirer tout de même, si l'on fait appel à l'hypothèse de Fick c'est-à-dire à l'hypothèse que, dans le dichromatisme, ce n'est pas la suppression d'une fondamentale qui se produit, mais la confusion due, par exemple, à un mélange, dans un même cône, des pigments rouge et vert.

Inversement, la théorie de Hering explique très bien la deutéranopie. C'est son triomphe, si je peux dire. Elle explique aussi une anomalie relativement très rare: la tétartanopie, mais elle échoue, ou tout au moins elle n'explique la protanopie et la tritanopie, avec leurs complexités, qu'à l'aide d'hypothèses additionnelles.

C'est, donc, en quelque sorte, la situation inverse de celle de Young qui expliquait très bien l'une des anomalies et expliquait les deux autres avec des hypothèses accessoires.

Mais alors il est bien évident que si l'on réconcilie les deux théories dans une théorie des zones, et si l'on place le défaut à un niveau différent, c'est-à-dire que si l'on place la protanopie au niveau de Young, celui de l'absence d'un pigment — peut-être la tritanopie aussi — au contraire si on explique la deutéranopie à un autre niveau qui est celui auquel fonctionne le schéma de Hering, à ce moment-là les difficultés sont certainement atténuées dans une grande proportion.

En conclusion, et bien qu'on ne puisse, je crois, énoncer aucune certitude, je crois que c'est dans le développement des théories des zones, mais probablement dans le développement au niveau même de la rétine, c'est-à-dire en recherchant aux divers étages mêmes des synapses rétiniennes des transformations qui puissent expliquer le passage, d'abord, des trois pigments de la théorie de Young au problème de la répartition de ces trois pigments en une certaine gamme possible de récepteurs, que nous révèlent les études sur les seuils différentiels et sur certains effets d'adaptation — enfin dans le troisième niveau qui est celui auquel s'élabore la réponse qui va partir dans le nerf optique et qui est celui dont, au fond, la psychologie fait usage, celui où justement les couleurs nous apparaissent être ce qu'elles sont et telles qu'on les voit dans le spectre — c'est par une analyse à ces divers niveaux de transformation des excitations que peut-être un schéma, dans l'avenir, sera possible.

J'espère, d'ailleurs, qu'il ne le sera jamais, car ce serait, à mon avis, extrêmement triste que la vision des couleurs soit définitivement expliquée.

Mais heureusement, comme Henri Poincaré l'a dit, il n'y a pas de problèmes résolus et de problèmes non résolus; il n'y a que des problèmes plus ou moins résolus.

Si notre réunion ici n'avait pour but que de faire un peu progresser ces problèmes, j'espère que tout de même elle laissera à nos successeurs suffisamment de travail pour que dans quelques années ou quelques dizaines d'années, peut-être nous-mêmes, et, en tout cas, nos enfants, puissent se réunir ici ou autre part, pour étudier encore les possibilités d'explication de la vision colorée.

DISCUSSION

PIÉRON

Puisque le Professeur Le Grand, après son très bel exposé, donne la place maintenant aux questions d'anomalies de la vision des couleurs, dans la mesure où elles peuvent fournir des éléments pour le choix d'un schéma convenable, je donne la parole au Dr. Dubois-Poulsen qui va nous donner des indications sur les anomalies congénitales ou acquises que l'on peut rencontrer.

DUBOIS-POULSEN

C'est une règle générale que la pathologie doit puiser ses explications pathogéniques dans les disciplines de base dans l'anatomie, la chimie, la physique et dans celle qui les résume toutes: la physiologie. Il est donc naturel que les pathologistes interviennent les derniers dans ces débats.

M. Piéron m'a prié de le faire en mon nom propre, mais aussi au nom de deux de mes collègues belges qui sont ici présents: M. Zanen et M. Verriest. J'espère ne pas les trahir. Néanmoins, s'ils estiment que je les ai mal interprétés, ils en seront quittes pour prendre la parole après moi dans la discussion.

Mon embarras est grand, car on a coutume de dire que la pathologie est la meilleure preuve de la théorie trichromatique. Effectivement, beaucoup de faits de cette théorie ont été recherchés et trouvés pour expliquer les anomalies de la vision des couleurs. D'autre part, celles-ci ont rendu service à la théorie trichromatique en permettant un certain nombre d'études, par exemple la recherche des fondamentales réelles de Koenig et celles d'autres auteurs comme Pitt ou Judd. Mais il a été dit aussi, au cours de ces journées que la pathologie était le plus sûr garant de la théorie tétrachromatique, si bien que la discussion des faits pathologiques ne peut certainement que décevoir les uns et les autres.

Elle apporte en réalité beaucoup d'obscurités, d'incertitudes et de points d'interrogation.

La pathologie chromatique se divise en deux grands groupes de faits. On doit envisager successivement les dyschromatopsies congénitales qui sont habituellement connues des spécialistes de la vision des couleurs, et les dyschromatopsies acquises qui commencent à peine à être déchiffrées et ne figurent pas encore dans les traités.

En ce qui concerne les dyschromatopsies congénitales, la théorie trichromatique fournit des cadres commodes et rigides de classification qui devraient permettre des diagnostics rigoureux. En vertu de cette théorie les dichromates sont privés d'une fondamentale et, par conséquent, n'en possèdent plus que deux. Ils ont, de ce fait, une bande neutre dans le spectre. L'aveugle au rouge, ou protanope, a sa bande neutre dans le vert-bleu qu'il confond avec le gris et avec le rouge; le deutéranope, je n'ose pas dire l'aveugle au vert, a une bande neutre dans le vert-jaune. Il confond le gris avec le vert-jaune et le pourpre; le tritanope, aveugle au bleu a une bande neutre dans le jaune et confond le gris avec le jaune et le bleu-violet. Tous font de grandes confusions entre les différentes couleurs, les nomment mal, et de plus établissent de curieuses proportions de rouge et de vert pour égaliser un jaune spectral.

Les trichromates anormaux ont gardé leurs fondamentales, mais une est affaiblie; ils n'ont pas de bande neutre, font des confusions moins graves, dénomment assez bien les couleurs et établissent des proportions très caractéristiques et cependant anormales, de rouge et de vert pour égaliser un jaune.

Les achromates ont perdu deux fondamentales et par conséquent ne sont plus capables de discrimination. Les uns voient mieux le jour que la nuit, les autres mieux la nuit que le jour. Ce qui permet de distinguer les achromates à cônes et les achromates à bâtonnets.

Voilà très simplifié le schéma et les critères cliniques sur lesquels devraient se faire les diagnostics. Mais il y a loin des théories à leur explication et dans la réalité on ne parvient jamais à faire complètement les diagnostics avec ce schéma. Il n'est pas difficile d'en donner des exemples. Les paradoxes sont nombreux pour qui examine les candidats à des postes de transport aériens, maritimes ou ferroviaires. Les observations suivantes proviennent des services de la S.N.C.F. région Est.

Voici d'abord dix malades qui devraient passer pour protanes.

Quatre répondent à la définition classique du protanomal. Trois, par contre, ont une bande neutre, mais désignent correctement les nuances spectrales et sont capables d'établir des égalisations chromatiques qui satisfont les normaux. Leur bande neutre et leurs confusions les désignent comme protanes, mais l'un distingue parfaitement le rouge, et l'autre étend son spectre jusqu'au rouge extrême.

Voici maintenant trois sujets qui seraient deutéranopes d'après la position de leur bande neutre, mais ils voient le spectre raccourci dans le rouge, et tous les trois établissent une excellente équation chromatique.

Ainsi sur 13 sujets, présentant tous un raccourcissement du spectre, 4 ont un comportement classique, 9 sont paradoxaux.

En ce qui concerne les deutanes, ils sont plus nombreux, on les recrute plus facilement. Voici les observations résumées de 16 d'entre eux. Trois correspondent au type deutéranomal classique sans bande neutre dans le spectre; trois ont une bande neutre dans le vert-bleu et ne peuvent pas faire d'égalisations chromatiques; ce seraient des deutéranopes classiques, mais ils distinguent le rouge extrême dans des proportions insolites. Dix sujets ont une bande grise dans le vert-bleu; ce seraient des dichromates mais ils distinguent toutes les nuances à l'exception du vert-bleu, du gris et du pourpre et ils font des égalisations chromatiques normales. Sur 15 deutanes, 13 sont paradoxaux. Les proportions de sujets difficiles à classer sont donc très grandes.

Cependant, dans ce qui parait être obscur et confus, quelques faits apparaissent avec netteté.

D'après la théorie classique, la dichromasie implique la présence d'une bande neutre, mais il y a des protanopies et des deutéranopies qui ne correspondent pas à ces descriptions car la bande neutre devrait coïncider avec la disparition de toute sensibilité différentielle dans les deux moitiés du spectre, or il existe une marge importante entre l'apparition de la bande neutre et le commencement des confusions.

La position de la bande neutre, d'autre part, n'est pas toujours aussi nette que le laisse prévoir la théorie. Il est souvent difficile de distinguer, par la bande neutre entre un protane et un deutane. Il faut dire qu'il n'y a pas loin de 498 mμ à 510 mμ.

Si l'on porte, d'autre part, les axes de confusions des protanes et des deutanes, comme l'a fait Pitt, sur le triangle des couleurs, on peut dire que les confusions s'orientent suivant un axe de direction générale vert-rouge oscillant un peu autour du blanc.

A ceci s'ajoute encore le fait que les courbes, les fondamentales dichromatiques de Pitt ne permettent guère de différencier protanopes et deutéranopes, et coïncident sur presque tout leur trajet. On arrive donc à une notion clinique *vague*, de dischromatopsie d'axe rouge-vert, comportant sans doute deux classes mais dont les termes ne sont pas si tranchés et opposés que ceux de la théorie classique.

Les courbes de sensibilité spectrale montrent encore qu'il existe tous les termes de passage entre les trichromates vert-rouge anormaux et les dichromates, si bien que tous les échanges sont possibles entre toutes les classes.

A ces faits s'opposent, par contre, une classe d'anormaux que nous pensions rares mais qui s'avèrent beaucoup plus nombreux depuis que nos procédés de dépistage se sont améliorés grâce en particulier aux travaux de Farnsworth. Ce sont les tritanopes. Chez ceux-là l'axe de confusion dans le triangle est diamétralement opposé dans son orientation qui est bleu-jaune. Leur bande neutre est dans le jaune et ils confondent le bleu et le gris. Ils font de multiples confusions dans les couleurs froides du spectre, mais non dans les couleurs chaudes. Ils donnent beaucoup moins de déboires dans leur dépistage et leur classement que les dischromatopes d'axe rouge-vert. Mais il ne faut pas se faire d'illusions. Leur connaissance est toute récente. Ils sont dépistés depuis très peu de temps. Il est bien certain que lorsqu'ils auront été plus complètement étudiés, les problèmes commenceront à affluer. Il y a d'ailleurs une troisième et même une quatrième variété qui se profilent derrière eux et qui promettent de grandes difficultés d'interprétation. Il s'agit de la tétartanopie avec ses deux bandes neutres. Lorsque nous dépisterons mieux les tétartanopes, nous serons peut-être encore plus embarrassés.

Néanmoins on serait tenté de dire, pour faire une synthèse de tous ces faits, que la perte de l'axe vert-rouge implique la conservation de l'axe bleu-jaune. Inversement, la perte de l'axe bleu-jaune implique la conservation de l'axe rouge-vert. On peut ajouter à cela que les anomalies unilatérales d'un seul œil ont permis à un certain nombre d'auteurs de dire que les protanes et les deutanes ne gardent que deux couleurs de part et d'autre de leur bande neutre et que ces deux couleurs sont du bleu et du jaune. D'autre part, il est bien évident que si le tritanope voit mal le bleu et le jaune, il voit parfaitement bien le rouge et le vert.

Il y a donc, semble-t-il deux couples antagonistes, ce qui évidemment trouve un certain nombre d'échos dans certaines théories. Mais les questions affluent de nouveau en foule. Pourquoi le jaune, couleur d'équilibre, qui ne se déplace pas dans l'effet Bezold-Brücke chez le normal, se déplace-t-il chez le protanope et chez le deutéranope? Chez le protanope, il vire vers le vert, chez le deutéranope, il vire vers l'orange.

Nous trouvons aussi des difficultés à interpréter les proportions différentes de vert et de rouge nécessaires pour égaliser un jaune dans l'équation de Rayleigh.

D'ailleurs, cette équation apporte aussi bien des difficultés, car si elle est assez fidèle chez le deutéranomal, il n'y a par contre aucune corrélation entre la protanomalie et la grandeur de l'équation. Les protanomalies prononcées à spectre raccourci dans le rouge peuvent très bien avoir des équations parfaitement normales. Il y a donc encore là des paradoxes qui ne s'expliquent pas bien avec les théories classiques. Dans ces conditions, la classification par couples est une commodité, mais elle pose des problèmes d'interprétation des mécanismes physiopathologiques. Or, les pathologistes sont toujours gênés pour donner des conclusions parcequ'ils ont conscience d'utiliser des appareillages déficients, n'ayant pas la précision désirable.

Il faudrait lancer un appel aux physiciens pour les prier d'aider les cliniciens à construire l'appreillage adéquat qu'ils réclament depuis longtemps et qui n'existe dans aucun de leurs laboratoires.

Il existe, enfin, une dernière question en ce qui concerne les dyschromatopsies congénitales. Il est possible que les faits paradoxaux observés proviennent de convergences génétiques qui se produisent sur le même individu.

Un individu peut associer un gêne de deutéranopie à un gêne de protanopie, et l'on peut ainsi concevoir tous les mélanges possibles et imaginables. Les généticiens se sont penchés sur ce problème et sont arrivés à établir des dominantes, mais leurs conclusions ne sont qu'approximatives. Il y a d'autre part des transporteurs d'anomalies chez lesquels l'anomalie n'est pas apparente. Des femmes, en particulier, transportent souvent des anomalies, mais elles ne sont pas apparentes dans leur phénotype.

L'étude détaillée de ces femmes décèle encore des anomalies de la vision des couleurs à caractères frustes qui ne cadrent pas très facilement avec les théories admises jusqu'à présent.

Lorsque nous étudions une dyschromatopsie congénitale, nous devons, non seulement étudier l'individu présent, mais nous devons encore le mettre dans le contexte de sa famille, et nous demander si les anomalies que nous constatons ne sont pas dues en réalité à des incidences génétiques beaucoup plus qu'à des insuffisances de théories.

Le problème reste néanmoins complexe, et il est difficile d'admettre d'emblée le dichromatisme avec les caractères qui lui ont été classiquement donnés.

Avant de quitter le domaine des dyschromatopsies congénitales, il faudrait encore parler des achromatopsies totales.

Il serait naïf de croire que l'anatomopathologiste va trouver en faisant des coupes dans la rétine de ces individus une absence de cônes ou une absence de bâtonnets.

Lorsqu'on dit qu'il y a des achromates à cônes et des achromates à bâtonnets, on exprime en réalité le fait qu'il existe des achromates ayant perdu leur fonction diurne et des achromates ayant perdu leur fonction nocturne.

Puisqu'ils ont perdu l'une de ces fonctions, on devrait s'attendre à ce que leur courbe d'adaptation à l'obscurité ne possède plus le point anguleux alpha qui sépare les deux segments photopique et scotopique de la courbe. Non seulement les achromates ont bien leur point alpha, mais ils en ont quelquefois deux et même aussi trois.

Cela jette, évidemment, un certain discrédit sur les conclusions qui peuvent être tirées de la présence de ce point. Au cours de ces débats, de nombreuses discussions ont négligé la présence du point alpha chez les achromatopes totaux.

Parlons maintenent des dyschromatopsies acquises. Elles constituent un monde à elles seules et on ne peut pas avoir la prétention d'en donner rapidement une idée complète ni même approximative.

Elles ont suscité chez les cliniciens beaucoup d'espoir pour la compréhension des anomalies colorées et des mécanismes de la vision des couleurs. Ils avaient pensé en abordant leur étude faire une comparaison fructueuse entre certaines lésions, leur siège, et les anomalies fonctionnelles qu'elles entrainent. La déception est grande, mais cela tient peut-être à ce que les procédés d'investigation ne sont pas encore suffisants et qu'il faut encore travailler. Dans l'avenir la moisson sera sans doute plus fructueuse. On distingue beaucoup de cas. Le premier groupe est celui des dyschromatopsies d'absorption. Elles sont dues à l'interposition d'un filtre entre la rétine et l'extérieur. Par exemple, le jaunissement du cristallin, le jaunissement du vitré, le jaunissement de la rétine. Elles n'ont pas beaucoup d'intérêt.

Dans les chromatopsies, l'individu voit le blanc coloré d'une couleur quelconque; du jaune, du vert, du rouge. Certaines se rattachent aux dyschromatopsies d'absorption car les milieux ont été colorés par une substance. C'est le cas, par exemple, des ictériques qui ont vu leurs milieux colorés par des pigments biliaires, donc du jaune.

D'autres chromatopsies sont dues à des toxiques, et sont beaucoup plus difficilement explicables.

Retenons une chromatopsie qui est due à des conditions physiques: c'est l'érythropsie des neiges. Elle se produit surtout chez les aphaques, c'est-à-dire chez ceux qui ont perdu leur cristallin ou chez des gens qui ont subi une large iridectomie, et qui, par conséquent n'ont plus le jeu de leur diaphragme pupillaire. La très grande lumière qui entre dans l'œil épuise les pigments et ces individus voient tous les objets colorés en rouge. Ces érythropsies des neiges ont beaucoup de rapports avec les expériences d'épuisement des pigments visuels qui sont faites sous de très fortes intensités lumineuses de plusieurs centaines de milliers de trolands.

On arrive par ces expériences à supprimer la visibilité de toutes les couleurs du spectre, sauf une qui est précisément le rouge (Ségal).

La récupération est extrêmement intéressante, car elle se fait à peu près dans l'ordre des couleurs spectrales, rouge, vert, bleu, violet. On ne sait pas ce que devient le jaune dans cette récupération. Est-t-il récupéré au moment où le couple rouge-vert est présent? ou au moment où le bleu au contraire est présent? Il serait très intéressant de le savoir, mais ces expériences laissent des traces durables pendant des semaines, et ne sont pas sans danger.

Il existe enfin une autre classe de dyschromatopsies qui simulent les dyschromatopsies congénitales. Elles ne font que les *simuler* seulement. A la vérité, elles en sont extrêmement différentes.

M. Zanen a particulièrement travaillé cette question par la recherche des seuils chromatiques qu'il étudie le long du spectre avec un appareil précis qu'il a fait construire pour cet usage qui lui permet de bien déterminer la grandeur des flux et de savoir très exactement à quelle longueur d'onde il a à faire, bref, de travailler avec beaucoup de précision.

Dans les dyschromatopsies congénitales, le déficit qu'il trouve est électif et localisé à une partie déterminée du spectre. Par contre, dans les cas pathologiques acquis, l'élévation des seuils est globale.

M. Verriest ici présent s'est également attelé à cette question. On peut, selon lui, reconnaître des malades qui ont, au contraire, acquis un système divariant.

Chez ces derniers, la bande neutre est large et beaucoup moins nettement centrée que dans les dyschromatopsies congénitales. La position varie beaucoup chez les malades du même type et aussi dans le temps, en fonction de la maladie.

D'autre part, les erreurs de reconnaissance des couleurs et leurs confusions sont très nombreuses mais sont beaucoup moins typiques que dans les dyschromatopsies congénitales.

On arrive néanmoins à définir grossièrement des axes rouge-vert et bleu-jaune, si bien que nous rejoignons les dyschromatopsies congénitales.

Là encore, la perte du rouge-vert entraine la conservation du bleu-jaune, et inversement. Il faut dire d'ailleurs que la convergence des deux anomalies bleu-jaune et rouge-vert donne des achromatopsies.

Ce qu'il y a de plus intéressant, c'est la confrontation de ces anomalies avec la nosologie.

A l'étage périphérique rétinien, les lésions portent de préférence sur le couple bleu-jaune pour réaliser une tritanopie. C'est le cas des lésions oedémateuses de la rétine, des choroïdites, des rétinopathies hypertensives, et même des dégénérescences pigmentaires acquises. Mais dès que la lésion siège plus loin sur le nerf optique, par exemple, et plus haut, dans le chiasma dans les voies optiques intracraniennes, alors c'est le couple rouge-vert qui est plus volontiers atteint.

Ce schéma est séduisant, mais il est beaucoup trop rigide. Les statistiques le dénoncent comme extrêmement flou, et il serait peut-être prématuré de faire d'emblée fond sur ces constatations. Il faut certainement accumuler d'autres expériences avant de pouvoir affirmer une pareille séparation des faits.

Mais il est évident que ce schéma trouve de nombreus échos dans ce qui a été dit dans ces dernières journées (existence de couples, par exemple, décelés dans la rétine par la technique de Svaetichin, existence aussi de couples dans le corps genouillé).

L'explication n'est pas facile à donner. On est en droit, néanmoins, de se demander pourquoi pareille électivité. Evidemment, nous l'ignorons. Mais ces faits ont un mérite: c'est d'obliger à considérer que la rétine n'est pas seule en cause dans le processus de la vision des couleurs, et qu'il ne faut pas oublier qu'elle n'est que la première étape sur les voies et les fonctions nerveuses de l'appareil visuel.

Le temps manque pour parler encore d'autres faits de pathologie chromatique qui sont cependant très intéressants. Il existe, en effet, des agnosies colorées. Certaines sont strictement limitées à des portions du champ visuel et n'atteignent pas la totalité. Il y a là des faits nouveaux qui ont une grande importance pour i'interprétation de la pathologie chromatique du lobe occipital. Il faudrait aussi s'étendre longuement sur le champ visuel.

On sait maintenant que les couleurs sont perçues toutes à l'extrême périphérie à condition d'y mettre le prix en intensité lumineuse. Dans le champ visuel les couplages rouge-vert et bleu-jaune existent encore. On peut susciter les complémentaires par des excitations portant sur la périphérie du champ. Mais là aussi existent des paradoxes. Un jaune monochromatique, même s'il a la même luminance, n'a pas exactement la même valeur qu'un mélange de rouge et de vert. Le mélange de rouge et de vert est perçu plus près du centre; le jaune monochromatique est perçu beaucoup plus loin vers la périphérie.

D'autre part, si l'on cherche dans le champ visuel quelles sont les couleurs invariables, c'est-à-dire celles dont la tonalité ne varie pas au fur et à mesure qu'on les déplace dans le champ, ou au fur et à mesure que l'on change leur intensité, on trouve qu'elles ne sont pas deux, comme dans les schémas de Bezold-Brücke, mais, une. Cette couleur est un jaune 585 mµ.

Il resterait encore à rappeler les discussions des campimétristes pour savoir si dans les cas pathologiques c'est la perception de la couleur qui disparait la première ou si c'est, au contraire, une sensation achromatique de blanc.

Il est impossible de s'étendre sur ces problèmes et comme le temps presse, il est nécessaire de conclure.

Il est évident que la pathologie constitue un excellent banc d'essai des théories de la vision des couleurs.

Faut-il être trichromatique? faut-il être tetrachromatique? j'avoue que je n'en sais rien.

Certains parlent en qualité de stimulus, ce sont les physiciens, ils sont surtout trichromatiques; les autres parlent en qualité de sensations, ce sont les psychophysiologistes, ceux-là ont tendance à être un peu moins trichromatiques.

On doit mettre l'accent sur un fait c'est que la trivariance n'est pas critiquable, c'est un fait bien établi que l'individu normal possède un système trivariant. Mais lorsque l'on veut déduire de ce système trivariant des classifications pathologiques, alors on se trouve considérablement gêné.

Les cas pathologiques sont toujours des dégradations du normal. Il semble évident que la dégradation pathologique d'un système trivariant ne peut donner que des systèmes divariants et monovariants.

Malheureusement, lorsqu'on essaie de comprendre le système divariant à la lumière de ces considérations, on se heurte à des cas cliniques paradoxaux et déroutants dont il est bon de prendre conscience.

PIÉRON

Dans ce domaine des anomalies de la vision, Dr. Rushton nous a apporté un des premiers faits qui peuvent être considérés comme essentiels, à savoir que chez un protanope il y a disparition d'un pigment normal.

Mais je crois qu'il a examiné aussi des deutéranopes. Voudraitil nous faire part de ses observations sur la deutéranopie?

RUSHTON

I feel a little diffident after what we have just heard of the tremendous variety of these things, because I must tell you that what I have now to show is taken from one deuteranope only, though it does confirm the results — a few of them — that I got on one other deuteranope.

But my work has practically always been confined to the medical students who come to me voluntarily as subjects and I would like, at this moment, to say how very grateful I am to these subjects for giving up so much of their time and for their co-operation.

Now, this meeting has heard suggestions of all kinds of pigment changes to account for colour blindness. I gave yesterday objective evidence that in protanopia there was a lack of one of the normal two pigments in the red-green range.

The symmetrical thing would be that the deuteranope has only the other pigment. But that is not the case.

We can find out what pigments they have by the technique of bleaching away all the red pigment with a bright red light, and then giving a total bleach to see what pigments had been left.

The deuteranope is bleached first with a bright red light and then with a total white light, the difference that is left is given by the points of Fig. 1. This is the curve of chlorolabe — the *protanope* sensitivity curve.

At Teddington last year* I suggested that it might be possible to turn a deuteranope into a protanope by bleaching all the red pigment away. And that is what happens here because, not only at the bright red level is there no red pigment left but only the green pigment; I have also found, though not accurately, that, in these circumstances, the deuteranope is a protanope in his red-green colour match.

* Rushton, W. A. H. (1958) *Nat. Phys. Lab. Symposium* (No. 8), H.M. Stationery Office, London.

Brindley (1953) has shown that after adapting to a very bright red light, a normal person becomes a protanope. I have often done that upon myself.

I asked my deuteranope (after he had been bleached with this bright red light) to match a red and green and I accepted his match when I did the same thing. I am sure from Brindley's work that I was in those conditions a protanope, and the spectrum appeared to me like a protanopic spectrum. So the deuteranope has been turned into a protanope, a confirmation by psychophysics of what the pigment measurements show.

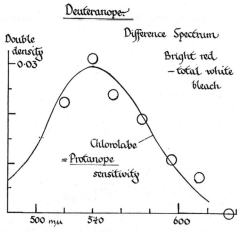

FIG. 1. ○ — difference spectrum of *deuteranope* between bleaching with strong red light (removing all erythrolabe) and a total white bleach. Curve:—the protanope sensitivity (Pitt).

Let us turn now to the question of how much chlorolabe there is in the deuteranope fovea and what other pigment is there.

In the slide I showed you yesterday (Fig. 3, p. 166). The circles indicate that a certain red light will bleach away half of the chlorolabe, and a full white light removes the other half. Now the last slide (Fig. 1) showed the results of exactly the same procedures upon the deuteranope, and the curve plotted is the change in chlorolabe between the red bleach and the white bleach, a change which we know from the protanope to be half the total change. So in the deuteranope the total amount of chlorolabe is twice what is shown in Fig. 1 and this plotted as the 'cholorolabe' curve in Fig. 2. If this curve is subtracted from the total curve (dots) we obtain the black squares, which correspond fairly well with the curve shown, which is the erythrolabe curve derived from the normal. But there is another way of obtaining this curve (if only two pigments are present). Bleaching with a deep red light has no effect upon chlorolabe in the protanope, and so in the deuteranope its effect should be upon erythrolabe only. The difference spectrum in this case (circles, Fig. 2) lies close to the black squares. I do not suppose that the erythrolabe in the deuteranope is different from that in the normal, and the divergence in Fig. 1 is probably due to some small systematic error which I must try to detect and eliminate.

Turning now to the question of why is the deuteranope monochromatic in the red-green range when he has *both* the pigments upon which normal colour vision

R

depends, two possibilities arise. Either there are two cones each with one kind of pigment, connected to the same optic nerve, or there is one class of cone with mixed pigments in the cone.

I have tried to separate these two possibilities by several methods in psychophysics of which I will only take your time to mention one which needs no description.

It is a very crude and simple repetition of what Stiles* has done so excellently — as you all know — with the increment thresholds. In this case I simply had a fairly large field, one half of which was green and the other half red+blue.

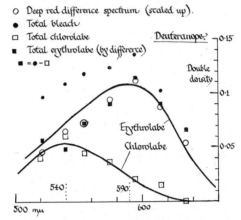

Fig. 2. Difference spectra in the *deuteranope*. Spectrum of erythrolabe (○) by bleaching with deep red light, (■) by difference between total bleach (●) and total chlorolabe (□).

The deuteranope himself matched the red+blue with the green so that they were quite identical and he couldn't tell the difference between them at all. Now I superposed a small flashing spot of light either upon the one half or the other of the field, and the flash was either red or green. The flash was adjusted in brightness to be just visible. It was found that the increment threshold was the same whether red was put on green or red was put on magenta, whether green was put on green or green was put on magenta, if the red and green flashes were matched to be the same for the deuteranope, all the increment thresholds were the same. There was no difference. No contrast at all.

With a normal subject, of course, a green is much easier seen against the red than against the green. The increment threshold is very different. But with the deuteranope it is identical. It is as though there is only one of the sensitivities of Stiles, which I will call πd, the Stiles mechanism in the deuteranope.

It follows at once that whatever is being mixed, whether nerves, or pigment, is mixed peripheral to the level at which the quasi-logarithmic transformation occurs. You could not get this relation if a logarithmic transformation in separate cones occurred first, and then the resulting signals were mixed.

Now, the logarithmic transformation occurs very early, obviously before the place where the electroretinogram arises. But the ERG is the earliest detectable

* STILES, W. S. (1939) *Proc. Roy. Soc. London* B., **127**, 64; (1959) *Proc. Nat. Acad. Sci. U.S.*, **45**, 100.

consequence of photolysis and the evidence we have suggests that it arises at the photo-electric transformation itself, and hence in the receptors.

If you accept that it arises in the cone, then the *mixture* is occurring in the cone, and I believe that that is the explanation: the deuteranope has only one class of cone and that contains a mixed pigment.

But, if the pigments are mixed in a single type of cone, we could then say something about the brightness produced by those two pigments. I would have no idea *a priori* whether the photolysis of erythrolabe or of chlorolabe should be the better at exciting the visual function, but I have a good idea of how we can find out.

All we have to do is to repeat on the deuteranope the experiment done on the protanope in that slide which you just saw (Fig. 3, page 166). That is to say, to bleach the deuteranope with two lights, a red and a green, which the deuteranope matched and found identical in brightness.

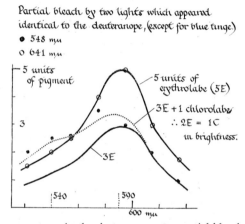

FIG. 3. Difference spectrum in the *deuteranope*. O—partial bleach with bright red light. ●—Bleach with green light which looked the same as that red to the deuteranope. Dotted curve is the difference expected if one unit of chlorolabe and three of erythrolabe were bleached.

In the case of the protanope there was only one pigment and the results of each bleach were the same. The deuteranope has two pigments, and the results will be different.

I used two lights, 548 mμ and 641 mμ, which the deuteranope had matched in intensity so that he said that they looked equal though 548 looked a little more blue than 641. Bleaching with 641 gives a bleach shown by the circles (Fig. 3), 548 gives the dots. The 641 mμ should be a light that affects erythrolabe only, and the difference curve corresponds to five units of erythrolabe. The 548 mμ curve corresponds to three units of erythrolabe plus one unit of chlorolabe. So, equating the bleaching of lights which appear equally bright

$$5 \text{ Eryth.} = 3 \text{ Eryth.} + 1 \text{ Chlor. } ... (1)$$

Subtracting 3 Eryth. from both sides, we conclude that the bleaching of one density unit of chlorolabe appears as bright as the bleaching of two density units of erythrolabe. If this is true, we can then do with the deuteranope what we did with the protanope, namely, to compare the amount of pigment with the luminosity curve.

Now we know from the physical measurements how much erythrolabe and how much chlorolabe there is in the eye, we know from equation (1) what weight to give to the two pigments, namely, double the weight for the chlorolabe, and this gives us the result shown in Fig. 4.

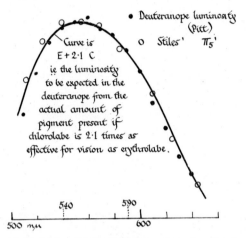

FIG. 4. ○—spectral sensitivity of Stiles' high intensity π_5' mechanism. ●—deuteranope spectral sensitivity. Curve—sensitivity to be expected from deuteranope pigments.

This curve plots the density of erythrolabe (Fig. 2) $+$ 2.1 times the density of chlorolabe. Dots show the deuteranope luminosity curve taken from Wright's book* derived, I think, from Pitt's measurements. But this luminosity fits very well with Stiles' recent π_5', which is the high luminosity value for π_5.

And therefore we can conclude that the πd, which was found above for increment thresholds in the deuteranope, was really π_5 of the normal eye. So that our final conclusion about the retina is given by this scheme:

We have a blue cone, about which I know nothing. A green cone, which has the sensitivity π_4, and which contains the pigment chlorolabe. A red cone, which has the sensitivity π_5', and which contains chlorolabe plus erythrolabe in the proportion shown in Fig. 2, with chlorolabe having twice the relative efficacity.

Then there is a logarithmic transformation and after this we can have whatever you like in the way of pools and interactions.

In the case of protanopes and deuteranopes I suggest that there are no changes in the normal structure of the retina. Both number of cones and nervous connections are normal. But, in the protanope, all the cones are simply of the π_4 type with chlorolabe inside, and in the deuteranope all these are just of the π_5 type with chlorolabe plus erythrolabe inside.

If they have only one kind of cone, then each cone will be equally excited by every wavelength in the red-green spectral range. If the subject were colour-blind in one eye and normal in the other, he would see the same colour from the two eyes when

* WRIGHT, W. D. (1946) *Researches on Normal and Defective Colour Vision*, London.

all the normal cones too were being equally excited. What is the colour which does excite the normal and π_5 cones equally? Red light excites mainly π_5, green mainly π_4, but yellow excites both to about the same extent. So one-eyed protanopes and deuteranopes would be expected to see yellow. And yellow is what they say they see.*

PIÉRON

M. Dekking a demandé la parole?

DEKKING

Physiology has derived great benefits from methods which I may call degeneration or disintegration methods. By some means, either chemical or physical, the structure you want to study is put under a stress, a strain, so that gradually it begins to break down and then you can see what happens. You see one function after the other dropping out and this is, of course, a very useful method. Even if it does not give you a clear insight into the structure you are studying, at least it gives you a clear insight in the deficiencies of your theory.

In retinal physiology this method has not been used very often; the only clear example I know is the degeneration of the electroretinogram by cold or alcohol to unravel the *a*, *b* and *c* waves. We can, however, degenerate the colour discrimination of the spectrum by using excessively high intensities, and most interesting things happen then. This is, of course, an old method which has been known for scores of years. Now, 8 years ago I showed that exactly the same thing can be achieved by quite another method — by intoxication of the retina by Tridione. In general, it may be said that if the same degeneration pattern is produced by two widely different agents, then this pattern is not accidental, but *must be based on some fundamental property of the system.*

What happens in both cases is this. First, all colours become less saturated and then, secondly, the green drops out completely and its place is taken by a pure white. After that the red becomes a pure and brilliant yellow, and at last the whole spectrum is a more or less white band, but not pure white. There always remains a blue tinge at the short wavelength end, and a yellow colour at the other end.

This blue-yellow system stands like a rock. You can raise your intensity as much as you like; you can intoxicate yourself as much as you dare, but you will not succeed in killing the blue and yellow impression, long after all discrimination of red and green is lost. I therefore consider the blue-yellow system as the older, the primeval one, and the red-green system as a younger and much more vulnerable acquisition.

In my opinion, the defect of both the Young-Helmholtz and the Hering theory is that they are symmetrical: the former is trisymmetrical, the latter bisymmetrical, and therefore neither of them can account for the unsymmetrical behaviour of colour sense. Of course, the Young-Helmholtz theory cannot explain the phenomenon described above at all. It considers yellow as a mixture of red and green. How can the *result* of a mixture (yellow) remain long after the *components* of that mixture (red and green) have disappeared completely?

The Hering theory is deficient in this respect, too, because it considers the blue-yellow system and the red-green system to be of equal standing. I think we could

* BRINDLEY, G. S. (1953) *J. Physiol. London,* **122**, 332; GRAHAM, C. H. & HSIA, Y. (1958) *Science,* **127**, 675.

cope with this much better if we assume an original, *primordial*, blue-yellow system which is extremely stable and remains under any condition of physical or chemical stress (and perhaps in dichromasy); and a *secondary* red-green system which has developed, so I would think, out of the yellow system.

Well, all this is as it may be. At any rate I can say this. In, for instance, neural conduction we have learned much from the degenerative action of nicotine, curare, atropine and so forth. I cannot conceive of a theory of neuro-conductivity which does not take into account, and does not explain, the action of nicotine and curare. In the same way, I cannot conceive of a colour theory worth that name which does not account for, and does not explain, the degeneration phenomena I have just described.*

PIÉRON

Le Dr. Wright doit nous parler, peut-être, de ses expériences sur la tritanopie.

WRIGHT

I hadn't really come prepared to speak about tritanopia. What I would like just to do very briefly is to summarize the experiments which we did carry out in 1952 on a number of tritanopes, then relate them to one or two more recent problems.

We found a number of tritanopes by means of an illustrated journal, *Picture Post*, in England, in which an article on defective colour vision was being published. And we included an illustration of a chart, which Commander Farnsworth had loaned me, capable of detecting tritanopes.

Although, by that means, we received replies from a very large number of the orthodox red-green defectives, we also established contact with some forty congenital tritanopes, of whom we were able to arrange for seventeen to come to the laboratory for testing and we confirmed on our colorimeter that they really were tritanopes. Of these seventeen, seven or eight came on a number of occasions for detailed examinations.

The measurements we took included the colour-matching curves, which proved in all cases to be dichromatic, that is to say, they could match all the colours in the spectrum by a mixture of two stimuli, one from the long-wave end of the spectrum and one from the short-wave end. We also recorded their wavelength-discrimination curves and their V_λ curves, and we deduced their confusion loci in the chromaticity chart.

In summarizing those results, I would first emphasize that the colour matching was dichromatic. Second, that while the wavelength discrimination was fairly normal in the red-yellow-green part of the spectrum, in the green-blue part of the spectrum there was virtually a discontinuity, indicating an absence of wavelength discrimination. In the violet part of the spectrum their discrimination appeared to be a good deal better than normal.

The confusion loci in the chromaticity chart converged on a point located just outside the violet region of the spectrum locus, which means that colours lying on zones radiating from that point were confused. This confirmed, for example, the confusion between blues and greens, and between yellow, white and violet.

This is the kind of result which, to my mind, supports rather strongly the Young-Helmholtz type of theory in which such confusions were predicted by Helmholtz

* Dekking, H. M. (1950) *Acta XVI Concilium Ophthalmologicum (Brittannia)*, p. 465, Brit. Med. Assoc. London.

many years before they were demonstrated experimentally. We can compare the tritanope with the case of the protanope, where the confusion loci converge towards a point just beyond the red end of the spectrum. This is entirely different from the tritanope but is in agreement with Helmholtz's prediction, if protanopia were due to the absence of a red receptor and tritanopia were due to an absence of a blue receptor.

In the case of protanopia, when we measure the V_λ curve, the maximum is shifted towards the short-wave end compared to the normal curve and there is a marked loss of sensitivity at the red end of the spectrum, which you would expect if the red receptor were absent.

In the case of the tritanope, it was very difficult to show that there was any significant loss in the V_λ values at the short-wave end of the spectrum, as you might perhaps expect if the blue receptor were missing. However, the spread in these values among the tritanopes is quite considerable, as it certainly is also among the normals, due no doubt to variations in yellow pigmentation in the optic media and the macula.

I would also emphasize that, in the case of the protanope, the convergence point in the chromaticity chart is a long way from the alychne, the locus of stimuli with no luminance. This means that the response associated with the red receptor contributes very markedly to the sensation of luminosity and, therefore, if that receptor were absent, you would expect it to have considerable effect on the V_λ curve.

On the other hand, the tritanope confusion point is very close to the alychne — I was going to say it might almost be on it — and therefore corresponds to a stimulus which contributes only very slightly to the total luminosity sensation. Hence, if the blue receptors were absent, you would not expect to find any noticeable effect on the V_λ curve.

So far, then, the results do fit in to a fairly orthodox Young-Helmholtz type of theory. However, there is an obvious difference in other respects between tritanopia and the other dichromatic defects, protanopia and deuteranopia.

The number of tritanopes, for example, is very much smaller. We estimated that perhaps one person in 25,000 might be a tritanope, whereas, of course, you may get 1 or 2 per cent of men who are protanopes or deuteranopes.

Also, the transmission of tritanopia from one generation to another obviously followed a very different pattern from the type of transmission associated with protanopia and deuteranopia.

Going on from tritanopia, the next step in the investigation ought to have been the study of tritanomalous vision, which we assume exists — an intermediate state between the tritanope and the normal — just as we have protanomalous and deuteranomalous vision intermediate between the protanope and deuteranope and the normal.

However, I have to confess that we ourselves, at least, have not done any work on tritanomalous observers and there is a difficulty here in really identifying and distinguishing them from people who have excess yellow pigmentation. I think this is a field still to be studied, but it is something we have not yet done.

I am interested also in the relation of congenital tritanopia with small-field tritanopia, which has been referred to here and was causing quite a lot of excitement a few years ago.

Recently there have been suggestions that small-field tritanopia is really a sort of fixation defect, since in order to demonstrate this loss of blue-green discrimination you fixate on a small field and hence produce local adaptation in the retina.

This, of course, is true. You do get some local adaptation effect and I would not personally deny that this may contribute to the tritanopic phenomenon. But we still have to explain why this local adaptation affects the blue-green discrimination in a different way from its effect on the red-yellow discrimination.

I also want to emphasize that, as far as our congenital tritanopes were concerned, I do not believe that their defect was due to fixation and adaptation. Although we made our tests on our colorimeter which has a fairly smallish field of one or two degrees, the people whom we studied usually knew that they were colour defective. They had had arguments with their wives, for example, about the colour of their shirts — whether they were blue or green. They were aware of and, in the correspondence which I had in the first place, they reported confusions between blue and green, for example in the game we call snooker — I don't know what it's called in France — but a game like billiards where you have coloured balls. They also reported a number of other subsidiary clues which were not associated with looking at the field in a colorimeter. One of the tritanopes was an artist who painted somewhat oddly, and the confusions which he made were in the tritanope sense.

As regards further work which is required, I think we need — and we are working on this — to relate tritanopic tendencies with the colour defects which you get in the peripheral retina.

I think some of our peripheral work has been mentioned — work by Moreland and work now being continued by Clarke at the Imperial College — and we are also doing some work on the colour confusions associated with acquired defects and with pathological states and ocular diseases. In this connection I was extremely interested in the paper which Dr. Dubois-Poulsen has just given us and I think there is a very big programme of work to be undertaken in that direction.

We obviously have a good deal of qualitative information about the losses of colour perception in such cases, but I am sure we need to supplement it with more exact types of measurements, such as wavelength discrimination, colour-mixture curves, V_V curves and so on.

Dr. Dubois-Poulsen mentioned a considerable number of colour deficiencies which did not seem to fit into the orthodox scheme and I think we must accept that in a mechanism as complex as the eye, the retina, the nerve paths and the visual cortex, we are bound to get all sorts of varieties of defect. My surprise generally is that when I am asked to examine some so-called odd subjects — from time to time the medical authorities on our railways have an employee whom they are not sure about and they send him to me — they do seem nearly always to fit into the more orthodox form of defect when we test them on our colorimeter.

We have to remember that differences of pigment, differences of acuity, differences of temperament, and so on, can all affect and be combined with their particular colour confusions.

There may be differences in adaptation, because one of the most recent pieces of work which has been carried out by McCree, in our laboratory, has been on the losses of colour discrimination when you fixate a colour. He has, rather to my embarrassment, discovered that the colour discrimination of quite an important fraction of the people in our own laboratory is very markedly reduced when they look steadily for a few seconds at the field of view of our colorimeter.

They are the sort of subjects whom I myself, if I had had them, might have brushed on one side as being poor observers and gone on to use other people who had better colour discrimination. I am sure now that that is quite a wrong approach and that there must be quite a large number of people who, at least under some conditions, lose their colour discrimination very quickly when they look steadily at a bipartite field with a dark surround.

Evidently, then, if you take such effects into consideration, the field is wide open for further studies, and all kinds of apparent abnormality must be expected. I am not personally prepared to panic and to abandon all our orthodox ideas but, on the other hand, I am well aware that we may have some unusual new data to account for.

PIÉRON

Nous continuerons et terminerons la discussion cet après-midi, avant de tâcher de dégager les lignes générales que l'on pourrait concevoir d'après l'ensemble de nos examens et de nos discussions.

Il y aura, en particulier aussi, à demander au Prof. Bouman de nous faire part de ses résultats qui doivent apporter des données intéressantes.

SÉANCE DE CLÔTURE

PIÉRON

Nous allons reprendre notre discussion interrompue ce matin, et tâcher de la terminer, avant d'en venir à essayer de dégager peut-être quelques données de cette réunion, et voir dans quelle direction on pourrait engager une recherche prochaine sur les points qui sembleront les plus intéressants.

Nous commençons tout de suite. Je donne la parole à Mrs. Hurvich qui aurait déjà dû prendre la parole ce matin.

MRS. HURVICH

Thank you, Professor Piéron.

I should like to say a few words, and I'll try to be as brief as possible, about the way we think the colour system operates in relation to some of the abnormalities of colour vision that were referred to by the speakers this morning.

Now, the slides you saw yesterday were all concerned with the opponent-colours formulation as it related to colour vision for a normal observer. And this formulation assumes that in the normal observer the photopigment absorptions are of certain shapes and magnitudes and that the neural system is operating at its maximal efficiency.

When it comes to abnormalities of the visual system there are two possibilities. One is that the photochemical system may be altered. And here we should divide the possibilities into subsections. There may be losses of photopigments; there may be combinations of photopigments in unusual ways; or there may be photopigments present that actually differ from those present in the normal human eye. The second possibility is that the photopigments themselves may not be altered at all, but that the alterations may occur in the nervous pathways.

Whether the abnormalities are of a congenital sort or whether they are of the sort produced by disease, or by some sort of degeneration caused by drugs or alcohol — the sort of thing we heard about this morning — the assumptions made about photochemical changes and those made about neural changes imply quite different characteristics of abnormal colour vision.

Fig. 1 is the slide you saw yesterday which we believe represents the net neural responses directly associated with the sensory responses of the normal system.

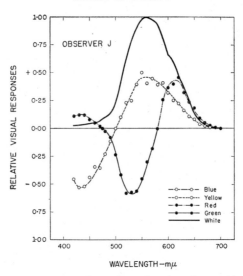

FIG. 1. Chromatic and achromatic response functions for equal energy spectrum for observer J.

Now, let us leave aside for a moment the possibility of photochemical changes. We can see that if we assume that the blue-yellow function is subsumed by one pair of opponent neural processes, and there is an independent pair that subsumes the red-green function, then a neural change might occur of the sort that causes a reduction in the efficiency of the red-green processes alone, and the magnitude of the red-green function, as this reduction continues, would be progressively reduced until finally, with complete loss of activity of that system, it would disappear completely. Associated with this loss in efficiency, we would expect a series of degrees of red-green sensory losses up to the point of complete extinction of red and green, resulting in a

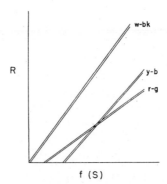

FIG. 2. Schematic representation of different functions relating response to stimulus energy in the three-paired neural systems.

condition of dichromacy. And, similarly, for reductions in the yellow-blue neural system.

In connection with the independent reductions in these functions and the implied differences in the physiological processes underlying them, we have not assumed — and our assumptions now are based on the psychophysical facts that require explanation — that the red-green and blue-yellow are equivalent in terms of the rate of response of the physiological systems with increase in stimulation, nor that their adaptive constants and properties are necessarily equivalent.*

In very schematic fashion we have visualized these physiological responses as varying in the manner shown in Fig. 2, with response as ordinate and some function of the stimulus intensity, whether logarithmic or power function, as the abscissa.† The assumption is that the three systems have different thresholds for response, and that they also show different rates of increase of response with increase in strength of stimulation. The thresholds, in order, show the achromatic to be most sensitive, the red-green the next most sensitive, and the yellow-blue to have the highest threshold but also to have a more rapid rate of increase with increase in strength of stimulation than does the red-green system.

Now, it is this assumption that really accounts for the hue changes and the saturation changes that occur as a function of intensity. And if the chromatic processes differ in this way with respect to intensity, it is probable that they are also differentially adaptive or that they drop out at different rates as functions of duration of stimulation. Also, as can be seen here, for very low stimulation levels the red-green process will be in action, the yellow-blue will not. And we believe that this is at least partially a factor in so-called small-field tritanopia in normal vision.‡

Now, if these systems do have these different characteristics, they would not necessarily be expected to drop out at equal rates when the neural system is diseased. We have no good guesses at the moment as to why the red-green one seems to disappear more often than the yellow-blue. But it is certainly not surprising, since we do not see how these systems can be physiologically equivalent in all respects if we are to explain the psychophysical data for normals.

If we can now go back again to the problem of the photochemical changes that can occur in abnormal colour vision, a possible assumption is that distortion in the biochemistry of the retina is possible, such that an individual can have three selective photopigment absorptions but that these three selective photopigment absorptions are different from the normal ones. Here

* HURVICH, L. M. & JAMESON, D. (1957) *Psychol. Rev.*, **64**, 384.
† HURVICH, L. M. & JAMESON, D. (1955) *J. Opt. Soc. Amer.*, **45**, 602.
‡ HURVICH, L. M. & JAMESON, D. (1958) *Nat. Phys. Lab. Symposium* (No. 8), H.M. Stationery Office, London.

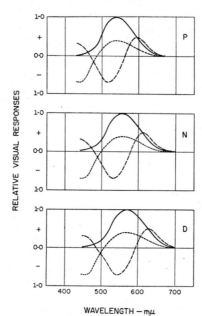

RELATIVE VISUAL RESPONSES

WAVELENGTH — mμ

FIG. 3. Chromatic and achromatic response functions for equal energy spectrum. For observers with protanomalous, normal and deuteranomalous photoreceptor systems and with normal strength visual response processes (Jameson & Hurvich, 1956).

we have an unlimited range of possibilities but the assumption that we have made is that all visual pigments would follow the rhodopsin-type form that Dr. Dartnall has found in all organisms that he has investigated.* We have assumed that the absorptions of the three deviant photopigments will have the same relation to each other as in the normal eye, but that the triad can be displaced with their maxima occurring either at shorter wavelengths, which would produce a protanomalous type of distortion, or that they can be shifted toward longer wavelengths, which would produce a deuteranomalous type of distortion.†‡

In the centre graph of Fig. 3 we have again represented the normal response functions when the eye has the normal photopigments. It shows the white function, the red-green function and the blue-yellow function. In the upper part we see the functions that would result in an eye that is still trichromatic, has three photopigments all of the rhodopsin-type again, but with displaced absorptions so that all the maxima of the photopigments now would occur at shorter wavelengths. Assuming the same relations to obtain between photopigment activity and excitation of neural responses, these are

* DARTNALL, H. J. A. (1953) *Brit. Med. Bull.*, 9, 24.
† HURVICH, L. M. & JAMESON, D. (1955) *J. Opt. Soc. Amer.*, 45, 602.
‡ JAMESON, D. & HURVICH, L. M. (1956) *J. Opt. Soc. Amer.*, 46, 1075.

the altered visual response functions that would result for this type of protanomalous individual. Here we assume that the neural system is functioning in a completely normal way. In the lower part of the slide we see the response curves that result, again from the assumption that only the

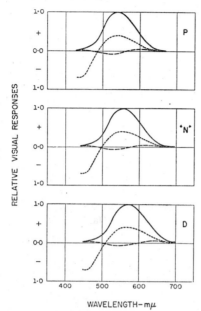

RELATIVE VISUAL RESPONSES

WAVELENGTH—mμ

FIG. 4. Chromatic and achromatic response functions for equal energy spectrum. For observers with protanomalous, normal and deuteranomalous photoreceptor systems and with impaired red-green response processes (Jameson & Hurvich, 1956).

rhodopsin-type photopigment absorptions have been shifted, but this time in the direction of longer wavelengths. In cases of this sort, as represented here, we would observe that these individuals would have distorted perceptions but not weakened perceptions. In other words, at any given region of the spectrum, the hues would be altered, but wavelength discrimination would not be any worse than that of the normal observer, even though this function would have a slightly different form.*

Another possibility is that, in any of these cases, in addition to photochemical shifts, we might also have neural weakening or neural losses.

The three cases in Fig. 4 would have the same photopigment distributions as the cases represented in Fig. 3. But here there is a loss in efficiency of the red-green chromatic system, so that the observer who has deuteranomalous distortions would also have relative weaknesses caused by the losses in red-green efficiency. We might also have an observer whose photochemical

* JAMESON, D. & HURVICH, L. M. (1956) *J. Opt. Soc. Amer.*, **46**, 1075.

S

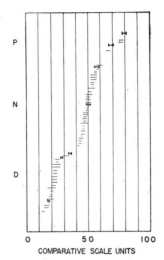

FIG. 5. Rayleigh mixture ratios. Heavy lines — theoretical ranges for observers with protanomalous, normal and deuteranomalous photoreceptor systems and with normal strength visual response processes (Jameson & Hurvich, 1956). Thin lines — comparable ranges for observers measured by Willis & Farnsworth (1952).

distributions were normal but again with a weakness in red-green introduced. And similarly for the protanomalous individual.

The existence of systems of this sort would present a very complicated picture of anomalous colour vision.* We would find, for example, a distribution of Rayleigh equations that departed in different ways from the normal.

In the case of the individual with a weakened red-green system, there would be evidence of a very large range of uncertainty in the Rayleigh equations, whereas the comparable individual in Fig. 3 would give the same Rayleigh equation mid-point, but there would be a small range within which the observer of that sort would make his adjustments since his sensitivity would be high.

Fig. 5 shows plots of Rayleigh ratios that were obtained by Farnsworth *et al.*† for a population including a number of normal observers whose mid-points plotted in this region, a number of deuteranomalous observers whose mid-points plotted in this region, and some protanomalous observers whose mid-points plotted here. And, in each of these instances, the extent of the line corresponds to the range of the ratios that the observer was willing to accept as a Rayleigh match.

I might add that these, the heavy lines with the bars, are computed Rayleigh ratios for theoretical observers who have various degrees of photopigment shifts either in the deuteranomalous direction, namely, shifted to longer

* JAMESON, D. & HURVICH, L. M. (1956) *J. Opt. Soc. Amer.*, **46**, 1075.
† WILLIS, M. P. & FARNSWORTH, D (1952) *Med. Research Lab. Rept. No. 190*, XI, No. 7.

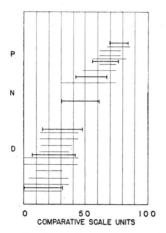

FIG. 6. Rayleigh mixture ratios. Heavy lines — theoretical ranges for observers with protanomalous, normal, and deuteranomalous photoreceptor systems and with red-green response processes of 0.03 normal strength (Jameson & Hurvich, 1956). Thin lines — comparable ranges for observers measured by Willis & Farnsworth (1952).

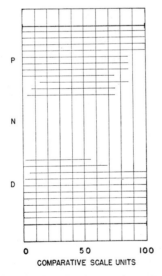

FIG. 7. Rayleigh mixture ratios. Heavy lines — theoretical ranges for dichromats with complete loss of red-green response processes (Jameson & Hurvich, 1956). Thin lines — comparable ranges for observers measured by Willis & Farnsworth (1952).

wavelengths, or in the protanomalous direction, shifted towards shorter wavelengths. The efficiency of the red-green neural system is normal.

In Fig. 6 we have a plot again of data obtained by Farnsworth *et al.** The

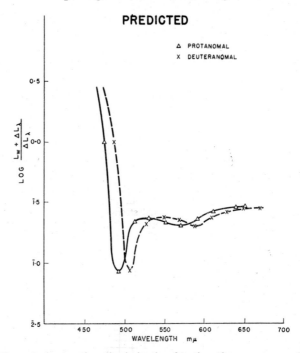

FIG. 8. Theoretical saturation-discrimination functions for a protanomalous and a deuteranomalous observer (Jameson & Hurvich, 1956).

mid-points of these matches are comparable to those we saw in Fig. 5, but the range is tremendously increased. Again, the heavy bars represent the theoretical computations of both ratios and ranges for individuals now assumed to have a partial loss in efficiency in the red-green neural processes.

And in Fig. 7 we have the situation where we are approaching, reaching, complete dichromacy. In this case the red-green loss is complete, or nearly so, and the mid-points, of course, become meaningless.

On Fig. 8 we have a set of predicted saturation discrimination functions for anomalous observers, a protanomalous and a deuteranomalous, as computed from the theoretical curves that we showed a little earlier.†

And in Fig. 9 are two sets of saturation discrimination data, determined by Chapanis, for a protanomalous and a deuteranomalous individual.‡ In this

* WILLIS, M. P. & FARNSWORTH, D. (1952) *Med. Research Lab. Rept. No. 190*, XI, No. 7.
† JAMESON, D. & HURVICH, L. M. (1956) *J. Opt. Soc. Amer.*, **46**, 1075.
‡ CHAPANIS, A. (1944) *J. Exp. Psychol.*, **34**, 24.

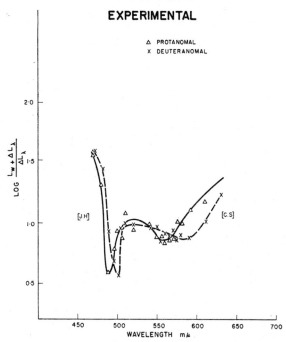

EXPERIMENTAL

FIG. 9. Saturation-discrimination functions (reciprocal of least colorimetric purity) for a protanomalous and a deuteranomalous observer measured by Chapanis (1944).

case, these anomolous individuals are still operating with trichromatic vision, but we can see the tremendous reduction in saturation in the green region, and I should like to suggest the possibility that tremendous reduction in saturation in the green, relative to the normal, may have something to do with the detection of a neutral point in the green, even when the observer shows evidence of trichromacy in other respects. This was mentioned this morning as one of the problems in this complex picture.

Saturation discrimination functions for complete dichromats are shown in Fig. 10. And, again, we have comparisons (the lines and the points) of experimental determinations* and theoretically predicted functions† for the protanope and the deuteranope.

Fig. 11 shows wavelength-discrimination functions. Again the lines and the points represent comparisons of theoretically predicted and experimentally determined — not ours, but other laboratories'‡§¶ — wavelength-discrimination functions for the deuteranope and the protanope.

* CHAPANIS, A. (1944) *J. Exp. Psychol.*, **34**, 24.
† HURVICH, L. M. & JAMESON, D. (1955) *J. Opt. Soc. Amer.*, **45**, 602.
‡ BRODHUN, E. (1892) *Z. Sinnesphysiol.*, **3**, 97.
§ LADEKARL, P. M. (1934) *Acta Ophthalmol.*, **12** (Supp. III).
¶ PITT, F. H. G. (1935) *Med. Research Council (Brit.) Spec. Rept. Ser. No. 200.*

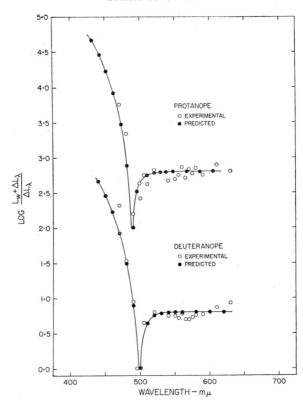

FIG. 10. Saturation-discrimination functions for protanopia and deuteranopia.
● — theoretical (Hurvich & Jameson, 1955). ○ — experimental results for a
protanope, W. M. and for a deuteranope L. P. measured by Chapanis (1944).

In conclusion, since the simple classical concepts do present so many difficulties for interpreting the data of abnormal colour vision, it has seemed to us worth while to examine closely an alternative scheme which considers both photochemical distortions and neural changes. This alternative scheme does, as I have tried to indicate in very summary fashion this afternoon, bring much systematic coherence to the very complex picture presented by the variety of ways in which colour vision seems to deviate from normality.*

* HURVICH, L. M. & JAMESON, D. (1957) *Psychol. Rev.*, **64**, 384.

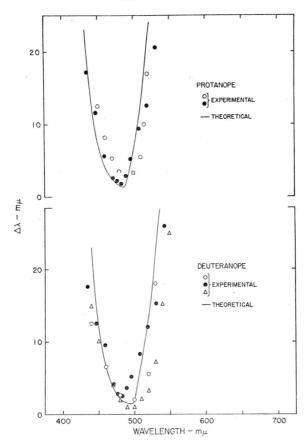

FIG. 11. Wavelength-discrimination functions for protanopia and deuteranopia. Upper graph: solid line — theoretical (Hurvich & Jameson, 1955); ○ — average experimental values for six protanopes measured by Pitt (1935); ● — average experimental values for three protanopes measured by Ladekarl (1934). Lower graph: solid line — theoretical; ○ — average experimental values for six deuteranopes measured by Pitt (1935); ◕ — averages for two deuteranopes measured by Ladekarl (1934); △ — values for one deuteranope reported by Brodhun (1892).

DISCUSSION

PIÉRON

Je donne la parole à M. Baumgardt.

BAUMGARDT

Je voudrais apporter quelques modestes compléments en la matière si riche que nous a présentée ce matin le Dr. Dubois-Poulsen.

Je reviens d'abord sur la constatation qu'on trouve toujours un point de brisure dans les courbes d'adaptation des achromatopes. Il paraît indiqué d'interpréter cet accident (point alpha) comme la manifestation d'un changement dans l'activité nerveuse intrarétinienne et non plus, comme on en avait l'habitude, comme le début de la manifestation de l'activité des bâtonnets. C'est au point de brisure que les cellules ganglionnaires géantes commencent à fonctionner et grâce à la convergence énorme que cela représente, le seuil doit baisser rapidement. Ce phénomène devrait s'observer indifféremment chez le normal, l'achromate typique et l'achromate atypique (à acuité normale) et c'est ce qui se passe effectivement.

Le Dr. Dubois-Poulsen a observé un phénomène très curieux lors de ses études du champ visuel.

Je rappelle la loi de Ricco: $I \times A^1 = \text{const.}$, où I est la luminance stimulante et A l'aire rétinienne stimulée. Cette loi est valable chez tous les individus normaux, pourvu que l'aire stimulée soit suffisamment petite. En vision extrafovéale, le diamètre d'un stimulus circulaire peut atteindre 1°, à 20° de la fovea, et au moins 15′, à 7° de la fovéa, sans que la loi de Ricco cesse d'être observée. Cette loi est, on le voit, l'expression du fait qu'une quantité de lumière donnée est liminaire, quelque soit l'aire des récepteurs qui l'absorbent.

Le Dr. Dubois-Poulsen a observé un assez grand nombre de cas pathologiques, où l'exposant de A dépasse l'unité. Cela signifie qu'avec la diminution du diamètre du stimulus, un individu requiert davantage de lumière et; finalement ne voit plus du tout, même si l'énergie lumineuse totale atteignant sa rétine est augmentée très considérablement.

Je ne pense pas qu'à présent ont ait proposé une explication de ce phénomène qui pourrait bien fournir une clé pour la compréhension de certains mécanismes nerveux intrarétiniens.

Or, j'ai testé longuement un sujet quasi achromatope présentant les propriétés suivantes: complètement achromatope typique aux faibles luminances ($\leqslant 1$ mLb), elle est protanope pure aux luminances élevées. Quand un jour je ramenais chez elle cette dame très âgée, je lui demandai: 'Pouvez-vous reconnaître la couleur de ce feu de signalisation?' — Elle répondit par la négative. Mais ayant approché les feux de quelques mètres, elle me dit: 'Maintenant je vois, ce sont des feux rouges ou jaunes.' C'était bien des feux rouges et mon sujet les avait vus sous un angle de plusieurs degrés. Ceci m'a fait concevoir une expérience dont je vous montrerai les résultats.

Voici la sensibilité normale en vision du jour; c'est la courbe photopique CIE La courbe en pointillé correspond au sujet achromatope. Le déplacement vers les courtes longueurs d'onde (effet Purkinje) est de 25 mμ environ. J'ai fait avec ce sujet des expériences de dénomination des couleurs, en faisant varier, comme

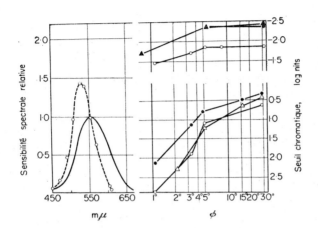

Fig. 1. A gauche: la sensibilité spectrale normale (courbe photopique CIE) et la sensibilité spectrale du sujet achromatope mesurées par égalisation au niveau de 0,52 mLb. Effet Purkinje de 25 mμ environ.

A droite: le seuil chromatique du même sujet, en fonction de l'angle visuel sous lequel est vu le test (en bas). En haut: seuils chromatiques jour un sujet normal.
O > 610 mμ; ● 605 mμ; Δ 470 mμ.

paramètre, le diamètre du test que je lui présentais. Lorsque le niveau lumineux était assez élevé et le diamètre du test suffisamment grand, le sujet répondait: 'Rouge ou jaune' ou 'bleu' (j'ai évité des tests verts puisque le sujet présentait une bande neutre dans cette région du spectre).

La partie droite de la figure montre en abcisses et ordonnées logarithmiques la variation du seuil de luminance de reconnaissance de couleur en fonction du diamètre du test, pour la protanope-achromatope et pour un sujet normal. Non seulement les seuils chromatiques du sujet anormal sont de 2,5 unités logarithmiques plus élevés que ceux du sujet normal (ce qui justifie le terme quasi achromatique), mais leur allure en fonction du diamètre du test est très particulière. En effet, le sujet normal reconnaît les couleurs rouge, orange, bleu, sans augmentation du seuil de luminance lorsque le diamètre du test baisse de 30° à 5°, et entre 5° et 1°, la hausse du seuil est de l'ordre de 0,5 unités logarithmiques.

Par contre, le sujet étudié accuse déjà une baisse de 0,5 unité logarithmique entre 30° et 5°, et cette baisse s'accentue ensuite très fortement et atteint et dépasse même 2 unités entre 5° et 1°. En somme, pour un stimulus de 1° de diamètre, le rapport des seuils de reconnaissance de la couleur des sujets anormal et normal est de 4,5 unités (30.000 fois), tandis qu'il n'est que de 2,5 unités (300 fois) pour un stimulus de 30° de diamètre. Ce fait ne peut s'expliquer par des hypothèses concernant des pigments photosensibles. Le parallélisme entre ces propriétés des sujets étudiés et l'observation du Dr. Dubois-Poulsen est frappant. Ici également le coefficient x de la loi

$$I \times A^x = \text{const.}$$

qui relie l'intensité liminaire de reconnaissance de la couleur I à l'aire stimulée A est nettement supérieur à l'unité chez le sujet anormal, ce qui n'est pas facilement compréhensible. Il est à espérer que d'autres observations nous permettront un jour de conclure au sujet des mécanismes nerveux rétiniens qui sont à la base de la sensation de couleur.

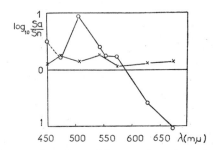

Fig. 2. Sensibilité spectrale crépusculaire Sa du sujet achromatope atypique, divisée par la moyenne Sn des sensibilités spectrales crépusculaires de deux sujets normaux. O vision fovéale; × vision excentrique (11,5°).

Je vous présente encore le cas de deux achromatopes atypiques que j'ai pu étudier grâce au Dr. Weale qui les a vus avant moi et qui a rendu possible leur venue à Paris où je les ai testés longuement.

Il s'agit d'un jeune homme de 20 ans et d'une femme de 35 ans. Tous les deux ont une vision fovéale normale et une acuité excellente, respectivement 20/10 et 15/10. En dehors des tests habituels, voici quelques résultats significatifs que vous fournissent ces courbes relatives à l'un des sujets. La ligne horizontale y signifie la sensibilité spectrale du normal (en l'occurrence, la moyenne de la sensibilité spectrale de deux sujets normaux). Cette présentation est une transformation mathématique qui montre bien mieux qu'une simple confrontation de deux courbes de sensibilité l'écart de la normale de la sensibilité spectrale de sujet étudié.

On voit qu'en vision crépusculaire fovéale l'achromatope atypique est fortement déficient dans le rouge. La sensibilité y rappelle celle des protanopes dans la forme et en ce qui concerne l'écart quantitatif. On remarque une sensibilité supranormale dans le vert qui atteint son maximum à 505 mμ et dont l'ampleur exclut toute erreur fortuite. Par contre, la sensibilité spectrale en vision extrafovéale est tout à fait normale.

La sensibilité spectrale diurne du même sujet montre le même aspect que le tracé précédent relatif à la vision crépusculaire fovéale. Mais l'accident dans le vert-bleu y est beaucoup atténué bien que toujours significatif.

Conclusion — En qualifiant de normale la sensibilité spectrale des achromatopes atypiques (à acuité visuelle normale) on exagère quelque peu. Ceux que j'ai testés et tous ceux qui l'ont été par d'autres avec des moyens modernes, présentent une

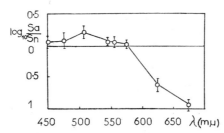

FIG. 3. Sensibilité spectrale diurne, fovéale *Sa* du sujet achromatope atypique, divisée par la moyenne *Sn* des sensibilités spectrales diurnes, fovéales de deux sujets normaux.

très forte déficience dans le rouge et lorsqu'on opère en vision crépusculaire, on peut découvrir une sensibilité supranormale dans la région du vert-bleu qui est moins marquée en vision diurne. Les résultats obtenus avec mon second sujet achromatope s'accordent dans le rouge avec ceux que je viens de vous présenter, tandis que l'accident dans le vert-bleu y est moins prononcé, bien que significatif en vision crépusculaire.

Les résultats que je viens de discuter ont été obtenus au cours d'un grand nombre de séries de mesures qui se sont prolongées sur, respectivement, 15 jours et 5 jours. Leur signification statistique est assurée.

J'en retiens ici une chose importante. Chez les achromatopes atypiques (achromatopes à cônes), il y a tendance à une sensibilité supranormale dans la région de 505 mμ, en vision fovéale, c'est-à-dire en vision des cônes et même en vision diurne. Ceci corrobore l'idée défendue précédemment ici, que les cônes sont bien susceptibles de contenir de la rhodopsine, au moins en adaptation à l'obscurité ou à un faible niveau d'éclairement.

FARNSWORTH

There is one basic psychological concept which I think we've been missing in this meeting and which is throwing speaker after speaker off on to the wrong track. We are seeking special mechanisms which we don't need!

I would like to speak — not as a psychophysicist, but as a psychologist — about some very simple things. They are so simple that I don't even know that the phenomena have ever had a name. We'll call it the concept of sensory equilibrium.

It is this: that no organism can stay for long in a condition of disequilibrium, of unbalance. This is true not only of the general 'feeling' tone of the organism as a whole, but it's true of all the avenues of sensory stimuli.

We learned in elementary psychology that if the sensory stimuli are shifted towards the negative or towards the positive on the 'pleasant-indifferent-unpleasant' scale that the *I* or point of Indifference changes. In sound phenomena we know that our base-line of silence 'quality' will change depending on the general level of white noise or the ambient level to which we are exposed. When the taste sensation is heavily affected by drugs or radiation there is a new balance upon an equilibrium, depending upon the flavours that are missing. For instance, after a massive dosage of penicillin a patient may find that water tastes salty, but that a saturated solution of salt water doesn't taste any more salty than the ordinary water; what was formerly the 'water taste' has been moved over to a new position of equilibrium.

So it is with all the senses, and so it is particularly with the eye.

The problem is not new. As a fallacy it is related to the classical 'stimulus error'. Professor Piéron in his introduction to this conference repeatedly called attention to the need to beware of misinterpretation.

Do you remember Dr. Hurvich looking at Professor Piéron and saying: 'You mean there's a little man up there somewhere that kind of balances all this out'?

Yes, there is a little man up there. There's a little man in the cortex that balances the incoming stimuli received over a period of time and refers all new incoming stimuli to the average state of stimuli in that modality, and this mechanism is already present in the cortex. As I have briefly indicated, this is a matter of common experience. If we accept that there is such a mechanism, why do we have to ask for a special mechanism to do that same thing in each colour phenomenon that we discuss? If we demand it for colour vision, then we would postulate special interpretive mechanisms for all the other senses, which is duplication quite contrary to the neurological austerity of animal physiology.

It is not *necessary* to postulate a peripheral mechanism of opposites in order to obtain it cortically — perceptually.

For example, these questions were asked by Dr. Hurvich: 'How can this theory of three independent processes be made to account for the apparent linkages that seem to occur between specific pairs of colours? Why do the hues drop out in pairs — for instance in congenital anomaly and so on?' In other words, if you have normally a red, green and blue mechanism and the green drops out, why is it that the individual sees in yellow and blue?

I answer that it's because the organism seeks a new state of equilibrium. Not for long, even in a normal like you or I, do reds and blues remain purely red and blue under a red-blue (purple) light. It is difficult to believe that a colour defective can long maintain a state of disequilibrium in which purple remains purple and neutral is never experienced. Even when a normal is adapted to purple lighting, whites tend to regain their balance on white and the separate incoming stimuli assume sensations of opposite polarities of blueness and not-blueness (yellowness).

And so it would be with the other two of the three types of colour deficiency of which we know. Hecht proposed the above dilemma for himself when he found evidence of luminosity deficiency in deuteranopes indicating loss of the green mechanism. Reasoning as a physiologist — not as a psychologist — he was unable to reconcile this fact with the reported yellow-blue vision of dichromats. Graham is somewhat on the horns of the same dilemma.

The only objection that I can see to Prof. Rushton's fine, simple theory is that he too has fallen into the stimulus error. His model implies that, if we have three channels to the brain, those three channels — like three pipe-lines in which red ink and green ink and blue ink are flowing — are going to arouse these same three sensations in the cortex regardless of circumstances. On the contrary, all we have are incoming codes which must be interpreted cortically with relation to each other and to the mean — accept this simple concept and we don't need a Fick hypothesis, we don't need an opponent-colours theory.

PIÉRON

Nous remercions Mr. Farnsworth pour son exposé d'un point de vue psychologique qui supprimerait évidemment toutes les recherches, si l'on s'accommodait d'une théorie aussi générale.

Je ne ferai qu'une objection quand il s'agit de phénomènes corticaux: au point de vue cortical, on n'a jamais d'anomalies monoculaires, parce que chaque hémisphère reçoit deux projections provenant de l'un et l'autre œil, et, par conséquent, nous ne pourrions pas observer un deutéranope monoculaire si la deutéranopie était d'origine corticale. Donc, nous pouvons affirmer que l'origine en est dans la rétine même, et il y a là un problème de mécanisme qui se pose; je crois donc que les efforts que l'on fait ne sont pas vains.

M. Verriest a demandé la parole.

VERRIEST

A propos des dyschromatopsies congénitales, je voudrais vous présenter les résultats d'un travail personnel récent.[*]

Il s'agit d'une série de déterminations de la relation entre l'éclairement et l'acuité visuelle de 0,1 à 0,6, d'une part dans un groupe de 19 sujets normaux et, d'autre part, dans des groupes de 14 sujets protanomaux, de 16 sujets protanopes, de 17 sujets deutéranomaux et de 16 sujets deutéranopes.

Nous avons fait ces déterminations en lumière blanche (2680°K) et en lumières colorées par interposition de filtres.

Pour chaque acuité de chaque couleur, j'ai calculé — pour chaque groupe de sujets — la moyenne des seuils d'éclairement en échelle logarithmique décimale, ainsi que l'écart quadratique moyen qui se rapporte à cette moyenne.

Les différences entre les valeurs moyennes obtenues dans les différents groupes de sujets anormaux et les valeurs moyennes normales correspondantes ont été également calculées, de même que le degré de significativité de ces différences.

Voici l'essentiel des résultats (Fig. 1).

Les sujets normaux donnent des courbes plus raides en lumière bleue que dans les autres régions spectrales: c'est un fait bien connu.

En lumière blanche, la courbe est significativement élevée pour la deutéranopie (+0,13-+0,20 U.L.), ainsi que pour la protanopie et la protanomalie (+0,3-+0,4 U.L.). Ces résultats sont en concordance parfaite avec ceux de Hecht, Hsia et Shlaer (1949),[†] qui se rapportent à une acuité visuelle de 0,29 en lumière blanche. Comme nous avons fait appel à des groupes plus nombreux de sujets, nous avons à présent la preuve que ces différences sont significatives.

Les autres résultats ne correspondent à aucune donnée de la littérature.

Il y a, en lumière rouge, une *diminution* significative des seuils pour les deutéranomaux (de −0,16 à −0,21 pour 0,3 à 0,5). Dans cette région spectrale, les seuils sont évidemment extrêmement élévés pour la protanopes et pour les protanomaux.

En lumière verte et en lumière bleue, il y a une augmentation significative des seuils pour les deutéranopes (env. +0,20 U.L.). Fait important: les seuils des protanopes en lumière bleue peuvent être considérés comme normaux. Celà est en contradiction avec Hecht (1930),[‡] qui estimait que les protanopes regagnent dans le bleu tout ce qu'ils perdent dans le rouge.

Signalons encore que deux sujets atteints d'héméralopie essentielle et appartenant à la descendance de Nougaret ont donné des seuils absolument normaux en lumière blanche.

[*] Verriest, G. (1958) *Ann. Opt. ocul.*, **4**, 53.
[†] Hecht, S., Hsia, Y. & Shlaer, S. (1949) *Docum. ophthal.*, **3**, 138.
[‡] Hecht, S. (1930) *J. Opt. Soc. Amer.*, **20**, 231.

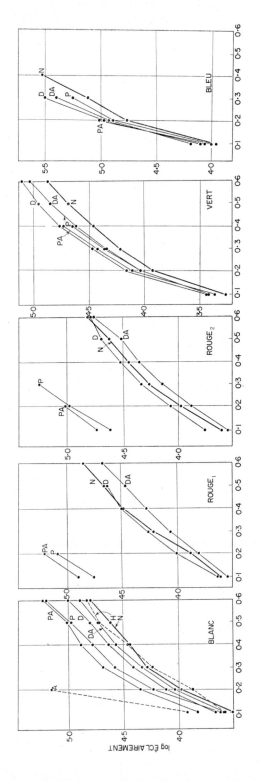

ACUITÉ VISUELLE

Fig. 1. Relation entre l'acuité visuelle et l'éclairement en lumière blanche (température de couleur: 2680° K) et en lumières colorées (par inter-position de filtres). Ordonnées en échelles logarithmiques décimales de hauteurs arbitraires mais constantes pour chaque condition expérimentale.

Moyennes correspondant à des groupes de sujets normaux (N), protanomaux (PA), protanopes (P), deutéranomaux (DA) et deutéranopes (D). Les écarts significatifs sont signalés dans le texte. A: achromatopsie typique. H: héméralopie essentielle (sujets appartenant à la descendance de Jean Nougaret).

Évidemment, les données qui se rapportent aux seuils d'acuité visuelle sont d'une interprétation plus complexe que celles qui se rapportent aux seuils de perception de luminances.

Chez les sujets normaux, l'acuité visuelle photopique n'est pas sensiblement influencée par la couleur de l'éclairage et il y a donc peut-être une indépendance entre les processus de différenciation chromatique et ceux de la perception des luminances, quoiqu'on doit tenir compte des micro-mouvement oculaires.

Même si l'on admet que toutes les fonctions visuelles photopiques reposent sur les mêmes récepteurs, il est évident que, pour chaque région spectrale, le seuil d'éclairement correspondant à une acuité visuelle donnée dépend non seulement de la quantité relative de chaque pigment dans l'aire étudiée, mais aussi de la distribution des pigments dans les différents cônes. Bien entendu, dans les dyschromatopsies congénitales, certains pigments seront parfois absents, et, dans les systèmes trichromatiques anormaux, leurs courbes d'absorption seront sans doute anormales, puisqu'il s'agit de systèmes d'altération, selon la terminologie de von Kries. D'autre part, il est probable qu'il y a aussi, dans toutes les dyschromatopsies congénitales, une proportion et une distribution pathologiques des différents types de cônes.

J'ai également étudié d'autres fonctions visuelles non colorées dans des groupes de sujets normaux et de sujets atteints de dyschromatopsies congénitales.

Je dirai d'abord un mot à propos des sommations spatiales dans le champ visuel, puisque M. Baumgardt a soulevé le problème.

Mon expérience personnelle se rapporte à la modalité un peu particulière de sommation spatiale photopique, que l'on peut étudier grâce à la méthode cinétique du périmètre de Goldmann.

Dans ces conditions expérimentales, les sommations étaient très nettement pathologiques dans l'achromatopsie totale et tout à fait normales dans les types ordinaires de dyschromatopsie, comme la protanopie, la protanomalie, la deutéranopie et la deutéranomalie.

Je citerai encore, brièvement, quelques résultats comparatifs se rapportant à la courbe d'adaptation à l'obscurité, mesurée sur les seuils globaux. Dans l'achromatopsie totale, le point anguleux principal se trouve souvent nettement plus haut que chez les sujets normaux. D'autre part, chez les protanopes, le début de la courbe est normal, mais il y a une élévation très significative du deuxième segment, en plein domaine scotopique. Le temps étant limité, je bornerai mon exposé à ces quelques constatations.

PIÉRON

Il y a un point sur lequel le Prof. Bouman ou son collaborateur, le Dr. Walraven, peut apporter des données assez intéressantes au point de vue expérimental, en rapport avec un des points qui sont discutés — à savoir s'il peut exister une réception photopique qui ne soit pas de nature à être fournie par des éléments chromatiques.

En effet, il se trouve que, dans des conditions de stimulation assez brève, au seuil, on peut obtenir un intervalle photochromatique dans la fovéa — et que, pour l'excitation du rouge et du vert, les valeurs quantiques auraient des seuils différents.

Le Dr. Walraven a la parole.

WALRAVEN

Some aspects in absolute threshold behaviour have been successfully connected with quantum-statistical considerations. In these studies yes-no experiments with flashes for three types of visual functions were involved: firstly, the frequency of seeing curve giving the chance for perception as a function of flash intensity; secondly, the threshold energy versus stimulated area; and thirdly, the threshold energy versus exposure time. Incidentally, also, combinations of these functions like dependence of threshold energy for moving sources on velocity were considered. The experimental results were compared with those of a rather elaborate theoretical treatment of quanta-statistical nature. Namely, do the visual functions reflect the consequences for the need of a twofold coincidence to reach the threshold, or a three-, four-, five- or even morefold coincidence?

Now, the mathematical treatment is pretty complicated, but it can easily be proved in an empirical way that, for instance, Piper's law points to the need for a twofold coincidence at the threshold. This means two quanta have to be absorbed within two mutual, sufficiently closely situated receptors and more or less simultaneously in order to perceive light. Two such absorptions can be and mostly are sufficient under dark-adapted conditions. Non-mathematicians, like physiologists, can convince themselves of the mathematics needed, by throwing a large number of small pieces of paper on the floor and studying the chance of having two within an arbitrary chosen mutual distance D as a function of the average number per unit area.

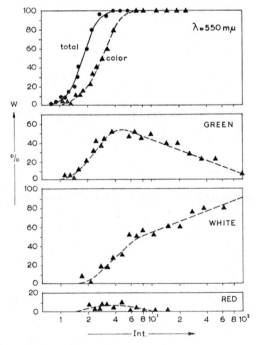

FIG. 1. The frequencies of perception curves for the different perceived colour qualities for the wavelength 550 mµ.

Most authors use only the f.o.s. curve for determination of the order of coincidence required. This has led to conflicting results because of the great influence on this curve from secondary psychological conditioning of the test subjects.

In our opinion the threshold energy versus stimulated area gives the most accurate information on the problem, such that $E(:) (ot)^{k-1/k}$ in which E is threshold energy, o stimulated area and t exposure time.

Now, we investigated the possibilities of applying these ways of approach on colour naming after having checked that the central fovea also reflects a twofold coincidence behaviour in absolute thresholds. Monochromatic flashes were presented and test subjects were asked to name these as white, colourless, red, green,

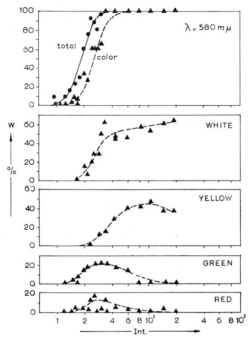

FIG. 2. The frequencies of perception curves for the different perceived colour qualities for the wavelength 580 mµ.

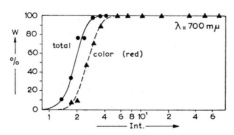

FIG. 3. The frequencies of perception curves for the different perceived colour qualities for the wavelength 700 mµ.

T

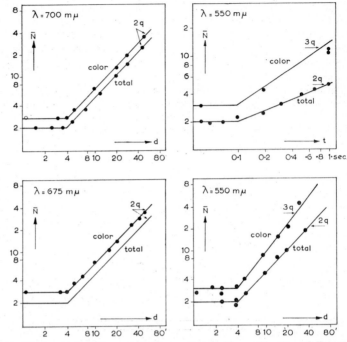

FIG. 4. Energy at absolute — and colour — threshold as a function of diameter for different wavelengths.

yellow, or blue. In Figs. 1-4 some of the results are presented. It is clearly seen that in the red an achromatic zone exists, independent in size from the stimulated area, contrary to green in which the achromatic zone increases with area.

This difference in slope of colour threshold as a function of area between red and green is also found in saturation discrimination as is seen in Fig. 5.

In our opinion these facts point to the existence in the red of a system giving achromatic signals when stimulated by two quanta and of a second less sensitive system giving 'red' signals, when two quanta are absorbed in it. For the sake of completeness it is mentioned here that the same results are found for the case in which red sensations occur for two twofold coincidences in the system giving achromatic signals at one twofold coincidence. The necessity for acceptance of the possibility of sensibilization to red perception by achromatic signals far apart from each other, makes this possibility, however, less probable.

In the green a receptor system behaves achromatically when two quanta are absorbed in it and the selfsame receptor system or another one reacts green when there are three quanta absorbed.

In Figs. 6, 7, 8 the rapid increase with intensity of yellow perceptions in a very small wavelength region is demonstrated. This seems again to be most easily compatible with the independence of the red and green signals in the retina, the yellow being the result of the combined stimulation of them.*

* BOUMAN, M. A. & WALRAVEN, P. L. (1957) *J. Opt. Soc. Amer.*, **47**, 834-9; (1958) *Nat. Phys. Lab. Symposium* (No. 8), H.M. Stationery Office, London.

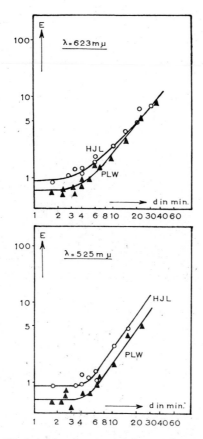

FIG. 5. Saturation discrimination in terms of degree of saturation in percentages times area as a function of diameter for λ = 623 and λ = 525 mμ.

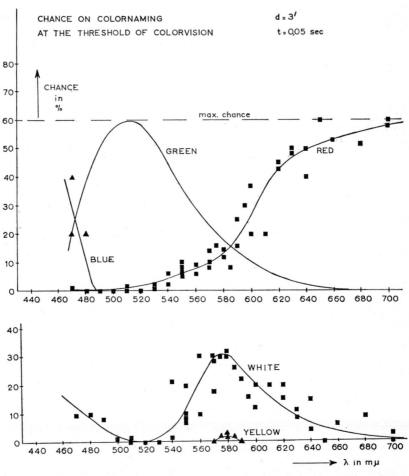

FIG. 6. The percentages of the colour qualities at the threshold energy level for colour vision (60 per cent coloured perceptions). All for small short flashes.

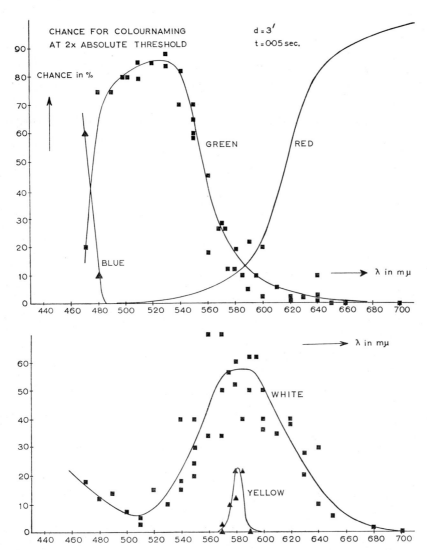

FIG. 7. The percentages of the colour qualities at twice the threshold energy level for colour vision (60 per cent coloured perceptions). All for small short flashes.

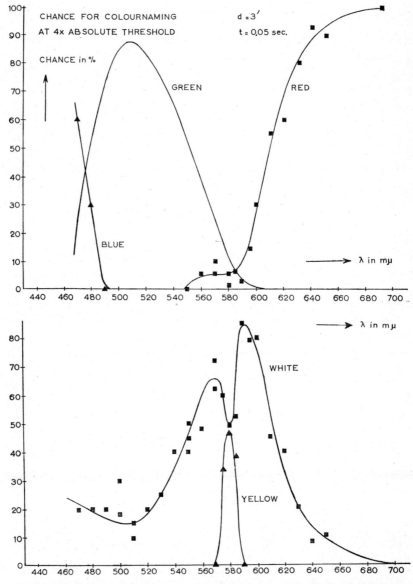

Fig. 8. The percentages of the colour qualities at four times the threshold energy level for colour vision (60 per cent coloured perceptions). All for small short flashes.

MONNIER

Si l'on considère sous un angle fonctionnel assez large le problème de la discrimination chromatique, on acquiert l'impression que cette fonction est couplée dans une certaine mesure à une autre fonction optique: la discrimination des formes. S'il est vrai que dans le règne animal, la discrimination des formes apparaît très souvent indépendante de toute vision chromatique, il est vrai également qu'il existe beaucoup d'espèces animales chez lesquelles la discrimination des couleurs va de pair avec la discrimination des formes. Les abeilles du Professeur von Frisch par exemple sont très démonstratives à ce point de vue.

Il existe toutefois d'autres arguments en faveur d'une synergie fonctionnelle entre la fonction chromatique et la fonction spatiale. Ainsi, nous avons mentionné le fait que la forme de la réponse du cortex visuel varie dans une certaine mesure simultanément en fonction des facteurs couleur du stimulus, surface d'illumination et localisation de la dérivation à l'intérieur de l'aire striée. Les latences de la réponse sont différentes par exemple dans la région antérieure, moyenne ou postérieure de cette aire. La forme elle-même de la riposte peut varier, du fait que des composantes nouvelles se manifestent à l'intérieur de la phase positive primaire, dans certaines conditions de stimulation chromatique, de surface d'éclairement et de dérivation du cortex visuel. Il est donc logique d'admettre qu'une discrimination chromatique, même rudimentaire, puisse être couplée de façon adéquate à la perception spatiale des messages.

Il sera utile d'étudier, à l'avenir, le problème de la vision chromatique, non seulement sous l'angle des unité cellulaires, mais d'examiner aussi dans quelle mesure la qualité chromatique est associée au signe local, et dans quelle mesure elle renforce ce signe. Un signe local, doublé d'une certaine qualité chromatique, peut avoir pour corollaire une réponse corticale différente selon la zone du champ visuel dans lequel se projette le message rétinien.

PIÉRON

Je crois que nous arrivons à un moment où il serait utile de dégager, dans la mesure du possible, les données principales ressortant de notre colloque.

Evidemment, il n'est guère possible de prétendre faire une synthèse dans un domaine où nous avons été en présence de problèmes si nombreux, si variés et si discutés.

Cependant, je crois que l'on pourrait porter l'accent sur quelques points dans le but de favoriser une certaine direction, ou plutôt: plusieurs directions, de recherches, de nature à être fructueuses.

Si nous prenons, tout d'abord, l'inventaire zoologique auquel on serait tenté d'attribuer la valeur d'une représentation générale, il est à noter que les lacunes sont encore extraordinairement graves — que, vraiment, dans la connaissance des espèces qui possèdent probablement une vision chromatique, la recherche fonctionnelle sur les caractères de cette vision n'a pas été faite d'une façon satisfaisante dans la plupart des cas.

Mais il y a déjà des données, en particulier, vous l'avez vu, en ce qui concerne les abeilles.

Il est bien certain qu'il y a là des espèces qui sont particulièrement aptes à des dressages, et pour lesquelles, étant donné les études qui ont déjà été poursuivies, on se rend compte du gros intérêt qu'il y aurait à préciser les lois propres de cette vision chromatique des abeilles, comme on cherche à le faire pour la vision de l'homme lui-même.

En particulier, il y a tous les problèmes d'équations chromatiques, qui permettraient de mieux comprendre la structure de cette vision particulière pouvant dépendre simplement d'un certain décalage de pigments sensibles.

Mais il est difficile, semble-t-il, d'obtenir des précisions sur la nature de ces pigments.

Jusqu'ici, on a échoué. On peut souhaiter qu'une étude neurophysiologique, difficile aussi, puisse tout de même être entreprise, et il y a en particulier à déterminer, s'il est possible, le rôle réel d'une ommatidie isolée, car c'est là une très grosse question que de savoir si une ommatidie peut suffire pour fournir les trois systèmes supposés de cette vision chromatique.

Le domaine des poissons est, évidemment—surtout avec les recherches de Svaetichin — un domaine où l'on peut trouver un matériel vraiment précieux, pour les neurophysiologistes.

D'où la nécessité d'études histologiques et fonctionnelles plus complètes.

Il est remarquable, par exemple, que nous ne savons rien de la vision chromatique éventuelle de la brême.

La brême n'aurait pas, d'après Svaetichin, de modulateurs. Or, elle est extrêmement riche en cônes volumineux, entre lesquels, d'après des coupes comme en a publié Rochon-Duvignaud, on voit se glisser des filaments minces qui proviennent des bâtonnets.

Quand l'œil a été préalablement éclairé, vous savez que, chez ces poissons, les bâtonnets, en réalité, se déplacent et vont fuir la lumière, rejoindre les pigments, s'enfoncer, en quelque sorte, dans la masse pigmentaire.

Or cela facilite l'enlèvement complet des bâtonnets, ce qui permet d'avoir, avec une rétine théoriquement mixte, une rétine à cônes.

Seulement, si la brême ne possède pas la vision des couleurs, c'est un point fort important, que de le vérifier, et ainsi de se rendre compte que la vision photopique ne donne pas la garantie d'une vision des couleurs.

Les achromates humains à vision fovéale que l'on est en train d'étudier sont des cas exceptionnels, mais il est fort possible que chez les animaux nous trouvions pas mal d'espèces qui ont des capacités de vision photopique, à côté de la vision scotopique, sans avoir pour cela des mécanismes de discrimination chromatique.

Mécanismes de discrimination dont nous pourrions voir alors — justement par la comparaison de la brême avec d'autres poissons—qu'ils font défaut lorsqu'on n'a que des réponses toujours du même type, tandis que, dans les cas où il y a discrimination chromatique, au niveau du système nerveux rétinien, on peut avoir des types de réponse différents, sur lesquels la discrimination se fondera.

Nous avons donc besoin d'études fonctionnelles sur les poissons.

D'autre part, cette possibilité peut intéresser les biochimistes, car, tout de même, on dit: 'Il est difficile d'avoir des animaux avec des rétines à cônes purs' — mais si un poisson aussi commun que la brême et qui peut atteindre une assez grande taille, peut être débarrassé de ses bâtonnets, de telle sorte qu'il nous offre des rétines photopiques, des rétines à cônes purs, des efforts d'extractions de pigments, dont jusqu'ici le Dr. Dartnall nous a montré qu'ils avaient été vains, pourront peut-être donner des résultats.

A l'autre extrémité, pour les vertébrés, les mammifères nous intéressent particulièrement.

Or, il est tout à fait remarquable de voir que, sur l'animal le plus commun et le plus utilisé, le Chat comme vous l'avez vu, le désaccord est total au sujet de la capacité de discrimination chromatique.

Il est évidemment désolant de rester, comme nous sommes obligés de le faire, aujourd'hui, devant cette impossibilité de conclure de façon certaine.

Nous ne savons pas s'il s'agit d'une indifférence particulièrement marquée de l'animal à des couleurs qui ne l'intéressent pas du tout — ou bien s'il s'agit vraiment d'une incapacité foncière de discrimination chromatique.

Je crois, tout de même, que cela est soluble.

A l'heure actuelle, il me semble qu'avec un conditionnement à des stimulations de chocs électriques douloureux chez le chat — qui est fort sensible à ces stimulations douloureuses — si réellement la couleur est le seul signe qui puisse l'avertir, et s'il n'utilise pas ce signe, cela doit vouloir dire que ce signe n'existe pas pour lui.

Par conséquent, je crois que nous pourrions demander que des expériences sérieuses et définitives sur le chat nous fixent à cet égard.

D'autre part il est certain que nous avons quelques mammifères, que l'on connaît — mais il y en a peut-être d'autres — dont les rétines sont des rétines à cônes purs.

Nous en connaissons trois espèces: chez des sciuridés, l'écureuil gris, la marmotte et le spermophile. Par conséquent, il semble que ces animaux-là doivent être mis au premier plan dans les recherches que l'on peut avoir à effectuer, aussi bien du côté de la neurophysiologie que de la biochimie.

Mais, encore une fois: il nous faut des expériences fonctionnelles qui manquent complètement; pour la marmotte et le spermophile, nous ne savons rien de leur capacité de discrimination chromatique.

Ils ont, évidemment, des rétines à cônes purs. Mais, encore une fois, ce n'est pas une preuve suffisante.

Par conséquent, nous avons besoin que les zoopsychologues viennent collaborer avec tous les autres techniciens de la vision des couleurs pour nous fournir à cet égard des renseignements qui sont indispensables.

D'autre part, il est aussi très souhaitable que, dans toutes les stations où l'on étudie la physiologie et la psychophysiologie des chimpanzés, qui, eux, nous le savons, sont parfaitement identiques à l'homme dans leur capacité visuelle — ce qui permet de dire que toute expérience sur un chimpanzé est une expérience qui vaut pour l'homme — on s'occupe d'avantage de nos problèmes.

Or on s'occupe de beaucoup de choses chez les chimpanzés, mais il faut reconnaître que la neurophysiologie chromatique, jusqu'ici, n'a pas fourni beaucoup de données.

C'est donc un souhait que l'on peut émettre que l'on songe, devant des chimpanzés, à étudier aussi les mécanismes de la vision des couleurs.

Dans les méthodes que l'on peut employer, il y a évidemment à voir les effets des adaptations chromatiques dont nous savons quelle est l'importance au point de vue des essais d'analyse de la fonction visuelle, dans la fonction de vision des couleurs. On peut envisager des adaptations monochromatiques prolongées.

D'autre part, on pourrait songer à utiliser — mais dans des conditions plus satisfaisantes — cette méthode de Le Gros-Clark: Que se passe-t-il chez le chimpanzé qui, à la naissance, est élevé dans des conditions déterminées d'éclairement? Nous savons, quand il est élevé à l'obscurité, qu'il y a une dégénérescence dans les cellules ganglionnaires de la rétine. Les expériences de Chow, Riesen et Newall, qui ont paru l'année dernière, l'ont parfaitement démontré.

Ils ont pris trois chimpanzés nouveau-nés, dont l'un a été laissé à l'obscurité pendant près de trois ans, avec quelques minutes de lumière, seulement, par jour. Un autre placé à l'obscurité entre les âges de huit et vingt-quatre mois. Un troisième, de la naissance à sept mois, mais avec de la lumière diffuse pendant un certain temps chaque jour.

Chez tous, la vision, en réalité, ne s'est pas développée fonctionnellement, en ce sens que les animaux se comportaient, ou à peu près, comme des aveugles.

Mais, chez les deux premiers il y avait, avec maintien des récepteurs dans leur état normal, une dégénérescence très marquée de la couche des cellules ganglionnaires, celles-ci—semble-t-il—n'ayant pas fonctionné, ont dégénéré ou, en tout cas, n'ont pas obtenu le développement qui se produit normalement.

Eh bien, que se passerait-il si nous élevions des jeunes chimpanzés, non pas à l'obscurité complète, mais dans une lumière complètement privée de certaines radiations? par exemple, complètement privée de radiations rouges?

Est-ce que, dans ce cas-là, fonctionnellement, on observera l'équivalence d'une protanopie? ou bien est-ce qu'il se développera normalement au point de vue visuel, d'une façon totale? Et, au point de vue de la structure de la rétine, trouvera-t-on des modifications qui ont été en relation avec l'absence possible de fonctionnement de certains des éléments, de certains des circuits?

Ce sont là des expériences, qui, me semble-t-il, sont de nature à pouvoir rendre des résultats intéressants, qu'ils soient positifs ou qu'ils soient négatifs.

En tout cas, je crois que des expériences de cet ordre seraient particulièrement utiles, et par exemple, en supprimant toutes les ondes supérieures à 550 mμ au cours du développement.

Voilà, en ce qui concerne l'étude chez les animaux, ce qu'on peut espérer au point de vue des directions générales de recherche—encore une fois, des études fonctionnelles beaucoup plus nombreuses, des études histologiques également, qui portent sur des animaux particulièrement intéressants, et peut-être alors des recherches neurophysiologiques et des recherches biochimiques qui seront en rapport avec l'intérêt particulier de certaines espèces animales.

C'est là ce qui concerne le premier aspect, celui d'une participation de la zoologie et des psychozoologistes aux problèmes que nous avons à envisager.

Un deuxième point concerne le problème photochimique.

Là, je dois dire que si, en apparence, il y a un peu de découragement à ne pas obtenir, comme on le désirerait, en solution tous les pigments qui seraient capables de rendre compte de la discrimination chromatique, puisqu'il faut bien admettre à la base qu'il y a des pigments ayant des électivités réceptrices conditionnées par leur structure—peut-être avec des petites modifications seulement dans leurs absorptions, en tout cas nous avons eu un tableau qui est vraiment, à la pointe des recherches actuelles, grâce au Prof. Rushton, au Dr. Dartnall, au Dr. Weale, et nous avons eu une indication des lignes dans lesquelles on peut espérer obtenir des explications assez cohérentes.

Les pigments n'ont pu être isolés. Tout de même on les décèle. En particulier, les données du Prof. Rushton chez les deutéranopes, chez les protanopes, et chez les normaux, paraissent d'une très grande importance. Il semble que, là, il a établi des données de base qui ont un caractère véritablement décisif.

Il est évident qu'il n'a pas pu, du côté de l'élément bleu, obtenir de résultats; les difficultés techniques l'en empêchant.

Mais le système pourrait paraître parfaitement cohérent quand on le lie, du moins, an mécanisme neurophysiologique. Du côté neurophysiologique, on peut dire que nous avons des indications actuelles qui sont d'un intérêt absolument capital.

En effet, nous voyons qu'il peut y avoir des phénomènes d'excitation et des phénomènes d'inhibition dans des conditions qui paraissent extraordinairement semblables.

Il peut se produire, à certains niveaux — nous ne sommes pas complètement informés à quel niveau — des phénomènes d'hyperpolarisation ou de dépolarisation. Nous savons que la dépolarisation est excitatrice, et que l'hyperpolarisation est inhibitrice.

Nous savons aussi qu'il y a des cellules qui sont des cellules 'on', qui, pour certaines d'entre elles, fournissent une réponse pendant tout le temps de la stimulation lumineuse, avec des fréquences de réponses proportionnelles au logarithme de la luminance.

Par conséquent, il y a là des systèmes qui expliquent complètement, peut-on dire, le comportement d'une certaine vision lumineuse.

Mais il y a des systèmes qui ayant une activité répétitive spontanée, continue, se trouvent, au contraire, arrêtés par une stimulation lumineuse.

Et alors, c'est quand la stimulation cesse qu'ils repartent avec une fréquence initiale plus grande — d'autant plus grande que la luminosité a été plus forte — qui repartent au moment de la cessation.

Des phénomènes de ce genre sont tout de même à rapprocher de ce que l'on peut envisager dans des phénomènes de contraste.

Nous voyons qu'un système complémentaire — je ne précise pas davantage — peut comporter, d'un côté, une excitation au cours de la stimulation, et, pour un autre élément, qui appartiendrait au couple, des réponses qui vont, au contraire, se produire au moment de la cessation.

Quand, après avoir regardé une lumière rouge, nous voyons, à l'obscurité, une lumière qui est bleue-verte, nous pouvons nous demander s'il n'y a pas là la manifestation de cet effet *off* d'un système particulier.

Il est bien certain que les choses sont complexes, et nous les voyons de façon trop simple en ce moment.

Il y a aussi des éléments *on-off*. Nous ne savons pas très bien comment ils se relient, mais leur existence et leurs manifestations nous fournissent tout de même déjà des données qui nous permettent d'expliquer certains des caractères de la vision chromatique.

A côté, par conséquent, de ce fait général commun à toutes les sensibilités, c'est-à-dire d'une réponse qui dure pendant la durée de la stimulation et qui, en effet, est d'autant plus grande, en fréquence pour des influx, et pour les potentiels lents initiaux en amplitude de voltage, avec une gradation qui n'est pas du tout ou rien, mais qui commande le tout ou rien des cellules ganglionnaires, en fonction du logarithme de la luminance, nous avons d'autre part un ensemble — au point de vue neurophysiologique — qui commence à devenir extrêmement intéressant, avec les processus opposés d'excitation et d'inhibition dont le jeu complexe ouvre des aperçus extrêmement prometteurs.

Le fait, d'ailleurs, général, puisque l'on envisage souvent les problèmes généraux — le fait général de possibilité de couplages antagonistes, nous le connaissons très bien.

Nous le connaissons très bien dans les canaux semi-circulaires. Nous savons, que, quand il y a rotation d'un côté, il y a, sous l'influence de l'inertie du liquide des canaux, un mouvement de la cupule dans un sens, qui entraîne des effets inhibiteurs sur une décharge continue de cellules réceptrices qui marchent tout le temps, et subissent alors un ralentissement, alors qu'il y a accélération en sens inverse, par un effet excitateur.

Il y a aussi dépolarisation ou hyperpolarisation, sous l'influence d'une stimulation qui a comme seule différence une inclinaison sur la droite ou une inclinaison vers la gauche.

Est-ce que nous n'avons pas là quelque chose qui nous permet de penser qu'il peut se produire des processus analogues dans les mécanismes visuels?

Si nous en arrivons aux schèmes généraux des mécanismes, nous avons vu que les deux grandes tendances continuent toujours à s'opposer. Il y a là comme un mécanisme antagoniste qui se maintient dans les pensées des chercheurs!

Ce que je tiens à dire, c'est que je crois qu'il est vain de chercher à expliquer les modalités des messages qui forment la base des interprétations perceptives dans les processus photochimiques directement, sans faire appel à cet intermédiaire nécessaire qui est la réponse des éléments nerveux interposés entre les récepteurs et les cellules ganglionnaires, au sein de la rétine.

Il est regrettable que nous ne sachions toujours pas — c'est là que les rétines de poissons pourront certainement servir — nous ne savons toujours pas si la réaction initiale est une réaction de libération de médiateurs ou si c'est, au contraire, déjà une formation d'un potentiel électrique.

Il est fort probable que, quand nous avons des potentiels antagonistes, il doit y avoir des intermédiaires comportant des processus électriques.

Mais, enfin, il est possible aussi — on en a des exemples — que des médiateurs engendrent de la polarisation ou de la dépolarisation.

Par conséquent, là, la question est entièrement posée: phénomènes initiaux électriques ou phénomènes d'ordre sécrétoire par médiateurs chimiques?

Au point de vue de la réception initiale, nous ne le savons absolument pas, à l'heure actuelle. C'est un des gros points sur lesquels l'avenir permettra de répondre.

Nous ne pouvons donc pas dire qu'à l'heure actuelle nous ayons des éléments pour répondre d'une façon définitive en ce qui concerne le schéma général de la réception chromatique commandée dans l'œil lui-même, avant toute intervention psychologique, toute intervention perceptive.

Je me demande s'il n'y aurait pas intérêt à faire ce qui a déjà été tenté, c'est-à-dire, faire de l'analyse factorielle.

On parle de trois variables, de quatre variables, de cinq variables — mais est-ce que nous ne pourrions pas obtenir quelques indications sur le nombre des variables au moyen d'une analyse factorielle?

Il y en a eu une faite par Nowell-Jones, en 1948, qui a utilisé les données de Coblentz et Emerson, en s'adressant aux sensibilités de 92 sujets à 20 radiations de longueur d'onde différentes, allant de 493 à 678 mμ égalisation, d'ailleurs, établie par *flicker-photometry*, avec toute les réserves qu'on doit faire sur l'exactitude de cette méthode. Les intercorrélations étant calculées Nowell-Jones trouve qu'il y a trois facteurs qui sont nécessaires et suffisants, dans une analyse centroïde, et il donne les poids en ces facteurs des différentes longueurs d'onde qui ont été utilisées.

Cela ne paraît pas très satisfaisant comme distribution, mais on a des valeurs de saturations positives et de saturations négatives — ce qui peut être parfois aussi intéressant quand on songe aux oppositions des couples.

Seulement, ce n'est pas avec les données de visibilité pure et simple que l'on peut faire valablement une telle analyse, d'autant qu'on peut toujours, justement, poser le problème: N'y a-t-il pas certaine indépendance entre la visibilité, la lucivité spectrale, et les réponses fournies par les récepteurs proprement chromatiques?

Aussi je crois qu'il serait nécessaire de procéder, chez un grand nombre de sujets — 92 est un nombre acceptable, il faut environ une centaine de sujets — à une étude aussi complète que possible de toutes les équations chromatiques, de la position spectrale du jaune, de sa largeur spectrale, des équations, naturellement, de Rayleigh et d'Engelking, en même temps que de la lucivité spectrale et du résultat des phénomènes d'adaptation.

Si nous avions, chez 100 sujets, des données numériques précises sur tous ces éléments-là, et si l'on procédait alors à une analyse factorielle, on pourrait peut-être obtenir quelque idée plus précise du nombre de facteurs indépendants auxquels on est obligé de faire appel.

Il me semble que ce serait un voeu à émettre que soit entreprise une recherche, qui ne devrait pas être celle d'un homme, mais qui devrait être celle d'un certain nombre de services de recherches, utilisant les mêmes méthodes, chacun sur un nombre limité de sujets, mais qui pourraient ensuite alors se réunir, à condition que dans chacun d'eux et chez chaque sujet toutes les mêmes mesures soient effectuées de la même manière. Voilà, il me semble, un voeu que pourrions émettre — de cette recherche spéciale, de cette recherche collective qui pourrait être instituée pour déterminer alors ce qui n'a pas été fait sérieusement jusqu'à présent: une analyse factorielle.

Est-ce que sur ce point vous êtes d'accord?

Je vous demande de bien vouloir intervenir à cet égard.

Mon effort de synthèse est un effort très imparfait, et je n'ai pas naturellement eu le temps le moins du monde de réfléchir sur cet ensemble de données.

Je ne fais qu'apporter de vagues suggestions, et je serais heureux de savoir ce que ceux d'entre vous qui veulent bien prendre la parole pourront ajouter.

LE GRAND

Oui, je crois certainement qu'une analyse factorielle — qui est une donnée récente dans l'utilisation scientifique — est utile, malgré tout je ne suis pas sûr qu'elle suffise.

Ce n'est pas parce qu'on fait des mesures sur beaucoup de gens et qu'on les étudie ensuite factoriellement qu'on est sûr d'avoir des résultats.

J'avoue que je n'ai jamais aimé beaucoup la manie des astronomes qui aiment mieux faire deux cents mauvaises mesures qu'une seule bonne.

Je crois que la statistique est très utile, mais la qualité des mesures qu'on fait l'est encore plus. L'idéal c'est d'avoir beaucoup de mesures bonnes.

PIÉRON

Bien sûr.

LE GRAND

Dans ces conditions, je suis tout à fait de votre avis qu'il est utile d'essayer de promouvoir des recherches statistiques.

Il y en a très peu, au fond. Je me rappelle que, dans le *Journal of the Physical Society*, il y a une vingtaine d'années, on a publié les données sur quelques sujets étudiés complètement.

Cela avait paru très remarquable à l'époque, d'avoir leur courbe de sensibilité différentielle, leurs composantes trichromatiques, etc. Mais je crois qu'il est nécessaire aussi que les techniques expérimentales soient bien étudiées.

PIÉRON

Oui. Il me semble qu'il faudrait qu'une commission précise la nature exacte des mesures et les techniques exactes de ces mesures.

Ce n'est qu'à cette condition que les résultats pourraient être réunis et comparés.

LE GRAND

Parce qu'on ne peut faire de bonnes statistiques qu'à partir de bonnes mesures — et de bonnes mesures qu'à partir de bons appareils. En France, malheureusement, nous sommes moins favorisés, peut-être, que nos collègues étrangers.

Comme le Dr. Dubois-Poulsen l'a rappelé ce matin, les médecins, en particulier, sont gênés par l'absence d'appareillage pour l'étude de la vision.

Si l'on pouvait fournir, à des prix raisonnables, des colorimètres du type Wright, par exemple, que l'on puisse distribuer — je ne demande pas que celui du Dr. Stiles soit répandu à un grand nombre d'exemplaires, parce que comme il tient une pièce entière à lui tout seul, on n'aurait peut-être pas beaucoup de crédits ni d'endroit pour le répartir dans l'univers; mais enfin un du type Wright, simplement, appareil qui fournit facilement des stimuli spectraux bien dépourvus de lumières parasites aux entrémités du spectre, avec une intensité suffisante dans les courtes longueurs d'ondes — ce qui est la grosse difficulté dans la plupart des appareillages, et, d'autre part, qu'il ne soit pas d'un maniement trop compliqué.

C'est, évidemment, un des instruments-types qu'il faudrait mettre à la base de ces études.

Mais je suis entièrement d'accord avec le Professeur Piéron que si on peut distribuer entre un nombre suffisant de laboratoires un appareillage bien étudié, et faire ainsi de l'analyse factorielle, ce serait certainement un très gros progrès dans l'étude de la vision des couleurs.

PIÉRON

Est-ce qu'un point encore, qui a été peu envisagé, peut aussi fournir des données intéressantes? J'avoue que là je n'ai pas d'opinion, mais je serais heureux si le Prof. Riggs pouvait nous dire ce qu'il pense de l'utilisation de l'électrorétinogramme au point de vue de la recherche de ces mécanismes de discrimination chromatique?

RIGGS

As it's already late, Professor Piéron, I don't wish to take time for details.

I should like to say simply that the research on the human electroretinogram occupies a sort of intermediate position between the neurophysiological work with micro-electrodes and the psychophysical work on human vision. The ERG is in fact the only electrical recording technique that can be employed with the intact organism without doing damage to the structure. Consequently it has a certain interest for us in comparison with the psychophysical data that can be obtained from the same individuals.

However, we are prevented from going into the eye and finding there the origin of function within structure, as we can do in animal research. Tomita,* Svaetichin,† Brindley,‡ and others, have studied the origins of electrical responses by micro-electrode methods.

I would like simply to say that, in order to get meaningful data on the colour system with the human ERG it has been necessary to resort to certain techniques, such as the use of light-adapting fields, the use of flicker and the use of short pulse stimuli, in order to accentuate the photopic responses. Now that these techniques have been developed, meaningful data on colour are emerging from the various laboratories around the world in which the human ERG is being recorded.

One thing that comes out is that some of the old ideas were certainly false about the responses of the photopic system. For example, we know at present that red, green and blue lights all yield responses under photopic conditions that are rather similar in wave-form but somewhat different in latent time and in magnitude of response. It is now clear that we do not have opposite polarities in the responses of rods and cones, or in the responses to one colour as compared with another. Instead, we find that both positive and negative components of the ERG can be elicited by any colour of stimulus. This is even true of the 'X-wave', a form of response first described by Motokawa§ and later shown in the work of Adrian,¶ Armington,** Bornschein†† and many others.

The X-wave consists primarily of a positive wave of the ERG, but it is preceded by a negative wave. The X-wave is most easily seen in response to bright red light. It is absent or very nearly absent in protanopes — so that the electroretinogram has been shown to give the same conclusion as Professor Rushton's paper, in showing that the absence of response occurs at the retinal level.

This is one positive example, then, where the human electroretinogram has been able to contribute something to our understanding of colour vision and colour defect. Other examples, which I do not have time to describe, include studies of photopic luminosity functions and studies of selective adaptation to lights of various wavelengths.

    * Tomita, T. & Torihama, Y. (1956) *J. Physiol. Soc. Japan*, **6**, 118.

    † Svaetichin, G. (1956) *Acta Physiol. Scand.*, **39**, Suppl. 134.

    ‡ Brindley, G. S. (1956) *J. Physiol. London*, **134**, 360.

    § Motokawa, K. & Mita, T. (1942) *Tôhoku J. Exp. Med.*, **42**, 114.

    ¶ Adrian, E. D. (1945) *J. Physiol. London*, **104**, 84.

  ** Armington, J. C. (1952) *J. Opt. Soc. Amer.*, **42**, 393.

  †† Bornschein, H. (1953) *Z. für Biol.*, **105**, 454.

PIÉRON

Il me reste à vous remercier de tout l'effort que vous avez fait, pour ce que vous nous avez apporté, pour les discussions que vous avez soutenues, et pour l'attention que vous avez donnée à ces exposés qui vous ont tenus pendant ces journées au cours de séances assez longues.

Merci.